THANATOCHEMISTRY

A Survey of General, Organic, and Biochemistry for Funeral Service Professionals

James M. Dorn
Barbara M. Hopkins

A RESTON BOOK
PRENTICE-HALL, INC., Englewood Cliffs, New Jersey 07632

Library of Congress Cataloging In Publication Data
Dorn, James M.
   Thanatochemistry: A survey of general, organic and
biochemistry for funeral service professionals.

   Includes bibliographies and index.
   1. Chemistry.   2. Undertakers and undertaking.
I.   Hopkins, Barbara M.   II. Title.
QD31.2.D654 1984   540′.24614   83-26889
ISBN 0-8359-7640-8

This book is dedicated to every student who has ever been subjected to the phrase "..., but for most of you this is just a review."

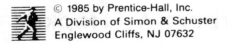
© 1985 by Prentice-Hall, Inc.
A Division of Simon & Schuster
Englewood Cliffs, NJ 07632

10

Printed in the United States of America

CONTENTS

Fundamental to the study of mortuary science is a basic understanding of general, organic, and biochemistry. After teaching chemistry to mortuary science students for several years and reviewing many introductory textbooks, the authors have found no single chemistry textbook to satisfy the needs of these students. Frequently students have little previous knowledge of chemistry or, due to unpleasant earlier experiences, are afraid of chemistry. Many students do not realize that chemistry is basic to other sciences, such as microbiology, that are important in the embalming process. In response to these observations, this textbook presents in an understandable manner the essen-

monia. Our emphasis, and hopefully that of the student, is on understanding rather than memorization. We hope to lead the student to an appreciation for chemistry. Obviously some facts must be memorized, but our goal is far broader than enabling the student merely to list chemical facts.

Chemistry uses mathematics as a tool. The use of this tool generates a new fear when the student is confronted with problem solving. To help dispel this fear, we give examples of solved problems and common mistakes. This approach will help the student to avoid the pitfalls which cause most of the frustrations felt by beginning students of chemistry.

PREFACE

tial facts of chemistry and the chemical aspects of other sciences related to mortuary science.

Before one can appreciate the chemical processes occurring after death, one must understand biochemical processes. To study biochemistry, students must first learn some organic chemistry and inorganic chemistry. Our textbook begins with general chemistry. Some topics discussed are measurements, matter and energy, the nature of matter, changes in matter, chemical reactions, solutions, ionization, and selected compounds such as oxygen, hydrogen, water, and am-

The second section of the book presents organic chemistry: nomenclature, reactions, and uses of fundamental compounds. This information provides the foundation for the third section on biochemistry, in which the chemical nature of proteins, enzymes, carbohydrates, and fats are illustrated and integrated with the decomposition reactions occurring after death. The final section deals with special topics pertinent to embalming. This furnishes the capstone for the student of mortuary science, drawing together all the previous concepts into an integrated framework.

GENERAL CHEMISTRY

The following are the instructional objectives in chemistry as formulated by the Curriculum Committee of the American Board of Funeral Service Education.

Upon satisfactory completion of a course in funeral service education, the student shall be able to:

a. list potentially harmful chemicals used in the preparation room, and the precautions to be taken with each;

b. specify representative chemicals in embalming fluids (arterial, cavity, and accessory) and give their respective functions;

c. give the essential characteristics of autolysis, hydrolysis, fermentation, and putrefaction in the area of the chemistry of decomposition;

h. give the essential characteristics of carbohydrates, lipids, and proteins in the area of basic biochemistry;

i. define organic chemistry and describe the characteristic features of aliphatic and cyclic compounds, hydrocarbons, alcohols, aldehydes, ketones, acids, esters, ethers, and amines;

j. identify a list of elements and their valences, radicals, ions, compounds, and reactions related to problems faced by the embalmer and funeral director, and give their symbols, formulas, and equations.[1]

The previous objectives were formulated to remedy a situation concisely summarized by Oatfield:

Embalming is a craft trade learned by apprenticeship, rather than a science. Embalmers

Chapter 1

INTRODUCTION

d. describe the basic theories and laws of chemistry and relate their importance to both the living and deceased;

e. identify the physical states of matter and differentiate between physical and chemical changes;

f. identify the characteristic features of solutions, suspensions, and emulsions, and the processes of diffusion including osmosis, dialysis, and hydrolysis;

g. demonstrate an understanding of common laboratory procedures and the common units of scientific measurement;

are in large measure empiricists, taking the solutions devised by the chemists of the fluid houses, and applying them to their work, without knowledge of the constituents or of the chemistry involved.[2]

---

[1] Curriculum Study Committee Report to the American Board of Funeral Service Education, October 1974.

[2] Harold Oatfield, "Literature of the Chemical Periphery—Embalming," Advances in Chemistry Series, No. 16, A Key to Pharmaceutical and Medicinal Chemistry Literature, November 1954.

In the craft of embalming, that is, so much has been passed down by tradition that the underlying scientific principles have become clouded. However, the principles do exist, and this textbook will demonstrate that there is a sound scientific basis for the embalming procedure.

DEFINITION OF CHEMISTRY

When most people think of chemistry they tend to dwell on the last two syllables of the word, which suggest that there is something "mysterious" about the subject. The etymology of "chemistry" takes us in two directions. First, the Greek word *chemeia* means an infusion, literally "poured into." Second, *alchemy*, the predecessor of chemistry, had its roots in ancient Egypt. The Greeks had named Egypt *Kemi*, meaning black lands, because of the rich black color of the soil. The word "chemistry" can be traced to this same origin, since alchemy was commonly regarded as the "black art."[3] Perhaps the most mysterious factor is that the word itself, unlike many other sciences, does not end in "ology." Admittedly, however, the word "chemistrology" is somewhat cumbersome!

To begin to remove the mystery, the standard definition of chemistry is the study of

○ the nature of matter and
○ the changes that matter undergoes.

This definition is incomplete until we define matter. *Matter* is anything that occupies space and possesses mass. Note that the word "mass" is used instead of the more familiar term "weight." This will be explained in

more detail when we define the units of chemical measurement later in this chapter.

What do we mean by the "nature of matter"? Two things: the composition of a particular kind of matter and the forces holding its parts together. For example, the common substance water is composed of hydrogen and oxygen. Each of these parts could be further described as being composed of a nucleus and one or more electrons. In a similar manner, each nucleus is composed of particles, of which protons and neutrons are the most important from a chemical viewpoint. The structure of all matter may be analyzed similarly.

The forces holding the hydrogen and oxygen together constitute what are referred to as *chemical bonds*, and the forces holding the nuclei of these constituents together are the *interactions* among the particles in the nucleus. All these terms describing matter will be explained in Chapter 4.

The second part of the definition of chemistry involves the changes that matter undergoes. These changes can be classified as physical or chemical. A physical change is defined, somewhat negatively, as one that does not cause a change in chemical composition of a material. A common physical change is the melting of ice or the boiling of liquid water. In both cases, the chemical composition of the matter is the same before and after the change. As you would expect, chemical changes are those that result in the formation of new substances. In such changes, the chemical compositions of the substances involved are different before and after the change. An example of a chemical change is the decomposition of water into hydrogen gas and oxygen gas when an electric current passes through it. You will be learning more about chemical changes, since they are the major concerns of a study of chemistry.

[3] Harry Wain, *The Story Behind the Word*, 1958. Courtesy of Charles C Thomas, Publisher, Springfield, Illinois.

Accompanying physical and chemical changes are energy changes, which are some of the most important types of changes that matter undergoes. *Energy* is usually defined as the ability to do work and is divided into kinetic and potential. *Kinetic energy* is energy of motion. *Potential energy* is energy that is inherent in a system before an act or process occurs. An important form of potential energy is *chemical energy*, which is stored in chemical substances and released during chemical reactions. One example of chemical potential energy is that which is stored in food and released by metabolic reactions for maintenance of bodily functions.

In discussing energy, we should always remember that matter and energy are really two different forms of the same thing. This idea has been accepted since the time of Einstein. For practical purposes the two concepts may be viewed as separate, since they remain distinct in normal chemical reactions. A familiar manifestation of energy is heat. Later in this chapter we will discuss its measurement.

DIVISIONS OF CHEMISTRY

Different ways to approach the study of chemistry are commonly referred to as the *divisions* of chemistry. Inorganic, organic, and biochemistry are the major divisions. To understand what is meant by inorganic chemistry it is helpful to first define organic chemistry, since inorganic means "not organic." Unfortunately, the term "organic chemistry" is a misnomer. Originally organic chemistry was the study of compounds that could be produced only by living organisms. This definition was found to be in error in 1828 when Wöhler synthesized urea, a compound normally produced by animals. His laboratory synthesis was performed by heating a nonliving compound, ammonium cyanate. This experiment revolutionized thinking concerning organic chemistry, since it showed that a compound classified as organic could be formed from a nonliving substance. To remove from the definition of organic chemistry a link to a living source, organic chemistry since the time of Wöhler has been defined as the study of certain carbon compounds. *Biochemistry* or *physiological chemistry* is the current term for the study of substances produced by living organisms. The origin of this name is the Greek word *bios*, which means *life*.

Since inorganic chemistry refers to nonliving substances, it is the study of minerals and other inanimate materials commonly found in the earth. Unfortunately, certain compounds such as carbon monoxide, carbon dioxide, the carbonates, and the bicarbonates are included in the study of inorganic compounds. Therefore, no clear-cut distinction can be made between inorganic and organic chemistry on the basis of carbon content alone.

To distinguish among the different aspects of chemistry, the following definitions are used:

○ *Inorganic chemistry* is the study of compounds containing elements other than carbon, especially minerals found in the earth.

○ *Organic chemistry* is the study of certain carbon compounds.

○ *Biochemistry* is the study of compounds produced by living organisms.

○ *Embalming chemistry* is the study of those types of matter and changes in matter related to the disinfection and preservation of a human remains. Certain aspects of all three of the major divisions of chemistry are incorporated into embalming chemistry.

CHEMICAL MEASUREMENTS

Chemistry, which essentially is an experimental science, is based on making measurements. In order to standardize measuring procedures, all scientists use a common set of units. The standard set of units known as the International System of Units (SI units from the French name, Système Internationale) was established in 1960 by the International Bureau of Weights and Measures. These units may be better known to the student as the metric system since the basic SI units and metric units generally are the same.

Chemists are involved in making measurements of physical quantities, of which we will consider four: length, volume, mass, and heat. Each quantity has a standard unit and divisions and multiples of the standard that are based on graduations of ten. Although the standards differ, the divisions and multiples are expressed by a system of prefixes which are consistently used in expressing all four of the physical quantities. (See Table 1-1.)

Length

The standard unit of length is the meter (m). Other important length units are the decimeter (dm), centimeter (cm), millimeter (mm), micron or micrometer (μ), and kilometer (km). Appropriate abbreviations are given with each quantity. By considering the prefixes, we can see that 1 m = 10 dm = 100 cm = 1000 mm = 1,000,000 μ and that 1000 m = 1 km.

Volume

The standard unit of volume is the liter (l). One other important volume unit is the milliliter (ml). There are 1000 ml in one liter. The milliliter is sometimes called a cubic centimeter (cc). A cube having a length, width, and height each equal to one centimeter has a volume of one cubic centimeter. Since one milliliter of water will fill this cube at 4° centigrade, it is consistent to say that one milliliter equals one cubic centimeter.

Mass

The standard unit of mass is the kilogram (kg). Smaller mass units are the gram (g) and the milligram (mg). The prefixes indicate that 1 kg = 1000 g and 1 g = 1000 mg. Mass measurements are most frequently made in the laboratory in units of grams. To relate mass to volume, one gram of pure water occupies a volume of one milliliter at 4° centigrade. Therefore, the density of pure water is 1.00 gram per milliliter at this temperature. Densities are always calculated by dividing the mass of a substance by the volume occupied by that mass. The density of water is of interest, since its maximum occurs at 4° centigrade. When cooled below or heated above this temperature, water expands so that its density decreases.

Throughout this discussion we have used the term "mass" instead of "weight." In ordinary conversation the two are often interchanged. Actually, they refer to different concepts. By definition, the *weight* of an object is a measure of the gravitational force exerted on it by the earth. As an object moves farther from the earth's center of grav-

Table 1-1   Prefixes used in measurements

deci	$\frac{1}{10} = 0.1$
centi	$\frac{1}{100} = 0.01$
milli	$\frac{1}{1000} = 0.001$
micro	$\frac{1}{1,000,000} = 0.000001$
deca	10
hecto	100
kilo	1000
mega	1,000,000

ity, this force and the weight of the object decrease. On the contrary, *mass*, which indicates the quantity of matter present in an object, does not change as distance from the center of gravity changes. Throughout this text, *mass* will be used to express a quantity of matter.

Heat

The final physical quantity is a measurement of energy in the form of heat. The standard unit is the calorie (cal), defined as the quantity of heat necessary to raise the temperature of one gram of water 1° centigrade at 15° centigrade. At other temperatures slightly different quantities of heat are required for this change. In metabolic processes the calorie is often too small a unit, so a kilocalorie (Kcal), equal to 1000 calories, is used. The kilocalorie is also symbolized as 1 Cal. Therefore 1 Kcal = 1000 cal = 1 Cal.

CHAPTER SUMMARY

The origins of chemistry can be traced to the ancient Greeks and Egyptians. Since those early days, chemistry has developed into a systematic study of the nature of matter and the changes that matter undergoes. Matter, which is anything that has mass and occupies space, can change physically or chemically. These changes are also accompanied by changes in energy.

Since there is great variety among the different types of matter, chemistry is divided into inorganic, organic, and biochemistry. Each division contributes to embalming chemistry, which is the study of those types of matter and changes in matter that are related to the disinfection and preservation of a human remains.

Chemistry is an experimental science. Central to it is the making of measurements.

The units for these measurements are those of the metric system. The quantities of length, volume, mass, and heat are frequently measured during a chemistry experiment. Associated with each quantity is a standard unit and divisions and multiples of these units.

QUESTIONS

1. Define: chemistry, matter, energy.
2. What is the principal difference between inorganic chemistry and organic chemistry?
3. How is biochemistry related to organic chemistry?
4. What is the relationship of inorganic, organic, and biochemistry to embalming chemistry?
5. Name some of the inorganic compounds of carbon.
6. Why is the metric system used in chemical measurements?
7. Name the four basic units of the metric system and give their standard abbreviations.
8. Define the metric unit of: length, volume, mass, heat.
9. Give the decimal equivalent of the following prefixes:

    (a) deci   (b) centi
    (c) milli   (d) micro
    (e) deca   (f) hecto
    (g) kilo   (h) mega

10. What is the linear equivalent of one milliliter?
11. How many cubic centimeters are found in one liter?
12. Give the following metric equivalents:

    _____ 0.01 meter
    _____ 0.01 gram
    _____ 0.001 liter
    _____ 1000 calories
    _____ 1000 meters
    _____ 0.1 liter

In Chapter 1 we defined matter as anything that occupies space and possesses mass. We will now look more closely at matter by studying its properties. Matter is characterized by two general types of properties: physical and chemical.

PHYSICAL PROPERTIES

Physical properties are characteristics that can be observed without altering the chemical composition of a substance. Some of these properties of matter we experience daily with our senses. Typical ones are color, odor, and taste. When we say that lemons are yellow, apples are red, or describe the color of oranges, we are stating a physical property of any of these fruits. The same is true when

are all familiar with the existence of three states of water exhibited by ice, liquid water, and water vapor. In each state water's chemical composition is the same, but the physical manifestation of the water is different. Each state is a different physical property of water.

There are other physical properties that we are not as aware of in everyday experiences. Some examples are a substance's melting point and boiling point, its solubility in other substances, and its density with the associated property of specific gravity. The melting point and boiling point of a substance are closely related to the property of state of matter. The *melting point* of a substance is that temperature at a given pressure at which a substance changes from the solid state to the liquid state. For pure water this occurs at 32°F or 0°C. The *freezing point* of

Chapter 2
PHYSICAL AND CHEMICAL CHANGES

we taste a sour lemon or enjoy the fragrance of certain flowers. These everyday occurrences are simple observations of physical properties.

Another common physical property is the *state* in which a type of matter exists at a given temperature and pressure. The typical states of matter are solid, liquid, and gas. More will be discussed about the characteristics of these states in Chapter 3. For now, we

a substance is the same as its melting point, since the process of freezing is the opposite of melting. When freezing, a substance changes from the liquid state to the solid state.

The other property associated with states of matter is the *boiling point*. It is defined as that temperature at which a substance changes from the liquid state to the gaseous state. This property, like the freezing point, is pressure dependent. For pure water at a pressure of one atmosphere the boiling point is 212°F or 100°C. All substances have their own characteristic melting and boiling points as measurable physical properties which can be used to identify them.

Another identifying physical property of a substance is its *solubility*. This concept will be fully discussed in Chapter 9. Most people are familiar with the old adage that "oil and water do not mix." This is an expression of the differences in solubility of oil and water. Another familiar example of solubility is that it is possible to add salt to water and see it dissolve. Similarly sugar dissolves in water. When we measure how much salt or sugar will dissolve in a given amount of water, then we are quantitatively evaluating the physical property of solubility.

Another quantitative physical property is a substance's *density*, which expresses the relationship between its mass and the volume occupied by that mass. Mathematically, density is defined as mass per volume. The normal density units for solids and liquids are grams per milliliter, and the units for gases are usually grams per liter. Based on its mathematical definition, three types of calculations can be performed concerning the density of a substance. The following examples illustrate these calculations.

Example 1   A piece of copper has a mass of 268 grams and a volume of 30.0 milliliters. Calculate the density of copper.

Solution 1   Applying the definition of density:

$$\text{density} = \frac{\text{mass}}{\text{volume}} \quad \text{or} \quad D = \frac{M}{V}$$

$$D = \frac{268 \text{ g}}{30.0 \text{ ml}}$$

$$D = 8.93 \text{ g/ml}$$

This problem is solved by direct, simple substitution of the known quantities, the mass and volume of the copper, into the density expression. The student should note that the correct answer has units. To state the density as 8.93 without units is incorrect. Any answer which represents a physically measurable quantity must be labeled with the proper units.

Example 2   What is the mass of 15.0 liters of air? The density of air is 1.29 grams per liter.

Solution 2   The mathematical definition of density

$$D = \frac{M}{V}$$

is rearranged to solve for the mass by multiplying both sides of the equation by volume so that

$$DV = M$$

Substituting the data from the problem,

$$1.29 \text{ g/l} \times 15.0 \text{ l} = 19.4 \text{ g}$$
$$M = 19.4 \text{ g}$$

It is important to remember that the units of the volume must be the same as the volume units of the density. If the problem asked, "What is the mass of 15,000 ml of air?" this volume would be changed to 15 liters before multiplication times the given density.

Example 3   What volume is occupied by 36.0 grams of mercury? The density is 13.6 grams per milliliter.

Solution 3   As in Example 2, rearrangement of the basic density definition is necessary:

$$D = \frac{M}{V}$$
$$DV = M$$

followed by division of both sides of the equation by density:

$$V = \frac{M}{D}$$

Substituting the data from the problem,

$$V = \frac{36.0 \text{ g}}{13.6 \text{ g/ml}}$$
$$V = 2.65 \text{ ml}$$

In the laboratory the densities of solids are frequently determined by a procedure known as *displacement of water*. The technique cannot be used with solids that dissolve in water. The following example illustrates this method of density determination.

Example 4 A student fills a graduated cylinder with water so that it contains 5.00 milliliters. He then puts a piece of metal in the cylinder. The new water level is 8.50 milliliters. The metal's mass was determined to be 9.45 grams. What is the density of the metal?

Solution 4 The density can be calculated if the metal's mass and related volume are known. The mass is given in the problem, and the volume is determined from the increase in the water level as (8.50 ml − 5.00 ml) = 3.50 ml.

$$D = \frac{M}{V} = \frac{9.45 \text{ g}}{3.50 \text{ ml}} = 2.70 \text{ g/ml}$$

Since density is a physical property of a substance, this measured density could be compared to standard densities of metals as one indication of the identity of the metal.

A physical property that is closely related to density is *specific gravity*. For liquids and solids, this property is the ratio of the mass of the substance to the mass of an equal volume of water at the same temperature. In the form of an equation,

specific gravity

$$= \frac{\text{mass of the solid or liquid}}{\text{mass of an equal volume of water}}$$

Since specific gravity is a ratio of two masses, it has no units.

Example 5 The mass of a calibrated volumetric container is 5.3692 grams. When filled with water the container has a mass of 9.6824 grams and when filled with an unknown liquid the mass is 12.4629 grams. What is the specific gravity of the unknown?

Solution 5 Since the same container was used to measure the masses of the water and of the liquid, they are equal volumes.

mass of water
= mass of container and water minus mass of container
= 9.6824 g − 5.3692 g
= 4.3132 g

mass of unknown liquid
= mass of container and unknown liquid minus mass of container
= 12.4629 g − 5.3692 g
= 7.0937 g

specific gravity

$$= \frac{\text{mass of liquid}}{\text{mass of equal volume of water}}$$
$$= \frac{7.0937 \text{ g}}{4.3132 \text{ g}}$$
$$= 1.6446$$

Another definition for the specific gravity of a substance is the ratio of the density of the substance to the density of water. This definition is especially useful if the density of water is expressed as 1.0 g/ml.

Example 6 Find the specific gravity of aluminum if it has a density of 2.7 g/ml.

Solution 6 This problem uses the relationship

$$\text{specific gravity} = \frac{\text{density of aluminum}}{\text{density of water}}$$

$$\text{specific gravity} = \frac{2.7 \text{ g/ml}}{1.0 \text{ g/ml}}$$

$$\text{specific gravity} = 2.7$$

In this section we have described several physical properties. Observations of color, odor, and taste hopefully begin to remove the mystery from chemistry. Others such as state of matter, melting point, boiling point, solubility, density, and specific gravity are more abstract. For all these characteristics it is important to remember that they can be observed without changing the chemical composition of a substance.

An important substance you will use as an embalmer is arterial embalming fluid. Some physical properties of a representative fluid are summarized in Table 2-1.

The color in the fluid is due to dyes that are frequently added for cosmetic purposes. The specific chemicals necessary for embalming have pungent odors. To mask these, floral

Table 2-1 Physical properties of an arterial embalming fluid

Color	Red or orange
Odor	Pungent or pleasant
Taste	Not available due to toxic nature
Solubility	Water soluble
Density	Approx. 1.05 g/ml

or spicy reodorants are often components of the fluid. Since water is the primary vehicle (solvent) in embalming fluid, the other components by necessity are soluble in it.

CHEMICAL PROPERTIES

A chemical property of a substance is a characteristic that can be observed when the substance is interacting with other forms of matter. The interaction results in alteration of the chemical composition of the substance. A chemical property is shown when a substance burns. When it burns, a substance such as carbon in wood or in a match unites with oxygen and forms a new substance. Another example of a chemical property is the interaction of certain substances with water. When sodium is added to water, two new substances, hydrogen gas and sodium hydroxide, are formed. Most commonly we think that substances simply dissolve in water. The term "universal solvent" is frequently applied to water. However, some substances, like sodium, chemically interact with water. In later chapters you will learn how to distinguish between these two actions of water. A third chemical property is the effect on matter of substances known as acids and bases. Anyone who is a fan of horror movies has seen the villain immerse bodies in vats of acid, producing alterations in their chemical compositions!

Observations of chemical properties are the basis of interactions that we refer to as *chemical reactions*. Chemistry's main subject matter is a study of these changes.

PHYSICAL AND CHEMICAL CHANGES

A physical or a chemical change is a process that manifests either a physical or chemical property. Very common *physical changes* are changes in state. When ice melts, for example, three physical properties—water's characteristics as a solid and as a liquid and its melting point—are demonstrated. Another physical change is dissolving table salt in water. This change manifests the physical property of solubility. In both of these examples the chemical compositions of the substances undergoing the change have not been altered. This is very effectively shown by observing that salt and water tastes salty, the same as solid salt. Evaporation of the water from the salt water also shows that dissolving is a physical change. The original solid salt is present after this process.

The major difference between physical changes and chemical changes is the latter form new substances with their own chemical and physical properties. Examples of *chemical changes* are rusting of iron, burning of paper, cremation, souring of milk, and the decomposition of human remains. Each of these processes represents an interaction between a substance and other forms of matter, causing alteration of the chemical composition of the original material.

Let's study these chemical changes separately. When iron rusts, it unites with oxygen in the air, forming iron oxide. This change has produced a product with a new chemical composition. The new substance is called an oxide. Such substances are common chemical compounds. By definition an *oxide* is a substance containing two elements, one of which is oxygen. Oxides are also formed in the processes of burning paper and during cremation. Whenever matter is burned in the presence of oxygen, oxides are produced. Another name for this chemical change is *combustion*. In these changes, simple substances, such as iron and carbon, have united with oxygen, forming more complicated substances.

Other chemical changes are *decomposition* reactions. When milk sours, microorganisms change the sugar in the milk to simpler substances which smell and taste sour. Similarly the decomposition of human remains involves the breakdown of biochemical compounds into smaller, simpler types of matter. This chemical change is initiated by a process known as *hydrolysis*. The meaning of this word is "water breaking apart." In the presence of moisture, substances known as enzymes begin chemical changes which alter the original composition and properties of proteins, fats, and carbohydrates, which are the main constituents of a human body. The embalming process attempts to disinfect and preserve human remains, thereby slowing the rate of the chemical change of decomposition.

CHAPTER SUMMARY

Matter has both physical and chemical properties. We can observe the physical properties of a substance without changing its chemical composition. Some examples of these properties are color, odor, and taste. Others which are not so easily observed by our senses are the state in which a form of matter exists at a given temperature and pressure, the melting and boiling points of a substance, solubility, and density.

In contrast to physical properties, chemical properties of a substance are observed when the substance is interacting with other forms of matter. Examples are the ability of a substance to burn, its interaction with water, and how it is affected by acids and bases.

Changes in matter that manifest physical properties are physical changes. When chemical properties are demonstrated by a change, a chemical change occurs. The major difference between physical changes and chemical changes is that during chemical changes new substances with their own chemical and physical properties are formed.

QUESTIONS

1. Classify the following as physical or chemical properties:
    (a) Hardness. –P
    (b) Density. –P
    (c) Freezing point. –P
    (d) Combustibility. –C
    (e) Hydrolysis. –C
    (f) Volatility of perfume. –C
    (g) Solubility. – P
    (h) Corrosion of metals. –C
2. Classify the following as physical or chemical changes:
    (a) Tearing paper. –P
    (b) Making yogurt. –C
    (c) Burning paper. –C
    (d) Melting ice. –P
3. Define melting point, freezing point, and boiling point. For water give the value of each of these.
4. Name and explain a chemical property of water.
5. What is the main difference between chemical and physical changes?
6. Define oxide. Give three examples.

7. Why are specific gravities unitless quantities?
8. Carbon compounds are the subject matter of organic chemistry. The density of carbon is 3.51 g/ml. What volume does 250 grams of carbon occupy?
9. The density of silver is 10.5 g/ml. Estimate its specific gravity.
10. The density of oxygen is 1.43 g/l. What is the mass of 5.0 liters of oxygen?
11. Use these data to calculate the specific gravity of a certain arterial fluid:

Weight of container and fluid   12.3218 g
Weight of empty container   6.4212 g
Weight of container and water   10.6232 g

12. A material used in the construction of caskets is stainless steel, which is an alloy of iron, chromium, and nickel. An alloy is formed by melting together two or more metals. Calculate the density in g/ml of these metals from the following data:

3900 g of iron occupy 500 ml
36,000 mg of chromium occupy 5 ml
17,800 g of nickel occupy 2 l

In the last chapter one of the physical properties of matter that we discussed was the state in which the matter exists. The common ones are solid, liquid, and gas.

SOLID ⟶ LIQUID ⟶ GAS

For a given substance, its state of matter is determined by the amount of energy it possesses. Of the three common states of matter, the gaseous state is the most energetic, the liquid state is of intermediate energy, and the solid state has the least energy. The degree of energy of a state is reflected by the type of motion possessed by the particles. For example, in a solid the particles vibrate around fixed positions, in liquids the particles slide past one another, and in a gas each particle

ice cubes, a freezer removes heat from liquid water so it can solidify. When ice cubes melt, they do so by absorbing energy from their surroundings.

As you learned in the last chapter, a substance undergoes the transition from the solid state to the liquid state at its melting point. For every substance there is a specific quantity of heat that is absorbed to convert one gram of the solid to one gram of the liquid at the substance's melting point. This amount of heat is called the *heat of fusion*. If we apply this to water, 80 calories of heat must be absorbed in order to change one gram of solid water to one gram of liquid water at 0° Celsius or centigrade. Therefore, the heat of fusion of water is 80 calories per gram. This heat frees the solid particles from one another. They are then able to slide past each

Chapter 3
STATES AND
TYPES OF MATTER

possesses random, rapid motion independent of the other particles. Since heat is a form of energy, the change from solid to liquid to gas by a particular form of matter is accompanied by absorption of heat. If the reverse of this sequence occurs, heat is liberated.

Heat absorbed | SOLID ↑
                LIQUID | Heat liberated
↓ GAS

A familiar example of these concepts is the action of a refrigerator. In the formation of

other and manifest themselves as a liquid. Analogously, every substance has a *heat of vaporization*. This is defined as the amount of heat necessary to change one gram of a substance from the liquid to the gaseous state at the boiling point. The heat of vaporization of water is 540 calories per gram. When one gram of liquid water at 100°C absorbs 540 calories of heat, the attractive interactions between the liquid particles are broken so each particle can freely move in a random way with respect to the other particles in the gas.

The heat of fusion and the heat of vaporization represent quantities of energy that are absorbed by matter. When a substance changes from the liquid state to the solid state, it liberates the same quantity of heat as the heat of fusion. Similarly the change from gas to liquid releases the heat of vaporization. If steam condenses on someone's skin, the steam liberates heat, which is absorbed by the skin. Since water has a large heat of vaporization, the liberation of this heat can cause severe burns.

To describe the processes of liberation and absorption of heat, two frequently used terms are exothermic and endothermic. Any process that liberates heat is *exothermic* and one that absorbs heat is *endothermic*. To characterize the previously discussed phase changes with respect to exothermicity and endothermicity:

GAS $\longrightarrow$ LIQUID + HEAT

and

LIQUID $\longrightarrow$ SOLID + HEAT

are exothermic processes.

SOLID + HEAT $\longrightarrow$ LIQUID

and

LIQUID + HEAT $\longrightarrow$ GAS

are endothermic processes.

The setting of plaster of Paris is a good example of an exothermic chemical process that has a practical application to the embalming operation. It also provides a convenient way of remembering the release of heat energy involved in physical changes in states of matter. Plaster of Paris is commonly used in embalming to provide a matrix for reconstructing a cranial vault that has been broken by traumatic accident. It also may be used to seal the cranium in cases of cranial autopsy. Plaster of Paris is reacted with water to form a hard crystalline substance called gypsum. (The chemical nature of this process will be illustrated in further detail in a later chapter on hydrates and hydrolysis.) After the skull has been sealed with this substance and during the time the scalp is being sutured back over the cranium, the operator can actually feel heat being transmitted through the back of the skull. This attests to the exothermicity of the reaction:

plaster of Paris + water $\longrightarrow$ gypsum + heat

This reaction is also a helpful reminder of the energy exchange that occurs when there is a physical change in state.

Heat is absorbed

SOLID $\longrightarrow$ LIQUID $\longrightarrow$ GAS

Lower energy state   Higher energy state

The reverse is also true.

Heat is liberated

GAS $\longrightarrow$ LIQUID $\longrightarrow$ SOLID

Higher energy state   Lower energy state

If we insert the reacting mixture of plaster of Paris and water in place of the liquid in this expression and the crystalline gypsum as the solid, then:

LIQUID $\longrightarrow$ SOLID + HEAT
plaster of Paris + water   gypsum

This reminds us that in the transition from a higher energy state to a lower energy state, energy in the form of heat must be released. It is a simple matter to add in the missing state, gas. Thus we can generate the entire change-of-state sequence

GAS $\longrightarrow$ LIQUID $\longrightarrow$ SOLID

Heat is liberated

just by remembering that during the hardening of plaster of Paris heat is released. It is a simple matter then to reverse both the sequence and the heat direction to say:

SOLID ⟶ LIQUID ⟶ GAS

Heat is absorbed

This avoids memorizing such statements as

○ When a gas is converted into a liquid, energy in the form of heat is liberated.

○ When a liquid is converted into a solid, energy in the form of heat is liberated.

○ When a gas is converted into a solid, energy in the form of heat is liberated.

○ When a solid is converted into a liquid, energy in the form of heat is absorbed.

○ When a liquid is converted into a gas, energy in the from of heat is absorbed.

○ When a solid is converted into a gas, energy in the form of heat is absorbed.

because all this information can be generated by remembering that during the setting of plaster of Paris in the case of a cranial autopsy the back of the head feels hot.

SOLID ⟶ GAS

Some forms of matter undergo changes in state by which they pass directly from the solid state to the gaseous state. This process is called *sublimation*. A common example of sublimation that you can do in the laboratory is heating iodine crystals. The black crystals change into a purple gas without passing through the liquid state. Upon cooling, the crystals reform. The iodine crystals must absorb energy in order to sublime. A more practical example of sublimation can be observed during cold weather. At temperatures below the melting point of water, frozen wash hanging on a clothesline dries by sublimation.

Other examples of subliming substances are solid carbon dioxide, more commonly known as dry ice, and solid air deodorants. The process of sublimation is a physical change.

CHARACTERISTICS OF STATES OF MATTER

Since the solid form of a type of matter has the least energy in comparison to the liquid and the gaseous state, the solid form is the most ordered. Another way of comparing the order in the states of matter is by *entropy*, which is a measure of the amount of disorder or randomness. A shuffled deck of cards has more entropy than one that is not shuffled. Of the three states of matter, solids have the least entropy, gases the most, and liquids are intermediate. As we study specific characteristics of the states of matter, it is helpful to relate these comparisons of order to the properties.

Gases

The properties of the gaseous state of matter should be familiar to you from practical experiences. Three important properties are compressibility, expansivity, and diffusibility. *Compressibility* means that the volume of a gas may be decreased by increasing the pressure on the gas. Cylinders of gas under high pressure show this property. Gases can also be compressed by cooling. In contrast, a gas may increase its volume when heated; this is the property of *expansivity*. *Diffusibility* refers to the movement of gas if introduced into a container. If a bottle of ammonia is opened in a room, the odor is soon noticed in all parts of the room owing to diffusion of the gaseous ammonia throughout the room. In the preparation room the pungent odor of formaldehyde is present in all areas because of diffusion. Gases are characterized as having no fixed shape or volume but occupying the entire space of their container. If a gas is in a one-liter flask, the volume of the gas is said to be one liter. It is simple to express the volume of a gas, since it is equal to its container's volume.

In addition to volume, a second important variable to express concerning a gas is pressure. The definition of *pressure* is a force per unit area. Gases exert a pressure on the walls of their containers. As the gas particles collide with the walls, they exert a force on them which is considered a pressure. If the force is too large to be withstood by the container, an explosion may occur.

Pressure measurements   It is important to know how to measure gas pressures. A commonly measured pressure is that exerted by the atmosphere, which is a mixture of gases. Although you may not be aware of it, the atmosphere is pushing down on you, exerting a pressure, while you are reading this book. The simplest device used to measure atmospheric pressure is a mercury barometer. You can demonstrate and measure the pressure of the atmosphere by filling with mercury an 80-centimeter-long glass tube closed at one end and inverting it in a dish of mercury. The mercury level in the tube will fall until the pressure exerted by the air on the surface of the mercury in the dish supports the mercury in the tube. (See Figure 3-1.)

By measuring the height of the column of mercury between the surface of the mercury in the dish and the top of the column, you can determine atmospheric pressure. Such measurements are commonly expressed in millimeters of mercury. Another name for a millimeter of mercury is a *torr*. If this measurement is performed at sea level at a latitude of 45°, the mercury column supported

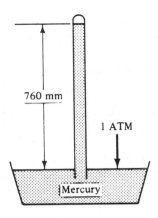

Figure 3-1   Mercury barometer

by the pressure of the atmosphere is 760 mm. This pressure is referred to as *one atmosphere*. By definition, one atmosphere (atm) equals 760 mm Hg or 760 torr. The pressure of the atmosphere varies with distance above sea level and with climatic changes. As one travels from sea level to a mountaintop where the air is less dense, the atmospheric pressure decreases. Anyone who has experienced shortness of breath when climbing to the top of a mountain is aware of the decreased atmospheric pressure. A meteorologist studies changes in atmospheric pressure in making weather predictions. A rapidly decreasing atmospheric pressure is indicative of an abrupt weather change.

Gas laws   Several laws describe the properties of gases in mathematical forms relating volume (V), pressure (P) applied to a gas, and temperature (T). We will look at Boyle's law and at Charles' law. The former describes the relationship between the volume of a gas and the pressure applied to the gas. At constant temperature, these two variables are inversely related. This means if pressure increases, volume decreases, and if pressure decreases, volume increases.

Example A gas occupies a volume of 100 ml at 23°C and a pressure of 1 atm. What volume will the gas occupy at 0.5 atm if the temperature stays constant?

Solution Since the pressure decreases, according to Boyle's law the volume must proportionately increase. Therefore, to find the new volume, multiply the initial volume by a ratio of the initial and final pressures that will make the volume increase. The correct ratio is 1.0 atm/0.5 atm.

$$V_{final} = 100 \text{ ml} \times \frac{1.0 \text{ atm}}{0.5 \text{ atm}}$$
$$= 100 \text{ ml} \times 2$$
$$= 200 \text{ ml}$$

In these problems, the student should understand the overall technique of the solution. Based on the pressure change, ask yourself if this will cause the volume to increase or decrease. Remember $P \downarrow V \uparrow$ and $P \uparrow V \downarrow$. Then multiply the initial volume by a ratio of the pressures reflecting the change. If the volume should increase, put the larger pressure in the numerator of the pressure ratio. If the volume decreases, put the larger pressure in the denominator of the ratio.

A practical example of Boyle's law is the increase in the volume of a balloon as it ascends to a higher elevation. Breathing is also an application of Boyle's law. From your anatomy studies you know that the lungs are located in the thoracic cavity, which is surrounded by the ribs and the diaphragm. During inhalation the diaphragm contracts and flattens, which increases the thoracic cavity's volume. The increased volume causes the pressure to drop in comparison to outside pressure, so air flows in. During exhalation the diaphragm relaxes and pushes into the thoracic cavity, decreasing its volume. The pressure in the cavity increases, forcing air out of the cavity.

The law that relates the volume of a gas to temperature is Charles' law. If the pressure on a gas remains constant, the volume is directly proportional to the temperature expressed in degrees Kelvin. The Kelvin temperature scale, often called the absolute scale, is related to the more familiar Celsius scale by the relationship:[1]

$$K = °C + 273$$

If the temperature is expressed in degrees Celsius, the corresponding temperature expressed in degrees Kelvin is found by adding 273 to the Celsius temperature. The number 273 is used, since it has been observed that if gas is cooled from 0°C to −1°C it contracts by $\frac{1}{273}$ of its volume. Theoretically, if a gas were cooled to −273°C, it would have zero volume. Practically this does not occur because the gas would liquify before reaching −273°C. In working Charles'-law problems, we must express the temperature on the Kelvin scale.

Example At one atmosphere pressure a gas has a volume of 2.0 liters and a temperature of 100°C. What will be the volume at 200°C, if the pressure remains constant?

Solution Change each of the temperatures to Kelvin.

$$100°C + 273 = 373 \text{ K}$$
$$200°C + 273 = 473 \text{ K}$$

Since the temperature is increasing, the volume will also increase. Using the same procedure as in the Boyle's-law problems, the new volume is found by multiplying the first volume by a ratio of the temperatures

---

[1] The Kelvin temperature scale does not use the degree sign.

that will increase it.

$$V_{final} = 2.0 \text{ liters} \times \frac{473}{373}$$
$$= 2.5 \text{ liters}$$

Example A gas occupies a volume of 250 ml at 25°C and 755 mm Hg pressure. Find the volume if the temperature is changed to −20°C with the pressure staying constant.

Solution

$$25°C + 273 = 298 \text{ K}$$
$$-20°C + 273 = 253 \text{ K}$$

Since the temperature is decreasing, the volume decreases.

$$V_{final} = 250 \text{ ml} \times \frac{253}{298}$$
$$= 212 \text{ ml}$$

Liquids

The individual particles in a gas are relatively far apart from one another. The particles also have high velocities. Owing to these properties there is minimal interaction between gaseous particles. If the pressure on a gas is increased or the temperature is lowered, interactions between the particles occur. When these interactions become strong enough to hold the particles together, the gas changes to the liquid state. Two experimental ways to liquefy a gas are to increase the pressure on it or to cool it.

The liquid state is intermediate in properties between the gaseous and solid states. Free space between the liquid particles is minimal, so liquids are practically incompressible. When placed in a container, liquids maintain their own volume. The particles cluster together, owing to attractive forces. Liquids also take on the shape of the bottom of their container. When added to another liquid without agitation, liquids diffuse, but

very slowly. This process can be observed by adding a drop of ink to water. After a long period of time, the water takes on the color of the ink because of diffusion.

After the properties of solids are discussed later in this chapter, the similarities between liquids and solids will be apparent. They are similar, since liquids are practically incompressible and maintain their own volume. Liquids are also similar to gases because they have no characteristic shape and they diffuse.

Another very important property of liquids is evaporation from open containers. In a liquid the kinetic energy of each particle changes as it collides with other particles. When particles near the surface obtain enough energy to overcome the attractive forces between them, these surface particles change to the gaseous state. This transition from liquid to gas is commonly referred to as *evaporation*. The kinetic energy of a particle is directly related to temperature. After the surface particles evaporate, those staying in the liquid state have a lower kinetic energy, which is manifested by a decrease in temperature. Evaporation is accompanied by cooling of the particles remaining in the liquid state.

A property of liquids related to evaporation is demonstrated by the following observation. If a liquid is placed in a container with a cover, the liquid level decreases to a certain point and then remains the same as time continues. The decrease in the level is explained by the escape of surface particles to the vapor state. Why does the level remain constant after a certain period? Since the container is covered, the gaseous particles are confined in the region above the liquid. As they collide with one another or with the walls of the covered container, they may transfer some of their energy to the collision partner, causing the particles to return to the liquid state. At the same time, some particles on the liquid's surface are increasing in energy by collisions and vaporizing. The constant liquid level represents the condition where the rate of molecules that return to the liquid is equal to the rate of molecules that escape from the liquid.

This condition of no net change in the liquid level represents a state of *dynamic equilibrium*. Whenever two opposing rates are equal, a state of equilibrium exists. The two rates in this example are condensation and evaporation. The equilibrium is described as *dynamic* to emphasize that there is activity even though it appears the process of evaporation has stopped. The molecules in the vapor state exert a pressure. At equilibrium it is referred to as the equilibrium vapor pressure. The magnitude of this pressure is characteristic of the liquid. The *equilibrium vapor pressure* is defined as the pressure exerted by a vapor when it is in equilibrium with its liquid. As temperature increases, the vapor pressures of liquids increase. Substances that have high vapor pressures should be kept in cool places when in closed containers.

During the process of evaporation, liquid particles slowly undergo the transition to the vapor state. In contrast to this relatively slow process, the rapid passage of liquid particles to the vapor state by forming bubbles is the process of *boiling*. Liquid particles generally obtain sufficient energy to boil by being heated. A liquid boils at a temperature called the *boiling point*, a physical property. At this temperature the vapor pressure of a liquid is equal to the pressure of the atmosphere on the liquid. When a substance boils, the atmosphere is actually pushed away by the vapor formed from the liquid. The prevailing atmospheric pressure determines the value of a liquid's boiling point. At one atmosphere pressure the boiling point is designated as the *normal boiling point*. For water, it is 100°C. If the atmospheric pressure is less than one atmosphere, as on a mountain, the boiling point decreases. Under conditions of high pressure, such as in a pressure cooker or an autoclave, boiling points higher than normal occur.

Solids

In a solid the particles are held tightly to one another by some type of bond. Owing to the forces between particles, solids have a definite shape and volume. Solids are nearly incompressible and do not expand significantly with increasing temperature. The strong attractive forces between the particles prevent expansion. Likewise, repulsive forces between the negatively charged electrons associated with each particle prevent compressibility. The interparticle distance is a balance between the attractive and repulsive forces.

Even though there is much order in solids, the particles are not motionless. They move back and forth, up and down, vibrating within limits of retaining the shape of the solid. If heat is added, the kinetic energy of the particles increases, until the solid breaks apart. This is the process we call *melting*. The temperature at which it occurs is the *melting point*. If heat is added to a solid at a temperature below the melting point, the solid will absorb the heat and increase in temperature until the melting point is reached. At this temperature the heat added to the solid will allow the transition from solid to liquid. We have already defined this quantity of heat as the *heat of fusion*. Each substance has a characteristic heat of fusion, which is reflective of the strength of the intermolecular forces of the solid.

During the melting process the temperature of the matter does not change. After all the solid is converted to the liquid state, any additional heat will increase the temperature of the liquid. Figure 3-2 should help you understand these concepts.

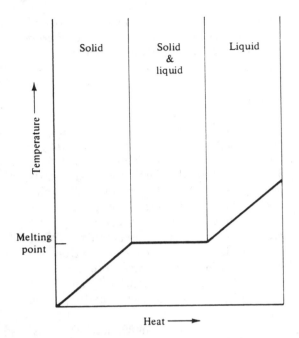

Figure 3-2 Melting point and heat of fusion of a solid

TYPES OF MATTER

We have defined chemistry as the study of matter and the changes that matter undergoes. We have also seen that matter may participate in physical and chemical changes. For further understanding, matter can be divided into pure substances and mixtures. Some *pure substances* that we have already mentioned are hydrogen, oxygen, carbon, mercury, aluminum, iron, water, carbon dioxide, and iron oxide. Examples of mixtures we have discussed are air, salt and water, and embalming fluid. In chemistry pure substances are classified as either elements or compounds. *Elements* are defined as substances that cannot be decomposed by further chemical means. *Compounds* are substances composed of two or more elements chemically united in a definite proportion by

weight. *Mixtures* are composed of two or more nonchemically united substances which are in no definite proportion by weight.

Elements

The basic units of matter are elements. Historically the ancient Greeks defined elements as substances which were not composed of more basic substances. They identified earth, air, fire, and water as the only elements. A similar idea was held by Lavoisier (1743–1794), who is called the Father of Chemistry. In his *Elementary Treatise on Chemistry*, which is regarded as the first chemistry textbook, he included a table of elements. Besides many substances that modern chemists consider to be elements, he listed light and heat as elements

Today 106 substances are identified as elements. A list of them is given in this book (Figure 4-1 in the following chapter). Like the Greeks and Lavoisier, we define elements as substances that cannot be decomposed by further chemical change. It is important to remember the "chemical change" in this statement. Certain nuclear reactions can decompose the elements, but in ordinary chemical changes elements are not decomposed. Of the 106 elements, 88 can be detected on earth. Of these oxygen is the most abundant. Silicon, which forms about one fourth of the earth's crust, is second in earthly abundance. In the entire universe, hydrogen is in greatest abundance (approximately 75%) followed by helium (23%).

Compounds

When elements join together chemically in a definite proportion by weight, compounds are formed. Three familiar compounds are water, carbon dioxide, and iron oxide. Each of these is a chemical union of elements in a definite weight (really mass) proportion. Water is formed by two parts hydrogen uniting with one part oxygen. Normal water always contains 2 grams of hydrogen for every 16 grams of oxygen. For a substance to be normal water, there must be a one-to-eight ratio between the grams of hydrogen and grams of oxygen. Similarly in carbon dioxide there is one part carbon to two parts oxygen with 12 grams of carbon combining with 32 grams of oxygen. For iron oxide, two parts iron combine with three parts oxygen. The gram relationship is 56 grams of iron with 48 grams of oxygen.

If you are in a state of panic at this point, ease the panic! More must be said about chemical unions before you can independently determine the numbers for the previous ratios. However, what you should understand is that every chemical compound has its own definite weight proportion of its constituent elements. The chemical and physical properties of the compound water that we daily experience are manifested only when two parts hydrogen and one part oxygen combine in the weight relation of one to eight. Other ratios don't yield water. These concepts were concisely stated in a law by Joseph Louis Proust, a Frenchman, in 1799. His *law of definite proportions* states that, when two or more elements combine, they always combine in a fixed or definite proportion by weight.

In contrast to elements, compounds can be decomposed by chemical changes. During such processes, they are decomposed into the elements from which they were formed. Four types of compounds are most important to your understanding of chemistry: oxides, acids, bases, and salts. We have already defined oxides as substances containing two elements, one of which is oxygen. Acids, bases, and salts will be defined in later chapters. You should begin to associate these general terms with types of compounds.

CHAPTER SUMMARY

One of the physical properties of matter is its state. The three common states of matter are solid, liquid, and gas. These states are determined by the amount of energy possessed. Gases are the most energetic, while solids have the least energy. Volume, pressure, and temperature are three important variables in the study of gases. These factors are related to each other by Boyle's law and Charles' law. The liquid state is intermediate between the gaseous state and the solid state. Liquids possess some properties of both of these states. The solid state is the most ordered of these three. However, even though the particles in a solid are tightly bonded to one another, they are not motionless.

Matter may also be classified according to its type or kind. The types of matter are elements, compounds, and mixtures. Elements and compounds are described as pure substances. They enter into chemical change. Mixtures do not enter into chemical change.

QUESTIONS

1. Name the three states of matter.
2. What determines the state of matter for any given substance?
3. Which state of matter is the most energetic? Which is the least?
4. Fill in the blanks:

_____ $\longrightarrow$ _____ $\longrightarrow$ GAS

Heat absorbed

_____ $\longrightarrow$ LIQUID $\longrightarrow$ ____

Heat liberated

5. For water list:
   (a) The heat of fusion.
   (b) The heat of vaporization.
6. Why are steam burns of the skin so severe?

7. Is the setting of plaster of Paris an endothermic or exothermic process? How can you recognize this? How would you reverse this process?

8. Define sublimation. Give two examples.

9. Define entropy. Which state of matter has the most entropy? Which has the least?

10. What are the three types of matter? Which of these are classified as pure substances?

11. Define element. How many elements are found in nature? List four examples.

12. Define compound. List the four types of compounds. Give two examples of each type.

13. Define mixture. List four examples of mixtures.

14. As far as the embalmer is concerned, what is the most important compound? The most important mixture? Is plaster of Paris an element, a compound, or a mixture? Classify gypsum in the same way.

In the last chapter we subdivided matter into elements, compounds, and mixtures. We will now study the building blocks of elements and compounds.

ATOMS

The smallest particle of an element is an atom. Picture yourself dividing a chunk of carbon into smaller and smaller pieces. If you have a microscopic instrument, the atom is the ultimate particle into which the chunk can be divided and still retain carbon's chemical and physical properties. For many years scientists believed that the atom was not composed of parts. Experiments performed in the late 1800s and early 1900s showed this idea to be incorrect. A new

Nucleus

The *nucleus* is described as small, since its diameter is about 1/10,000 of the diameter of the entire atom. Although it is very small, the nucleus contains most of the mass of the atom. The other important property of a nucleus is its charge. Why is it positively charged? We answer this question by studying the composition of the nucleus. It contains several types of particles. Of these, protons and neutrons are important for your understanding of chemistry.

Protons are positively charged particles with a mass approximately equal to the mass of one hydrogen atom. Each proton has a charge of 4.8×10^{-10} electrostatic units. For convenience this charge is referred to as $+1$. All atoms contain at least one proton. The

Chapter 4
ATOMIC STRUCTURE
AND CHEMICAL BONDING

theory about the nature of atoms was formulated. This theory, which is accepted today, says atoms are composed of a small, dense, positively charged nucleus that is surrounded by one or more negatively charged particles called electrons. We will consider a nucleus and one or more electrons as the major parts of the atom.

total positive charge on a nucleus is determined by the number of protons. This number, called the *atomic number*, gives the atom its identity. All atoms with only one proton are hydrogen atoms. All atoms with six protons are carbon atoms. Similarly all atoms with eight protons are oxygen atoms. The atomic number is symbolized by the letter Z. A table of the elements with their atomic numbers is shown in Figure 4-1. Other information listed there will be explained later in this chapter.

The other nuclear particle is the *neutron*. All atoms with the exception of simple hydrogen contain neutrons. As the word suggests, these particles have no charge. Their mass is approximately the same as that of the proton. A function of neutrons is to give the nucleus stability. In atoms with many protons, repulsions of the positive charges cause nuclear instability. The neutrons provide a buffering action by separating the positive charges from one another.

Electrons

Since atoms are known to be neutral, the positive charge of the nucleus must be balanced by an equal negative charge, which is provided by *electrons*. Each electron has a charge of minus 4.8×10^{-10} electrostatic units. Similar to the $+1$ designation for the charge of the proton, each electron is said to have a charge of -1. Since electrons and protons have the same magnitude of charge but one is negative and the other positive, a neutral atom has the same number of electrons and protons. A neutral hydrogen atom ($Z = 1$) has one electron. A neutral carbon atom with six protons has six electrons. The interaction of the positively charged nucleus and the negatively charged electrons is the force which holds an atom together. The concept of unlike charges attracting is fundamental to the structure of matter.

Atomic mass

The mass of an electron is $\frac{1}{1837}$ of the mass of a hydrogen atom. Since this is much less than the mass of a proton or neutron, an atom's total mass is mainly due to the protons and neutrons. For simplicity each of these particles is defined as having a mass of one unit. This assignment is based on the experimental procedure of comparing the masses of all elements to that of a particular atom of carbon. This special carbon atom has six protons and six neutrons and has an atomic mass of 12 units. Each of these units is an *atomic mass unit*, abbreviated amu, and represents one twelfth the mass of the special carbon atom. If the numbers of protons and neutrons for any atom are added together, the atomic mass is approximately determined. This sum is generally referred to as the element's *atomic weight*.

If this procedure is followed, all atomic weights should be whole numbers. A glance at the table of atomic weights (Figure 4-1 on the opposite page) shows that many elements have atomic weights that are not whole numbers. Consideration of the following situation will explain this apparent discrepancy. If you analyzed a large quantity of chlorine atoms, two types of nuclei would be found. Both types would have 17 protons, but some would have 18 neutrons and some would have 20. You would conclude that some chlorine atoms have an atomic weight of 35 and some 37. The weight of 35.453 amu listed in the table is an average value of many chlorine atoms. The averaging takes into consideration the natural abundance of the two chlorine nuclei. In your large collection of chlorine atoms, more would have 18 neutrons than 20. The weights listed for the other elements are also average weights that take into consideration the abundance of an element's nuclei with a varying number of neutrons.

Isotopes

Atoms of the same atomic number and different masses are called *isotopes*. The two types of chlorine atoms are isotopes. The only difference between them is their number

Table of atomic numbers and atomic weights

	Symbol	Atomic number	Atomic weight		Symbol	Atomic number	Atomic weight
Actinium	Ac	89	[227]*	Molybdenum	Mo	42	95.94
Aluminum	Al	13	26.98154	Neodymium	Nd	60	144.24
Americium	Am	95	[243]	Neon	Ne	10	20.179
Antimony	Sb	51	121.75	Neptunium	Np	93	237.0482
Argon	Ar	18	39.948	Nickel	Ni	28	58.70
Arsenic	As	33	74.9216	Niobium	Nb	41	92.9064
Astatine	At	85	[210]	Nitrogen	N	7	14.0067
Barium	Ba	56	137.34	Nobelium	No	102	[259]
Berkelium	Bk	97	[247]	Osmium	Os	76	190.2
Beryllium	Be	4	9.01218	Oxygen	O	8	15.9994
Bismuth	Bi	83	208.9804	Palladium	Pd	46	106.4
Boron	B	5	10.81	Phosphorus	P	15	30.97376
Bromine	Br	35	79.904	Platinum	Pt	78	195.09
Cadmium	Cd	48	112.40	Plutonium	Pu	94	[244]
Calcium	Ca	20	40.08	Polonium	Po	84	[209]
Californium	Cf	98	[251]	Potassium	K	19	39.098
Carbon	C	6	12.011	Praseodymium	Pr	59	140.9077
Cerium	Ce	58	140.12	Promethium	Pm	61	[145]
Cesium	Cs	55	132.9054	Protactinium	Pa	91	231.0359
Chlorine	Cl	17	35.453	Radium	Ra	88	226.0254
Chromium	Cr	24	51.996	Radon	Rn	86	[222]
Cobalt	Co	27	58.9332	Rhenium	Re	75	186.207
Copper	Cu	29	63.546	Rhodium	Rh	45	102.9655
Curium	Cm	96	[247]	Rubidium	Rb	37	85.4678
Dysprosium	Dy	66	162.50	Ruthenium	Ru	44	101.07
Einsteinium	Es	99	[252]	Samarium	Sm	62	150.4
Erbium	Er	68	167.26	Scandium	Sc	21	44.9559
Europium	Eu	63	151.96	Selenium	Se	34	78.96
Fermium	Fm	100	[257]	Silicon	Si	14	28.086
Fluorine	F	9	18.99840	Silver	Ag	47	107.868
Francium	Fr	87	[223]	Sodium	Na	11	22.98977
Gadolinium	Gd	64	157.25	Strontium	Sr	38	87.62
Gallium	Ga	31	69.72	Sulfur	S	16	32.06
Germanium	Ge	32	72.59	Tantalum	Ta	73	180.9479
Gold	Au	79	196.9665	Technetium	Tc	43	[98]
Hafnium	Hf	72	178.49	Tellurium	Te	52	127.60
Helium	He	2	4.00260	Terbium	Tb	65	158.9254
Holmium	Ho	67	164.9304	Thallium	Tl	81	204.37
Hydrogen	H	1	1.0079	Thorium	Th	90	232.0381
Indium	In	49	114.82	Thulium	Tm	69	168.9342
Iodine	I	53	126.9045	Tin	Sn	50	118.69
Iridium	Ir	77	192.22	Titanium	Ti	22	47.90
Iron	Fe	26	55.847	Tungsten	W	74	183.85
Krypton	Kr	36	83.80	Unnilhexium	Unh	106	[263]
Lanthanum	La	57	138.9055	Unnilpentium	Unp	105	[262]
Lawrencium	Lr	103	[260]	Unnilquadium	Unq	104	[261]
Lead	Pb	82	207.2	Uranium	U	92	238.029
Lithium	Li	3	6.941	Vanadium	V	23	50.9414
Lutetium	Lu	71	174.97	Xenon	Xe	54	131.30
Magnesium	Mg	12	24.305	Ytterbium	Yb	70	173.04
Manganese	Mn	25	54.9380	Yttrium	Y	39	88.9059
Mendelevium	Md	101	[258]	Zinc	Zn	30	65.38
Mercury	Hg	80	200.59	Zirconium	Zr	40	91.22

*A value in brackets is the mass number of the best-known or longest-lived isotope.

of neutrons; they both have the same number of protons and electrons. Since the electrons surrounding a nucleus determine its chemical properties, isotopes of an element undergo the same types of reactions. Other familiar isotopes are those of hydrogen. Simple hydrogen represents about 99.985% of the hydrogen in nature and has a nucleus of one proton and no neutrons. Two other isotopes of hydrogen are deuterium (one proton and one neutron) and tritium (one proton and two neutrons). Water containing deuterium is called *heavy water*. Tritium is a *radioactive* element. More will be said about radioactivity in a later chapter.

Energy levels, shells, and orbits

If an atom is composed of a positively charged nucleus surrounded by electrons, is it possible to tell the exact location of the electrons? Since electrons are so small and have high velocities, the answer to this question is no. However, theories have been developed that picture electrons traveling around the nucleus at certain distances in what are referred to as *energy levels*, *shells*, or *orbits*. These three terms are synonymous and for bookkeeping purposes can be labeled by the numbers 1, 2, 3, ... or the letters K, L, M, ... The numbers usually refer to energy levels and orbits and the letters to shells. Sophisticated mathematical calculations show that each shell, energy level, or orbit holds a certain maximum number of electrons. The K shell can hold 2 electrons, the L shell holds 8, the M shell 18, and the N shell 32. See the following:

Energy level	Shell	Maximum number of electrons
1	K	2
2	L	8
3	M	18
4	N	32

By applying this bookkeeping system to individual atoms, we can begin to understand chemical reactivity. In determining how to arrange electrons in atoms, remember that electrons tend to stay close to the nucleus and at the same time as far apart from one another as possible. The driving forces behind electrons' positions are attractions between unlike charges and repulsions between like charges.

Let us consider some simple examples. Look at Figure 4-2. The one electron in hydrogen is in the first energy level or orbit or the K shell. The two electrons of helium are also in the first energy level. Since this level can hold only two electrons, the positioning of electrons in lithium ($Z = 3$) will use both the first and second energy levels. If

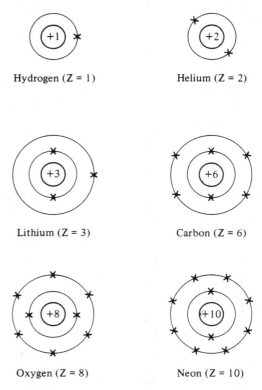

Hydrogen ($Z = 1$)   Helium ($Z = 2$)

Lithium ($Z = 3$)   Carbon ($Z = 6$)

Oxygen ($Z = 8$)   Neon ($Z = 10$)

Figure 4-2 Electron orbits and valence electrons

Table 4-1 **Atomic numbers and valence electrons**
of first 18 elements

Element	Atomic no.	Valence electrons
Hydrogen	1	1
Helium	2	2
Lithium	3	1
Beryllium	4	2
Boron	5	3
Carbon	6	4
Nitrogen	7	5
Oxygen	8	6
Fluorine	9	7
Neon	10	8
Sodium	11	1
Magnesium	12	2
Aluminum	13	3
Silicon	14	4
Phosphorus	15	5
Sulfur	16	6
Chlorine	17	7
Argon	18	8

we continue to fill in electrons, the second energy level is filled with neon ($Z = 10$). The student should be able to draw pictures such as in Figure 4-2 for all the elements from hydrogen ($Z = 1$) to argon ($Z = 18$).

For a specific atom the electrons in the outermost shell are called *valence electrons*. They determine the chemical properties of the atom. The number of valence electrons in an atom is also important, because, with a few exceptions, most atoms with the same number of valence electrons have similar chemical and physical properties. Table 4-1 lists the valence electrons for the first 18 elements.

Orbitals

As the electrons travel in their shells, is it possible to picture pathways in which they are moving? If very complicated mathematical equations are plotted, the results are three-dimensional pictures of the regions in space where electrons associated with a certain nucleus may be found. These plots are

called *orbitals*. Each orbital represents a probability of finding an electron at a given distance from the nucleus. The different shapes of orbitals are called $s, p, d, f, \ldots$. Each orbital can hold only two electrons, owing to instability caused by repulsions of negative charges. Our major concerns are the s and p orbitals.

For electrons in the first energy level (K shell) the type of orbital in which electrons have high probability of being located is an s orbital. Three-dimensionally it looks like a sphere with its center at the origin of an x, y, z coordinate system. (See Figure 4-3.) We picture the nucleus of the atom at this origin. The one electron in hydrogen and the two in helium will most likely be in an s orbital. To symbolize these positions, we use a shorthand system called the *electronic configuration* of an atom. It gives three important pieces of information: (1) the number of the energy level, (2) the type of orbital, and (3) how many electrons are in the orbitals. For hydrogen the electronic configuration is $1s^1$. The large 1 is the shell number, s is the type of orbital, and the small superscript written to the upper right of the s indicates that there is one electron in this s orbital. For helium the electronic configuration is $1s^2$.

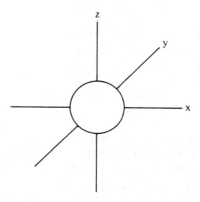

Figure 4-3 *s*-orbital

Earlier you learned that if an atom has more than two electrons, the third electron must go into the second energy level. What types of orbitals are available in this shell? The probability plots for the second level show another s orbital, which is spherical but larger than that of the first level, and a new type of orbital designated as p. Its shape is a three-dimensional figure eight oriented around an axis (x, y, z) in our model. (See Figure 4-4.) Whenever there is the possibility of electrons traveling in the shape called p orbitals, there are three possibilities, p_x, p_y, p_z. Since each orbital holds two electrons, a simple calculation shows why the L shell or second energy level can hold eight electrons:

L shell:	one s orbital	$2e^-$
	three p orbitals	$6e^-$
		$8e^-$

We can now write electronic configurations for lithium through neon. The electrons systematically fill the orbitals, so they are as close to the nucleus as possible (unlike charges attract) without repelling one another. Within a shell the electrons first fill the s orbital and then the p orbitals.

Li	($Z = 3$)	$1s^2 2s^1$
Be	($Z = 4$)	$1s^2 2s^2$
B	($Z = 5$)	$1s^2 2s^2 2p^1$
C	($Z = 6$)	$1s^2 2s^2 2p^2$
N	($Z = 7$)	$1s^2 2s^2 2p^3$
O	($Z = 8$)	$1s^2 2s^2 2p^4$
F	($Z = 9$)	$1s^2 2s^2 2p^5$
Ne	($Z = 10$)	$1s^2 2s^2 2p^6$

When writing electronic configurations, notice that all the electrons in p orbitals in a shell are grouped together. For example, nitrogen's configuration could be written $1s^2 2s^2 2p_x^1 2p_y^1 2p_z^1$, but for simplicity the p

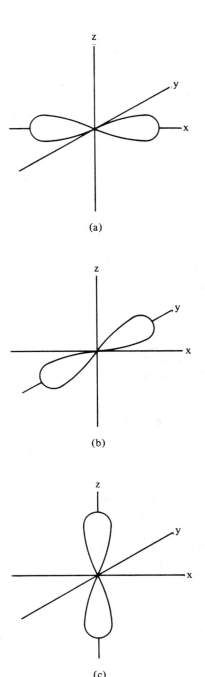

(a)

(b)

(c)

Figure 4-4 p_x (a), p_y (b), and p_z (c) orbitals

orbitals are grouped together as $2p^3$. When valence electrons are determined from the electronic configurations, the shell numbers must be considered. Again using nitrogen as an example, electrons in the $2s$ and $2p$ orbitals are added together so there are five valence electrons. A common mistake in determining valence electrons is to look only at the orbital that is written last. This procedure incorrectly says nitrogen has three valence electrons.

After the first two energy levels are filled, electrons fill the third level. In addition to an s orbital and three p orbitals, there are five d orbitals in the M shell. Each can hold two electrons. The N shell has an s orbital, three p's, five d's, and seven f orbitals. We will not be concerned with the pictures of the d and f orbitals. By knowing how many of each orbital are in the various shells, we can easily verify that the M shell can hold 18 electrons and the N shell 32.

Ions

Often in chemical interactions atoms lose or gain electrons. As a result there is no longer a balance between the positive charge on the nucleus and the negative charge of the electrons. The charged particles that result are called *ions*. If an atom loses electrons, it becomes a positively charged ion, since the number of protons in the nucleus will be greater than the number of electrons surrounding the nucleus. A negative ion is formed if an atom gains electrons, because then the number of electrons will be greater than the positive charge of the nucleus.

Electronic configurations can be written for ions. Consider lithium, which tends to lose one electron in reactions. A lithium ion has a charge of $+1$ and has an electronic configuration of $1s^2$. Magnesium ($Z = 12$) usually loses two electrons in reactions,

acquiring a charge of $+2$ with an electronic configuration of $1s^2 2s^2 2p^6$. Oxygen ($Z = 8$) gains two electrons, has a charge of -2 as an ion and an electronic configuration of $1s^2 2s^2 2p^6$. Do not be confused by the fact that both an ion of magnesium and an ion of oxygen have the same electronic configurations. The reason for this will become apparent when chemical bonding is studied. Also, remember that an atom's identity is determined by its atomic number, not by its electronic configuration.

THE PERIODIC TABLE

The elements vary considerably in their chemical and physical properties. It would be a formidable task to learn the specific properties of each of the 106 elements. Fortunately the elements can be arranged in a table so that the position of each on the table will indicate its properties. This grouping of elements is called the *periodic table*. (See Figure 4-5.)

The vertical columns in the table are called *groups* or *families*. Notice there are main groups labeled IA to VIIA, a group labeled 0, and subgroups labeled with Roman numerals and the letter B. The main groups and the zero group are the most important to us. Within each of these families the elements have the same number of valence electrons. The Roman numeral in front of the A is the number of valence electrons for that group. Hydrogen, lithium, sodium, potassium, rubidium, cesium, and francium all have one valence electron. Beryllium and all other elements in Group IIA have two valence electrons. The same idea is true for the other main groups. The elements in Group VIIA are collectively called the *halogens*. The elements in the 0 Group are very special. These are the *inert gases* or *noble gases* as

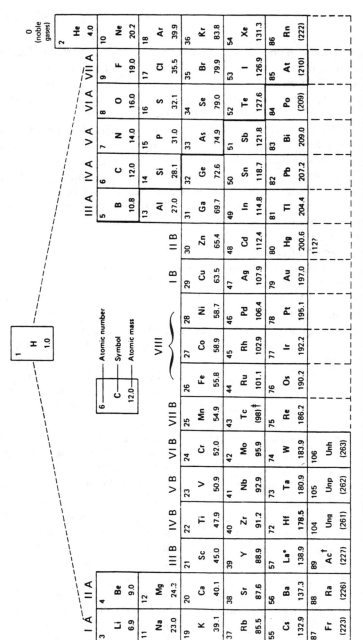

Figure 4-5 The periodic table

they are generally called today. Helium has two valence electrons and the others in this group have eight electrons in their outermost shell.

The rows on the table are called *periods*. Each element in a row has one more proton and one more electron than the element before it. The physical properties of the elements change from metal to nonmetal within a row from left to right. The elements to the left of the heavy line in each row are metals and those to the right are nonmetals. In chemical reactions metals have a great tendency to lose electrons and become positive ions. Nonmetals have a high tendency to gain electrons and become negative ions.

CHEMICAL BONDING

Atoms join together to form molecules. A *molecule* is the smallest unit into which a compound may be divided and still retain the properties of that compound. Notice the similarity between molecules and compounds, and atoms and elements. The forces that join atoms to one another are electrical in nature and result from changes in the electronic structure of the atoms. The net attractive interaction between two atoms in a molecule is called a *chemical bond*. Two important kinds of bonds are *ionic* and *covalent*. In either type of bond formation, atoms try to take on electronic configurations like the inert gases. Since these gases react only under very strenuous conditions, there must be something very stable about having two electrons in the valence shell as does helium, and eight valence electrons as do the other inert gases. In rationalizing the structure of a molecule, we must remember that atoms try to become "happy" by attaining the electronic configuration of an inert gas.

Ionic bonds

These bonds result from the transfer of electrons from one atom to another. When atoms gain or lose electrons, ions are formed. The electrostatic interaction between a positive ion and a negative ion is an ionic bond. The simplest ionic bond is formed between elements in the first family of the periodic table (exclude H) and elements of the seventh family. Two processes occur. First, if any element in the first family loses an electron, it will take on the electronic configuration of the inert gas with an atomic number one less. If the lost electron is transferred to any element in the seventh family, this gain of an electron gives the seventh-family element an electronic configuration of the inert gas immediately following it in its row. Consider the following:

Atom	Positive ion	Inert gas
Lithium $(3e^-)$	$2e^-$	Helium $(2e^-)$
Sodium $(11e^-)$	$10e^-$	Neon $(10e^-)$
Potassium $(19e^-)$	$18e^-$	Argon $(18e^-)$
Rubidium $(37e^-)$	$36e^-$	Krypton $(36e^-)$
Cesium $(55e^-)$	$54e^-$	Xenon $(54e^-)$
Francium $(87e^-)$	$86e^-$	Radon $(86e^-)$

Atom	Negative ion	Inert gas
Fluorine $(9e^-)$	$10e^-$	Neon $(10e^-)$
Chlorine $(17e^-)$	$18e^-$	Argon $(18e^-)$
Bromine $(35e^-)$	$36e^-$	Krypton $(36e^-)$
Iodine $(53e^-)$	$54e^-$	Xenon $(54e^-)$

The second step in ionic bond formation is the joining together of any of the previously formed positive ions with any of the negative ions. One of the most familiar ionic compounds is sodium chloride, ordinary table salt. Owing to the attraction between the unlike charges, ionic bonds are strong bonds. Ionic compounds generally are brittle, crystalline substances at room temperature and have high melting points.

Elements in the second family also form positive ions. To become "happy," these elements lose two electrons. The elements of the periodic table's sixth family can gain these two electrons to achieve configurations of inert gases. Examples of ionic compounds formed by this process are magnesium sulfide and calcium oxide. Ionic interactions also occur between Groups IA and VIA, and IIA and VIIA. Examples are sodium oxide and calcium chloride. A molecule of sodium oxide forms if two sodium atoms each lose one electron. One oxygen attains the inert-gas configuration by gaining the electrons. A molecule of calcium chloride forms from one calcium atom and two chlorine atoms.

Covalent bonds

These bonds are formed by the sharing of electrons between two atoms. Each bond contains two electrons, one from each atom. The simplest covalent substance is a diatomic (two atoms) molecule of hydrogen. Each hydrogen atom has one electron in the first energy level. Using H as a symbol for hydrogen and circles and crosses for electrons,

$$H° + ×H \longrightarrow H{°\atop×}H$$

The two electrons are equally shared by the two hydrogen nuclei. As in ionic compounds, the atoms bond in order to attain the stability of an inert gas. In the formation of the covalent bond of the hydrogen molecule, each hydrogen atom has the electronic configuration of helium. Other homonuclear (same type of nucleus) diatomics bond covalently. Consider chlorine with the valence-shell configuration of $3s^2 3p^5$. A chlorine atom differs from argon ($3s^2 3p^6$) by one electron. If two

chlorine (Cl) atoms share a pair of electrons, each has the argon configuration.

$$:\!\overset{\circ\circ}{\underset{\circ\circ}{C}}\!l^{\circ} + ×\overset{××}{\underset{××}{C}}l^{×} \longrightarrow :\!\overset{\circ\circ}{\underset{\circ\circ}{C}}l^{\circ}_{×}\overset{××}{\underset{××}{C}}l^{×}$$

The procedure that has been used in these examples to represent covalent interaction is: (1) draw the valence electrons on each individual atom and (2) bond the atoms so each obtains two or eight electrons and therefore has the electronic configuration of an inert gas.

The covalent bonds in hydrogen molecules and in chlorine molecules are called *single bonds*. By sharing one pair of electrons, two hydrogen atoms and likewise two chlorine atoms attain stability. Sometimes it is necessary to place more than one pair of electrons between two atoms to satisfy the inert-gas rule. Consider the formation of a diatomic oxygen molecule. Since oxygen has six valence electrons, $1s^2 2s^2 2p^4$,

$$:\!\overset{\circ\circ}{\underset{\circ\circ}{O}}\!: + ×\overset{××}{\underset{××}{O}}× \longrightarrow :\!\overset{\circ\circ}{\underset{\circ\circ}{O}}{°\atop×}\overset{××}{\underset{××}{O}}×$$

Also consider the bonding in nitrogen ($1s^2 2s^2 2p^3$) with five valence electrons,

$$\overset{\circ}{\underset{\circ}{°}}N° + ×\overset{×}{\underset{×}{N}}× \longrightarrow \overset{\circ}{\underset{\circ}{°}}N{°×\atop°×}N×$$

Stability is obtained in a diatomic nitrogen molecule only by a triple bond.

In all these homonuclear diatomic molecules, the electrons in the bond are shared equally by the bonding atoms. Since the atoms are of the same element, neither nucleus has a tendency to attract the electrons more than the other. If we compare the attractiveness for electrons of nuclei of all the elements, we find that some attract electrons more than others. A measure of the attractiveness of an atom for electrons is called *electronegativity*. On the periodic table this attractiveness of atoms for electrons increases in moving from left to right across a row and within a family from bottom to top. The most electronegative element is fluorine and the least electronegative is francium. Electronegativities influence the covalent bonding between atoms of different elements.

Let us consider the bonding in hydrogen chloride, a covalent molecule formed between one hydrogen atom and one chlorine. Following the same procedure as before,

$$H° + \overset{\times\times}{\underset{\times\times}{\times Cl}}\underset{\times}{|}^{\times} \longrightarrow H\overset{\times\times}{\underset{\times\times}{\overset{°}{\times}Cl}}\underset{\times}{|}^{\times}$$

In the molecule hydrogen is "happy" since it has the electronic configuration of helium, and chlorine is "happy" since it has the electronic configuration of argon. The electrons in the pair are not equally shared as they were either in the molecule of hydrogen or in the molecule of chlorine. The electronegativities of chlorine and hydrogen must be considered to fully describe the bond. The chlorine atom attracts electrons more than the hydrogen atom, so the electrons of the shared pair are more closely associated with the chlorine nucleus. The bonding is covalent, but the sharing is in favor of the chlorine. As a result a partial positive charge develops on the hydrogen atom and a partial negative charge on the chlorine atom. Owing to these slight charges, the bond is described as polar. Covalent bonds between unlike atoms are properly called *polar covalent bonds*.

Another very important molecule with polar covalent bonds is water. In its formation two hydrogen atoms bond with one oxygen atom.

$$H° + \overset{\times\times}{\underset{\times\times}{\times O\times}} + °H \longrightarrow H\overset{\times\times}{\underset{\times\times}{\overset{°}{\times}O\overset{°}{\times}}}H$$

Again, by bonding, each hydrogen has two electrons and the oxygen has eight. Since oxygen is more electronegative than hydrogen, oxygen has a partial negative charge and each hydrogen is partially positive. These polar bonds in water are the basis for many of its unique properties and influence its reactions.

Oxidation numbers

Oxidation numbers are positive and negative numbers that are assigned to atoms to show whether they bond to other atoms by gaining or losing electron density. Certain rules are followed in the assignment of these numbers. Atoms in ionic compounds that lose electrons have positive oxidation numbers corresponding to the charges they acquire in the formation of the ions. Similarly the atoms in ionic compounds that gain electrons have negative oxidation numbers. In the ionic compound sodium chloride, sodium's oxidation number is $+1$ and that of chlorine is -1.

In the formation of covalent compounds the assignment of oxidation numbers is somewhat more arbitrary. In a homonuclear diatomic such as a molecule of hydrogen, oxygen, nitrogen, fluorine, chlorine, bromine, or iodine, each atom has an oxidation number of zero. Since there is equal sharing of the electrons in these bonds, neither atom has really gained electron density in comparison to its bonding partner. When molecules form polar covalent bonds, the assignment of oxidation numbers gives both electrons in the polar bond to the more electronegative atom. The atom acquires a negative oxidation number and the other atom a positive oxidation number. Remember the polar covalent bonds in hydrogen chloride and water. Since chlorine is more electronegative than hydrogen, the chlorine has a -1 oxidation number and the hydrogen a $+1$. In water oxygen pulls an electron from two hydrogen atoms. As a result, oxygen is -2 and each hydrogen is again $+1$. It is convenient to remember that in most compounds, oxygen will have an oxidation number of -2 and hydrogen of $+1$. These rules do not apply if either oxygen or hydrogen is bonded to itself. In both ionic and covalent compounds, the sum of the oxidation numbers of the atoms of the molecule must be zero to show the neutral charge of the molecule.

CHAPTER SUMMARY

The smallest particle of an element is an atom. All atoms are composed of a nucleus and one or more negatively charged electrons. All nuclei are small, dense, and positively charged. One or more protons in a nucleus are the source of its positive charge. The number of protons, the atomic number, determines the identity of an element. Another nuclear particle is the neutron. It has no charge and gives stability to a nucleus. Atoms of the same element with different numbers of neutrons are isotopes.

In a neutral atom the number of protons equals the number of electrons. Plots of the mathematical probabilities of finding electrons at given distances from the nucleus are orbitals designated as s, p, d, and f. The elements in the outermost shell of an atom are the valence electrons. They determine an element's chemical properties. Elements are organized on the periodic table on the basis of similarities in chemical and physical properties.

Atoms form molecules by chemical bonds. An overall picture of bonding views ionic compounds and pure covalent compounds as two extremes. For the formation of ionic bonds, electrons are actually transferred from one atom to another. In contrast, the formation of a pure covalent bond results from the equal sharing of electrons between like atoms. Between these two extremes is the polar covalent bond. Sharing of electrons occurs, but the atom of greater electronegativity experiences the effects of the electron more than the nucleus of the electropositive atom. In all types of bonding, the goal of each atom is to attain the stability of the inert gas.

QUESTIONS

1. Describe the major parts of the atom.
2. State the distinguishing characteristics of protons, neutrons, and electrons.
3. An atom has four protons and five neutrons. What is its atomic number? What is its approximate atomic weight? Write its electronic configuration.
4. An atom has an atomic weight of 200. It contains 80 protons. How many neutrons does it have?
5. What are isotopes? State examples.
6. Draw pictures of the distribution of electrons in shells or energy levels for all elements from hydrogen ($Z = 1$) to argon ($Z = 18$). Indicate the number of valence electrons for each element.
7. What is an orbital? Draw pictures of s orbitals and p orbitals.
8. Write electronic configurations for
   (a) Sodium.
   (b) Phosphorus.
   (c) Argon.

(d) An ion of nitrogen with -3 charge.

(e) An ion of aluminum with $+3$ charge.

9. Why are oxygen and sulfur in the same family on the periodic table?

10. Where on the periodic table are
    (a) Inert gases.   (b) Metals.
    (c) Nonmetals.   (d) Halogens.

11. Show how the following bonds occur:

(a) Potassium chloride.

(b) Calcium iodide.

(c) Sodium oxide.

What kind of bonds are these?

12. Show bond formation in
    (a) I_2.   (b) CCl_4.   (c) N_2.
    (d) CH_4.   (e) H_2S.

13. Compare the electronegativities of
    (a) K and Br.
    (b) F, Cl, Br, I.

SYMBOLS

We live in a society that is in love with symbols. Everywhere we look we see GM automobiles, IBM computers, RCA televisions, and so on. These lettered symbols are nothing more than abbreviations for longer names. Most people know what is meant by AT&T or GE, but when they encounter Hg, O, or Na in a chemistry course they are quite easily flustered. The appearance of something like H_2SO_4 further unbalances their composure, and an expression such as

$$CuSO_4 + 2H_2O \longrightarrow Cu(OH)_2 + H_2SO_4$$

comes close to driving them into a state of abject panic. The problem is a lack of familiarity with the symbols. When we see symbols such as FTC, we can relate this to

acteristics we can go on to understand the interaction of the elements to form compounds, and the interaction of elements and compounds in other chemical reactions.

There are 88 elements that naturally occur in our surrounding environment. Of these only about 24 will be routinely used in chemical interactions. The symbols for these elements appear in two forms: one-letter symbols that are always expressed as a single capital letter, and two-letter symbols that always contain one capital letter and one lower-case letter.

A list of the typical elements with which we will be dealing and their symbols are shown at the top of the next page.

Of these 24 elements, 9 have one-letter symbols and 15 have two-letter symbols. The purpose is to distinguish among a number of

Chapter 5
CHEMICAL SHORTHAND: SYMBOLS, FORMULAS, AND EQUATIONS

an organization known as the Federal Trade Commission because we have heard it so many times and we are familiar with the characteristics of that organization. The connection between the symbol Fe and the element iron, however, is less clear because we have not been exposed to it enough and we are not familiar with the characteristics of the elements that these abbreviations represent. When we understand these char-

elements that begin with the same letter. For instance, since calcium, carbon, and chlorine all begin with the letter C, the symbol C can represent only one of them. The others must be distinguished on the basis of a two-letter abbreviation.

The list of elements provokes an additional question. What about the symbols in which the letters bear little or no resemblance to the original word? Inspecting the

Name	Symbol	Name	Symbol
Aluminum	Al	Magnesium	Mg
Argon	Ar	Manganese	Mn
Bromine	Br	Mercury	Hg
Calcium	Ca	Neon	Ne
Carbon	C	Nitrogen	N
Chlorine	Cl	Oxygen	O
Copper	Cu	Phosphorus	P
Fluorine	F	Potassium	K
Helium	He	Silver	Ag
Hydrogen	H	Sodium	Na
Iodine	I	Sulfur	S
Iron	Fe	Zinc	Zn

list, we can identify six elements that fall into this category.

- Copper   Cu
- Iron   Fe
- Mercury   Hg
- Potassium K
- Silver   Ag
- Sodium   Na

The symbols represent the original Latin words for these elements. Remember that chemistry is an ancient science with its roots in alchemy. Rearranging these elements alphabetically, we can try to make some sense of the symbolism.[1]

- Ag = silver: The Latin name for silver is *argentum*, which stems from a Sanskrit word that means "to shine." Thus silver was named for its white shiny appearance.

- Cu = copper: This metal has been known since ancient times. The chief supplier of copper to the Roman Empire was Cyprus. The metal became known as *cyprium* and eventually the Latin *cuprum*, from which we derive our symbol.

- Fe = iron: The discovery of iron dates back even farther than copper and is lost in the past. The Anglo-Saxon name, *iren*, describes the smooth appearance and feel of this metal. *Ferrum* is the Latin name for iron. *Farrarius* is the Latin word for blacksmith.

- Hg = mercury: The word *hydrargyrum* looks formidible enough until we break it down: *hydro* = water; *argyrum* = silver—literally fluid silver or quicksilver, as it is commonly known. The name is merely an appropriate description of this liquid metallic element.

- K = potassium: The Latin term for potassium is *kalium*. This is the Latinized form of the Arabic word, *kali*, for potash. It was originally obtained by leaching the ashes of burned wood and boiling down the lye in large open kettles. The residue, a white solid, was called *potash* because it was made from ashes in pots.

- Na = sodium: The common name for sodium is *soda*. This comes from the Arabic word *suda*, meaning headache, because soda was the chief remedy used for headaches by the ancient Arabians. *Natrium* is the derivation of the Latin word *natron*, which referred to a native carbonate of soda which was found in many dried-up lakes in Egypt. Immersion in natron solutions was one of the methods of ancient Egyptian embalming.

Every one of the elements and their respective symbols could be explained in a similar manner, but we must not lose sight of our goal, which is the manipulation of these abbreviations in order to illustrate chemical change.

A symbol represents:

- The name of the element.
- One atom of the element.
- The atomic weight of the element.

---

[1]Word origins are from Harry Wain, *The Story Behind the Word*, 1958. Courtesy of Charles C Thomas, Publisher, Springfield, Illinois.

FORMULAS

Compounds have been defined as two or more elements chemically combined in a definite proportion by weight. Both the chemical combination and the definite proportion by weight are determined by the atomic structure of the elements involved.

The previous section on atomic structure illustrated that in order to be "happy," elements have to either acquire or give up electrons to achieve the inert-gas configuration. That is why most elements in our environment are not present in their natural form but instead are found in a combined state as compounds.

The two or more elements that comprise a compound are called the *constituents* of that compound and usually involve a metallic portion (written first) and a nonmetallic portion (written last). Metallic elements generally have positive oxidation numbers while nonmetallic elements have negative oxidation numbers. These numbers are based on the valence electrons, which are located in the outermost orbit of the atom.

Now we can add the oxidation numbers to our list of the elements.

Symbol	Type	Oxidation number
Al	Metal	+3
Ar	Inert gas	0
Br	Nonmetal	−1
Ca	Metal	+2
C	Nonmetal	+4 or −4
Cl	Nonmetal	−1
Cu	Metal	+1 or +2
F	Nonmetal	−1
He	Inert gas	0
H	Special	+1
I	Nonmetal	−1
Fe	Metal	+2 or +3
Mg	Metal	+2
Mn	Metal	+4
Hg	Metal	+1 or +2
Ne	Inert gas	0

Symbol	Type	Oxidation number
N	Nonmetal	−3
O	Nonmetal	−2
P	Metal	+3
K	Metal	+1
Ag	Metal	+1
Na	Metal	+1
S	Nonmetal	−2
Zn	Metal	+2

Formulas represent the abbreviation for a compound. Just as GM may represent General Motors, KI is the abbreviation for potassium iodide (metal written first, nonmetal written second). The object of formula writing is to achieve an inert-gas configuration for each of the elements involved. The end result is that the compound formed has a net electronic charge of zero. Thus:

$$K^{+1} + I^{-1} = KI$$

because $1 - 1 = 0$ or $(+1) + (-1) = 0$.

Formula writing introduces the convention of position numbering. Formulas contain two types of position numbers, superscripts and subscripts. *Superscripts* are written above and to the right of the symbols. *Subscripts* are written below and to the right of the symbol. Where no subscript number appears, it is inferred to be 1, because by definition a symbol represents one atom of an element.

In chemical formulas, superscripts represent the oxidation numbers, whereas subscripts represent the *definite proportion by weight* in which the elements combine in order to achieve the inert-gas configuration (a net charge of zero).

Consider the formula for water, H_2O, which may be completely illustrated as follows:

superscript

$$H_2^{+1} O_{1\ (\text{implied})}^{-2}$$

subscript

A further expansion would show:

$H^{+1}H^{+1}O^{-2}$ Net charge: $1 + 1 - 2 = 0$

Oxygen needs two electrons to satisfy its outermost orbit. Since hydrogen has only one electron to give up, two hydrogens are needed to complete the outer orbit of one oxygen.

Any time two elements of opposite charges with the same oxidation numbers combine, there is no need to use subscript numbers. For example:

$K^{+1}I^{-1}$
$Ca^{+2}O^{-2}$
$Al^{+3}N^{-3}$

The net charge is automatically zero. However, problems arise when the oxidation numbers are different (as in the case of water) and that is why subscript numbers are used. For example, if we combine K^{+1} with O^{-2}, the formula is written K_2O for the same reason that water is written H_2O. However, if we combine Ca^{+2} with Cl^{-1}, the process is reversed and the correct formula is $CaCl_2$ ($Ca^{+2}Cl_2^{-1}$ or $Ca^{+2}Cl^{-1}Cl^{-1}$).

An interesting situation arises when both of the combining elements have oxidation numbers greater than one. For example:

Mg^{+2} and N^{-3}

The lowest common denominator for 2 and 3 is 6. Thus the formula becomes

$Mg_3^{+2}N_2^{-3}$ or Mg_3N_2

The reverse is similar. Combine Al^{+3} with O^{-2}:

$Al^{+3}O^{-2}$

The lowest common denominator is still six, but this time the formula is

$Al_2^{+3}O_3^{-2}$

Remember, when writing formulas:

1. Write the positive (metallic) part first and the negative (nonmetallic) part last.
2. Find the lowest common denominator.
3. Multiply the subscript number of each symbol by the superscript number.
4. Add the totals to be certain that the net charge is zero.

Sometimes a group of atoms behaves as if it were a single atom. This group has its own charge and name and is called a *radical*. Consider the following:

Name	Formula	Charge
Ammonium	NH_4	$+1$
Bicarbonate	HCO_3	-1
Chlorate	ClO_3	-1
Hydroxide	OH	-1
Nitrate	NO_3	-1
Nitrite	NO_2	-1
Carbonate	CO_3	-2
Sulfate	SO_4	-2
Sulfite	SO_3	-2
Borate	BO_3	-3
Tetraborate	B_4O_7	-2
Phosphate	PO_4	-3

In the writing of formulas, radicals follow the same rules as single atoms: positive part first, negative part last, net charge zero. Since there is only one positive radical in this list, they will usually appear at the end of the formula for a compound.

Combine sodium (Na^{+1}) with the hydroxide radical (OH^{-1}):

$Na^{+1}OH^{-1}$

Thus,

NaOH

Note that no subscript numbers are needed because the oxidation numbers are the same (both are 1).

The formula NaOH represents the combination of two units (one positive and one negative), but it also represents *three* elements: sodium (Na), oxygen (O), and hydrogen (H).

Combine calcium (Ca^{+2}) with hydroxide (OH^-):

$$Ca^{+2}OH^{-1}$$

In order to obtain the -2 necessary to counterbalance the $+2$ of the Ca, we must recognize that the two elements O and H are behaving as if they were a single unit, OH^{-1}. Therefore we *must* multiply *the entire unit* by two. To do this we place the radical in parentheses and place the subscript number *outside* the parentheses. This means that the correct formula for the combination of calcium and hydroxide is

$$Ca(OH)_2 \qquad (1)$$

not

$$CaOH_2 \qquad (2)$$

Expanding the first reveals

$$Ca^{+2}(OH)_2^{-1}$$

that is,

$$Ca^{+2}(OH)^{-1}(OH)^{-1} \qquad \text{Net charge zero}$$

Expanding the second:

$$Ca^{+2}O^{-2}H_2^{+1}$$

or

$$Ca^{+2}O^{-2}H^{+1}H^{+1} \qquad \text{Net charge } \underline{+2}$$

This second form, $CaOH_2$, is one of the most common errors made among beginning students of chemistry. Parentheses must be used to indicate that the entire radical (both the O and the H) is being multiplied by two. Since the subscript number multiplies *only* the symbol to which it is attached, OH_2 means that you are multiplying *only* the H and not the O. Remember that a radical is

defined as a *group of atoms* that behaves as if it were a single atom. The *group* has a unique name *and its own charge*.

Other radicals are handled in the same way. Combine sodium (Na^+) with the bicarbonate radical (HCO_3^-). Note that when the charge is 1 ($+$ or $-$) the number is implied and only the charge is shown. Some chemists follow through completely with this idea, and Ca^{+2} becomes Ca^{++}, SO_4^{-2} becomes SO_4^{--}, and so on:

$$Na^+HCO_3^-$$

The charges are both 1, so there is no need for additional subscript numbers. However, if we combine Ca^{+2} with HCO_3^-, we get

$$Ca^{+2}(HCO_3)_2^{-1}$$

In the final written formula, the superscripts are usually dropped. Thus

$$Ca(HCO_3)_2$$

is the correct formula for calcium bicarbonate.

MOLECULAR WEIGHT

If the formula for a compound is known, it is possible to calculate its molecular weight. In Chapter 4 you learned that each element has an atomic weight. The units of these weights are atomic mass units. For example, the atomic weight of hydrogen is 1 amu and of oxygen is 16 amu. If this concept is extended to compounds, the molecular weight of a compound is the sum of the atomic weights of all the atoms present in one molecule of the substance. Since the formula of water is H_2O, a molecule of water contains two atoms of hydrogen and one atom of oxygen. The molecular weight of water is 18 amu. This is calculated by

Hydrogen	1.0 amu
Hydrogen	1.0 amu
Oxygen	16.0 amu
Water	18.0 amu

If we add the idea of molecular weight to what has been said concerning formulas and compounds, we can say that a formula represents

○ One molecule of a compound.
○ The molecular weight of the compound.

NAMING OF COMPOUNDS

There are four types of compounds: acids, bases, salts, and oxides. Although each one of these types has its own method of naming and subclassification, there is a more general way to name all compounds according to their formulas. The simplest situation is one in which there is a compound containing a metal and a radical. The metal is named first and the radical second, just as the formula is written. Thus, $Ca(HCO_3)_2$ is named calcium bicarbonate, $Ca(OH)_2$ is calcium hydroxide, and $NaOH$ is sodium hydroxide. Note that the subscript numbers have no bearing on the names. Therefore $Ca(OH)_2$ is called calcium hydroxide, not calcium dihydroxide.

Combine Al^{+3} and SO_4^{-2}:

$$Al_2^{+3}(SO_4)_3^{-2}$$
$$Al_2(SO_4)_3 = \text{aluminum sulfate}$$

The other situation involved in naming compounds occurs when a metal element is combined with *one* other nonmetallic element. In those cases, the name of the metallic element remains intact, but the nonmetallic element acquires an *ide* suffix. Thus:

○ Al_2O_3 is named aluminum oxide.
○ Mg_3N_2 is named magnesium nitride.
○ $CaCl_2$ is named calcium chloride.
○ CaO is named calcium oxide.
○ KI is named potassium iodide.
○ H_2O (water) may be named hydrogen oxide!

In all the previous examples the names of the compounds did not reflect the presence of subscript numbers. If there is more than one possible combination of the constituents of a compound, then the subscript numbers do influence the name.

○ CO = carbon monoxide
○ CO_2 = carbon dioxide

○ SO_2 = sulfur dioxide
○ SO_3 = sulfur trioxide

Another influence on the naming of compounds is the oxidation state of certain elements called *bivalent metals*. Referring back to the table of oxidation numbers, we find three of these metals listed:

○ Cu: +1 or +2
○ Hg: +1 or +2
○ Fe: +2 or +3

The older naming method used the suffix *ous* for the lower oxidation number and *ic* for the higher number. Thus:

○ Cu (+1) = cuprous,
  Cu (+2) = cupric.
○ Hg (+1) = mercurous,
  Hg (+2) = mercuric.
○ Fe (+2) = ferrous,
  Fe (+3) = ferric.

○ FeO ($Fe^{+2}O^{-2}$) is called *ferrous* oxide.
○ Fe_2O_3 ($Fe_2^{+3}O_3^{-2}$) is called *ferric* oxide.

Contemporary nomenclature simply indicates in parentheses the oxidation state in

Roman numerals.

- FeO is called Iron(II) oxide.
- Fe_2O_3 is called Iron(III) oxide.

EQUATIONS

Symbols are abbreviations for elements and *formulas* are abbreviations for compounds. An *equation* is an abbreviation for a chemical change. We will discuss four types of these changes: synthesis, decomposition, double replacement, and single replacement.

WRITING EQUATIONS

When we wrote the formulas for all the previous compounds, we expressed the end result of a chemical change called *synthesis* or *combination*. For example, let us combine mercury with sulfur, keeping in mind that neutral atoms do not express their oxidation number until they are in the compound.

$$Hg^0 \quad + \quad S^0 = Hg^{+2}S^{-2} \text{ Net charge zero}$$
$$\text{unhappy} \quad \text{unhappy} \qquad \text{happy}$$

This abbreviation is called an equation because the = sign expresses a principle called the *law of conservation of mass*. The law may be stated as follows: In a chemical change, matter is neither created nor destroyed, merely changed in form. In other words, the total amount of what is produced is equal to the total amount of starting material. By convention, an arrow replaces the = sign to indicate the direction of the reaction.

$$\underset{\text{reactant}}{Hg} + \underset{\text{reactant}}{S} \longrightarrow \underset{\text{product}}{HgS}$$

Substances written on the left of the arrow are known as *reactants*. Substances written on the right of the arrow are known as *products*. One way to identify synthesis reactions is that there are two reactants, but only one product. Remember that elements chemically combine in a definite proportion by weight to form compounds. The definite proportion by weight is determined by the oxidation numbers. Because of their structures, certain atoms take the form of diatomic molecules. This means that whenever they are written by themselves they must contain a subscript of two. For example:

- Hydrogen (H_2)
- Oxygen (O_2)
- Nitrogen (N_2)
- Fluorine (F_2)
- Chlorine (Cl_2)
- Bromine (Br_2)
- Iodine (I_2)

Combining carbon with oxygen, the correct expression for the reactants is

$$C + O_2$$

because oxygen is diatomic. To complete the expression:

$$C + O_2 \longrightarrow C^{+4}O^{-2} \qquad \text{Net charge} +2$$

Therefore:

$$C + O_2 \longrightarrow C^{+4}O_2^{-2} \quad \text{Net charge zero}$$

It is merely coincidental that O_2 is the same on both the product and the reactants side. It does not combine that way. Oxygen and the other diatomic molecules are *only* written with the subscript two when they are *alone*. When they are combined, the subscript number reflects the definite proportion by weight of the compound in which these elements are merely one constituent. Thus:

$$H_2 + O_2 \longrightarrow H^{+1}O^{-2}$$

Therefore:

$$H_2 + O_2 \longrightarrow H_2^{+1}O^{-2} \quad \text{Net charge zero}$$

Not:

$$H_2 + O_2 \longrightarrow H_2O_2$$

because

$$H_2 + O_2 \longrightarrow H_2^{+1}O_2^{-2} \quad \text{Net charge} -2$$

BALANCING EQUATIONS

The last step in writing equations is called *balancing*. This step assures us that the = sign is valid and the law of conservation of mass is intact. However, it involves the introduction of a new position number called a *coefficient number*. This number is written to the left of and on the same level as the symbol or the formula. The coefficient number multiplies through everything in that symbol or formula.

$$2H_2 = 4H = H + H + H + H$$

coefficient subscript

As in the case of the subscript numbers, the absence of a coefficient number means that number is 1.

The first two equations required no balancing:

$$Hg + S \longrightarrow HgS$$

because

$$1\,Hg + 1\,S \longrightarrow 1\,HgS$$

Remember, the coefficient number multiplies *each part* of the symbol or formula.

In a similar manner:

$$C + O_2 \longrightarrow CO_2$$

because

$$1\,C + 1\,O_2 \longrightarrow 1\,CO_2$$

Therefore, each side has one carbon and two oxygens. However, in the last equation, the sides are *not* equal.

$$H_2 + O_2 \longrightarrow H_2O$$

because here

$$2\,H + 2\,O \longrightarrow 2\,H, \text{ but only 1 O.}$$

This is rectified by using the coefficient 2 on the right side of the equation.

$$H_2 + O_2 \longrightarrow \underline{2}\,H_2O$$

Remember, a coefficient is written to the *left* and at the same level as the symbol or formula.

A common error associated with this expression is

$$H_2 + O_2 \longrightarrow H_2O_{\underline{2}},$$

This is *doubly* wrong. *First*, as previously shown, this changes the definite proportion by weight and does not make the net charge equal to zero. *Second*, in balancing, *only* coefficient numbers are used.

Let us reexamine our progress:

$$H_2 + O_2 \longrightarrow 2\,H_2O$$
$$2\,H \quad 2\,O \qquad 4\,H, 2\,O$$

The oxygen is balanced, but the hydrogen on the product side is overloaded. The next step is to go to the left side of the equation, and, still using coefficient numbers, to balance the hydrogen.

$$\underline{2}\,H_2 + O_2 \longrightarrow 2\,H_2O$$
$$4\,H \quad 2\,O \qquad 2\,H_2O$$

Diagramatically:

$$\begin{array}{ll} HH \\ HH \end{array} + OO \longrightarrow \begin{array}{l} HHO \\ HHO \end{array}$$
$$4\,H \quad 2\,O \qquad 4\,H, 2\,O$$

The writing of a chemical equation may be summarized in three progressive steps.

1. Write the correct formulas for the reactants using subscript numbers and making the net charge of each zero.

2. Do the same thing for the products, again using subscript numbers and making the net charge of each zero.

3. Balance the equation, using coefficient numbers.

These steps are both progressive and mutually exclusive. That is, when you reach step 3, balancing, you may *not* go back and change subscript numbers. Conversely, coefficient numbers may *not* be used in steps 1 and 2, formula writing.

DECOMPOSITION

The second type of chemical change is *decomposition*, which is the opposite of synthesis. Decomposition is defined as the breakdown of a compound into its constituent parts. It is an extremely important reaction, since it is the process embalming attempts to retard. Decomposition of biochemical compounds is quite complex and is best introduced by a description of simple inorganic decomposition. Just as a synthesis reaction may be identified by the presence of two reactants and one product, decomposition is identified by the presence of one reactant and two products. The synthesis reaction

$$2 H_2 + O_2 \longrightarrow 2 H_2O$$

may be reversed by applying a current of electricity to water. H_2O, then, becomes the reactant, and its constituents become the products.

$$H_2O \xrightarrow{\text{electricity}} H_2 + O_2$$

Note again that when hydrogen and oxygen are written by themselves, they must be written with the subscript 2. The balancing proceeds in the same manner.

$$H_2O \longrightarrow H_2 + O_2$$
$$2 H, \underline{1 O} \qquad 2 H \quad \underline{2 O}$$

Therefore:

$$2 H_2O \longrightarrow H_2 + O_2$$
$$4 H, \underline{2 O} \qquad 2 H \quad \underline{2 O}$$

Thus:

$$2 H_2O \longrightarrow 2 H_2 + O_2$$
$$\underline{4 H}, 2 O \qquad \underline{4 H} \quad 2 O$$

Another example is the decomposition of mercuric oxide by heat. The name mercuric oxide indicates that this compound contains only two elements (definition of oxide). The word mercuric indicates the higher of two oxidation numbers of the bivalent metal mercury. Consulting the table yields the appropriate numbers.

$$Hg(ic) = +2, \qquad O = -2$$

The equation begins:

$$Hg^{+2}O^{-2} \longrightarrow$$

Since this compound contains only the constituents mercury and oxygen, the products must be

$$HgO \longrightarrow Hg + O_2$$

Oxygen is diatomic. Mercury is not diatomic. This completes steps 1 and 2.

Step 3—balancing:

$$HgO \longrightarrow Hg + O_2$$
$$1 Hg, \underline{1 O} \qquad 1 Hg \quad \underline{2 O}$$

Therefore:

$$2 HgO \longrightarrow Hg + O_2$$
$$2 Hg, \underline{2 O} \qquad 1 Hg \quad \underline{2 O}$$

Finally:

$$2 HgO \longrightarrow 2 Hg + O_2$$
$$\underline{2 Hg}, 2 O \qquad \underline{2 Hg} \quad 2 O$$

Diagramatically:

$$HgO \atop HgO \longrightarrow {Hg \atop Hg} + O\ O$$

2 Hg, 2 O   2 Hg   2 O

Remember:

o Subscripts are used *only* for formula writing.

o Balancing (coefficient numbers) satisfies the equals sign (definition of equation).

o The total amount of products must equal the total amount of reactants.

DOUBLE-REPLACEMENT (METATHESIS) REACTIONS

The third major type of chemical reaction is *double replacement*. Two significant examples are *neutralization* and *hydrolysis*. Both of these are integral to the understanding of essential embalming processes and will be referred to extensively throughout the remainder of this text.

Double-replacement reactions are identified by the presence of two reactants and two products, both of which are compounds. The products are obtained by "changing partners" of the plus and minus parts of the reactants. Consider, for example, the reaction between sodium hydroxide and hydrogen chloride.

Step 1: *First* we obtain the formulas for these reactants from the appropriate tables.

o Sodium hydroxide = sodium (Na^+) combined with hydroxide (OH^-).

o Plus part first, minus part second:

Na^+OH^-

o The oxidation numbers are both 1, so the formula is simply NaOH. Hydrogen chloride = hydrogen (H^+) combined with chlorine (Cl^-):

H^+Cl^- or   HCl

o The correct expression for the reactants is

$NaOH + HCl \longrightarrow$

This completes step 1. Note that no subscript numbers are necessary.

Step 2: Write the correct formulas for the products. The products are obtained by swapping the plus part of one reactant for the plus part of the other reactant. Thus, both parts are replaced (double replacement).

$$Na^+OH^- + H^+Cl^- \longrightarrow H^+OH^- + Na^+Cl^-$$

Since there is only one of each of the constituents of the reactants, and each of these has the same oxidation number, there is no need for the use of either subscripts or coefficients. If only everything could be this simple! Then there would be no need for steps 2 and 3.

Let us go to the other extreme so that all the steps in writing an equation will be fully illustrated. Write an equation for the reaction between aluminum hydroxide and hydrogen sulfate.

Step 1: Write the correct formulas for the reactants.

o Aluminum hydroxide = Al^{+3} combined with OH^-.

$Al^{+3}OH^{-1}$

Therefore:

$Al^{+3}(OH)_3^{-1}$ or $Al(OH)_3$

o Hydrogen sulfate = H^+ combined with SO_4^{-2}.

$H^{+1}SO_4^{-2}$

Therefore:

$H_2^{+1}SO_4^{-2}$ or H_2SO_4

○ Step 1 completed:

$$Al(OH)_3 + H_2SO_4 \longrightarrow$$

Step 2: Write the correct formulas for the products. Once again the products are obtained by changing partners.

$$Al^{+3}(OH)_3^{-1} + H_2^{+1}SO_4^{-2} \longrightarrow$$
$$H^{+1}OH^{-1} + Al^{+3}SO_4^{-2}$$

A new concept emerges: The only subscript numbers that are transferred to the products (right) side of this expression are those which are *part of a radical*. Therefore, SO_4^{-2} transfers intact. However, $(OH)_3$ is not a radical. OH^{-1} is the hydroxide radical. The reason for the subscript 3 is to give the *definite proportion by weight* when in combination with the Al^{+3}. When the OH^{-1} combines with something else, the definite proportion by weight will reflect the *new constituent*. Another common error:

$$Al(OH)_3 + H_2SO_4 \longrightarrow H_2(OH)_3 + AlSO_4$$

This violates both the rule concerning radicals, and the previously mentioned one about diatomic molecules.

Continuing with step 2:

$$Al(OH)_3 + H_2SO_4 \longrightarrow$$
$$H^{+1}OH^{-1} + Al^{+3}SO_4^{-2}$$

The proportion of hydrogen and hydroxide is correct, since the net charge is zero. However, aluminum is plus three and sulfate is minus two. The lowest common denominator is six. So the correct formula for aluminum sulfate is

$$Al_2^{+3}(SO_4)_3^{-2}$$

or

$$Al_2(SO_4)_3$$

Note that the radical is set in parentheses because the SO_4 represents two *different* elements, but the Al is not since it is a *two-letter*

symbol for one element. Thus:

$$Al(OH)_3 + H_2SO_4 \longrightarrow HOH + Al_2(SO_4)_3$$

This completes step 2. Step 3 cannot be commenced before completion of step 2.

Step 3: Balancing the equation. Remember:

○ Only coefficient numbers can be used.
○ Subscript numbers cannot be changed.

Therefore:

$$Al(OH)_3 + H_2SO_4 \longrightarrow HOH + Al_2(SO_4)_3$$

| 1 Al | 2 H | 1 H | 2 Al |
| 3 OH | 1 SO_4 | 1 OH | 3 SO_4 |

We first notice that there is more aluminum on the right. Thus:

$$\underline{2}\,Al(OH)_3 + H_2SO_4 \longrightarrow HOH + Al_2(SO_4)_3$$

| 2 Al | 2 H | 1 H | 2 Al |
| 6 OH | 1 SO_4 | 1 OH | 3 SO_4 |

And, since there is also more SO_4^{-2} on the right:

$$2\,Al(OH)_3 + \underline{3}\,H_2SO_4 \longrightarrow HOH + Al_2(SO_4)_3$$

| 2 Al | 6 H | 1 H | 2 Al |
| 6 OH | 3 SO_4 | 1 OH | 3 SO_4 |

Everything is now balanced with the exception of the water on the products side. Therefore:

$$2\,Al(OH)_3 + 3\,H_2SO_4 \longrightarrow \underline{6}\,HOH + Al_2(SO_4)_3$$

| 2 Al | 6 H | 6 H | 2 Al |
| 6 OH | 3 SO_4 | 6 OH | 3 SO_4 |

In summary:

Step 1. $Al(OH)_3 + H_2SO_4 \longrightarrow$
Step 2. $Al(OH)_3 + H_2SO_4 \longrightarrow HOH + Al_2(SO_4)_3$
Step 3. $2\ Al(OH)_3 + 3\ H_2SO_4 \longrightarrow 6\ HOH + Al_2(SO_4)_3$

Any double-replacement reaction can be successfully completed by following this procedure.

Upon initial observation, the foregoing seems to be extremely cumbersome, but you will find that it forms an important foundation for the expression of the many chemical changes which we will study next.

CHAPTER SUMMARY

When mercuric oxide is heated, it decomposes to yield its constituent elements mercury and oxygen. This is a formal statement of a chemical change, which may be abbreviated by a form of chemical shorthand called an equation. The equation for this change is

$$2\,HgO \longrightarrow 2\,Hg + O_2$$

A balanced chemical equation expresses the law of conservation of mass. The substances to the left of the arrow are called reactants. The substances to the right of the arrow are called products. Both the reactants and the products are abbreviated by symbols and formulas. This chapter shows a progression, starting with the simplest abbreviations for elements and ending with a logical method for balancing complex chemical expressions.

Three types of chemical equations are explained in detail: synthesis, decomposition, and double replacement. The fourth, single replacement, will be discussed in a later chapter.

QUESTIONS

1. What is the difference between:
   (a) OH and 2 OH.
   (b) OH_2 and $(OH)_2$.
   (c) $(OH)_2$ and 2 OH.
2. Write the names for the compounds represented by the formulas written in question 6.
3. Define:
   (a) Symbol.
   (b) Formula.
   (c) Equation.
4. Complete and balance the following reactions:
   (a) $C + O_2 \longrightarrow$
   (b) $H_2 + O_2 \longrightarrow$
   (c) $HgO \longrightarrow$
   (d) $H_2O \longrightarrow$
   (e) $AgNO_3 + HCl \longrightarrow$
   (f) $Ca(OH)_2 + HNO_3 \longrightarrow$
5. Identify the equations in question 4 according to type: synthesis, decomposition, or double replacement.
6. Write the formulas:

	Cl^-	OH^-	NO_3^-	O^{--}	SO_4^{--}	PO_4^{---}
Na^+						
Ca^{++}						
NH_4^+						
Al^{+++}						
Zn^{++}						
Fe^{+++}						

Up to this point we have discussed generalities about matter. Now we can put some of this background material to use and apply it to specific examples.

FACTS ABOUT OXYGEN

Oxygen is a nonmetallic element of great importance because it is the most abundant element on earth. It makes up 21% of the volume of atmospheric air and 89% of the weight of water. The name oxygen means "acid former." It was so named because the eighteenth-century chemist Lavoisier ob-

PHYSICAL PROPERTIES

The physical properties of oxygen are:

○ Colorless, odorless and tasteless gas.
○ Heavier than air.
○ Slightly soluble (about 3 ml per 100 ml at room temperature) in water.
○ Can be liquefied and solidified by extreme pressure and low temperature.

Knowing these properties can be valuable in situations other than the chemistry lab. If you realize that oxygen is heavier than air, this could help you escape from a burning building alive. In a fire, the smoke and heat rise and the oxygen sinks to floor level. Theo-

Chapter 6
OXYGEN

served that all the acids known to him contained this element. The symbol for oxygen is O, but its formula is O_2, since it is a homonuclear diatomic molecule. Its position in the upper right corner of the periodic table indicates that it is highly electronegative. Oxygen is a Group VI element. Therefore, it has six valence electrons and usually an oxidation number of -2 except when combined with itself.

retically you could fall to your knees and crawl out of the danger zone, utilizing the available oxygen. The only drawback is that many of the synthetic substances found in building and furniture materials give off toxic fumes when they burn that are also heavier than air. You can't avoid them by holding your breath, because some of these toxic substances are absorbed directly through the skin.

Knowing that oxygen is slightly soluble in water gives us an appreciation of aquatic life. Fish and other "gill breathers" utilize dissolved oxygen (DO) in water. They do not extract oxygen from water by decomposing it into its constituent elements. If they did, the oceans would become churning caldrons. In large bodies of water the dissolved oxygen content is constantly replenished by the action of wind and waves. When the DO is depleted, water becomes stagnant and favors the growth of anaerobic microorganisms which produce odors similar to those associated with the decomposition of human remains.

The liquefaction and solidification of oxygen provides us with a review of the states of matter and their relationship to energy. A gas is the most highly energetic state, a liquid is less energetic, and a solid possesses the least energy. When oxygen is first liquefied and then solidified, the process is accomplished by removing energy from the substance.

CHEMICAL PROPERTIES

The chemical properties of oxygen are:

○ Reacts with many substances slowly at ordinary temperatures but rapidly at high temperatures.

○ Reacts with many metallic and nonmetallic elements to form oxides.

○ Supports combustion. Note that this does not mean that *oxygen* burns. It means that oxygen helps other things to burn. In fact, it is helpful to define burning as the process of chemically adding oxygen to another substance with the production of an oxide.

○ Acts as an oxidizing agent.

Before the last property can be understood, the concepts of oxidation and reduc-

tion must be explained. These processes are involved in many chemical reactions. There are four ways to define *oxidation*:

(a) The addition of oxygen to a substance.

(b) The removal of hydrogen from a substance.

(c) The removal of electrons from a substance.

(d) The increase in oxidation number of a metal or metallic part of a compound.

Burning (combustion) is an example of the first definition. When oxygen is added to a substance, that substance undergoes oxidation. Since oxygen has caused this process, it is called an *oxidizing agent*. What happens to the oxidizing agent after it has performed its task? It is reduced. Reduction (not to be confused with decomposition) is the counterpart of oxidation and always accompanies it. The next chapter deals with hydrogen, which is the simplest form of a reducing agent. Since reduction is the opposite of oxidation, we obtain definitions of reduction by reversing the definitions of oxidation. Thus *reduction* is:

(a) The removal of oxygen from a substance.

(b) The addition of hydrogen to a substance.

(c) The addition of electrons to a substance.

(d) The decrease in oxidation number of a metal or the metallic part of a compound.

Since oxidation and reduction go hand in hand, the oxidizing agent is reduced and the reducing agent is oxidized. Considering again the example of burning, the substance burned undergoes oxidation and is the reducing agent. Simultaneously, oxygen undergoes reduction and is the oxidizing agent. The substance burned causes the oxygen to be reduced, and oxygen causes the burned substance to be oxidized

The other definitions of oxidation and reduction do not necessarily involve oxygen or the formation of oxides. The second definition is explained in Chapter 7. The other two definitions can be explained by considering an example involving oxygen and one in which oxygen does not participate. Consider the formation of carbon dioxide from the elementary substances carbon and oxygen:

$$C + O_2 \longrightarrow CO_2$$

The first definition says that carbon is oxidized, since oxygen is added to it. Oxygen must at the same time undergo reduction. The same conclusion can be drawn from the last two definitions of oxidation and reduction. When the molecule carbon dioxide forms, bonds occur between the one carbon and the two oxygens. These bonds are *polar covalent*. Oxygen is more electronegative than carbon, so the electrons in the bonds are pulled away from the carbon atom and toward the oxygen atom. In this way carbon is oxidized (loses electrons) and oxygen is reduced (gains electrons).

Application of the other definition of oxidation and reduction gives the same result. Recall from Chapter 4 that an oxidation number indicates if electrons have been added to or lost by a substance. Atoms that lose electrons have positive oxidation numbers and ones that gain electrons have negative oxidation numbers. Before the reaction forming carbon dioxide occurs, carbon and oxygen have oxidation numbers of zero, because neither has gained or lost electrons in comparison to its normal neutral state. After the reaction, the pulling of electrons away from carbon in the polar covalent bonds means carbon has a positive oxidation number in the compound. Likewise, in carbon dioxide, oxygen's oxidation number is negative. By

application of the oxidation-reduction definitions, carbon undergoes oxidation and oxygen undergoes reduction.

As another example of an oxidation-reduction process, consider the reaction resulting from passing electricity through a sodium chloride melt:

$$2 \, NaCl \longrightarrow 2 \, Na + Cl_2$$

In an ionic compound the oxidation number of each ion equals its charge. Sodium ion is $+1$ and chloride ion is -1. The individual oxidation-reduction reactions are

$$2 \, Na^+ + 2 \, e^- \longrightarrow 2 \, Na$$
$$2 \, Cl^- \longrightarrow Cl_2 + 2 \, e^-$$

The oxidation number both of elemental sodium and of chlorine gas (Cl_2) is zero. Since Na^+ gains electrons (decreases its oxidation number), it is reduced. The chloride ion loses electrons (increases its oxidation number). It undergoes oxidation.

A good way to remember the definitions for oxidation and reduction is: LEO GERs! That is,

Loss of Electrons is Oxidation
Gain of Electrons is Reduction

METHODS FOR THE PREPARATION OF OXYGEN

There are three significant methods for the preparation of oxygen.

Historical or classical method

This method was first used by Priestley in 1774 and consists of heating mercuric oxide.

$$2 \, HgO \xrightarrow{\text{heat}} 2 \, Hg + O_2$$

Mercuric oxide   Mercury   Oxygen

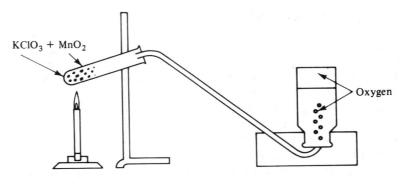

Figure 6-1 Apparatus for preparation of oxygen

Laboratory method

We heat a mixture of potassium chlorate and manganese dioxide.

$$2 \text{ KClO}_3 + \text{ MnO}_2 \xrightarrow{\text{heat}}$$

Potassium   Manganese
chlorate   dioxide

$$2 \text{ KCl} + 3 \text{ O}_2 + \text{ MnO}_2$$

Potassium   Oxygen   Manganese
chloride   dioxide

The apparatus used for this method is diagrammed in Figure 6-1.

Commercial method

There are two commercial methods for the preparation of oxygen. One is evaporation of liquid air. Air is a mixture of about 78% nitrogen and 21% oxygen. If the energy is removed by cooling to $-200°C$, the mixture liquefies. By taking advantage of the difference in boiling points of these two major components of air (B.P. of nitrogen, $-196°C$, B.P. of oxygen, $-183°C$), we can separate them. When the temperature is raised from $-200°C$ to $-196°C$, the nitrogen will boil off first, leaving nearly pure oxygen.

The other commercial method is electrolysis of water, as shown in the following equation:

$$2 \text{ H}_2\text{O} \xrightarrow{\text{electricity}} 2 \text{ H}_2 + \text{O}_2$$

Water can be decomposed into its constituent elements of hydrogen and oxygen by the application of an electric current.

Comparison of methods

In choosing any method of preparation, two factors, yield and cost, must be considered. Comparing mercuric oxide and potassium chlorate as potential sources of oxygen, potassium chlorate is substantially more economical. Consider the following:

$$2 \text{ HgO} \longrightarrow 2 \text{ Hg} + \text{ O}_2$$

Two molecules   One molecule

$$2 \text{ KClO}_3 \longrightarrow 2 \text{ KCl} + 3 \text{ O}_2$$

Two molecules   Three molecules

Two molecules of mercuric oxide yield only one molecule of oxygen, whereas two molecules of potassium chlorate yield three molecules of oxygen. In addition to a lower yield, mercuric oxide is considerably more expensive than potassium chlorate. However, neither of these substances is cost effective for commercial use. Therefore, air and water constitute the sources for commercial preparation of oxygen.

Relationship between preparation methods and properties of oxygen

These standard preparation methods of oxygen illustrate the physical and chemical properties of the element. Let us consider what happens in Priestley's method. Mercuric oxide, when heated, decomposes into its constituents. Since, by definition, these constituents are mercury and oxygen (Chapter 2 definition of oxides), let us identify these products by their properties. Mercury (*hydrargyrum*—"fluid silver") is readily identified by its physical appearance. However, the descriptive physical characteristics of oxygen indicates that it is a colorless, odorless, tasteless gas. Since this is not much help, we must use the most important chemical characteristic of oxygen for its identification: oxygen supports combustion.

What does "supporting combustion" really mean? It has already been stated that it does not mean burning. Oxygen is used to burn other things, but oxygen itself does not burn. Supporting combustion can be simplistically illustrated by saying, "We are taking a little flame and making it into a big flame." Anyone who has applied a bellows to a fireplace or a wood stove has employed this principle. Oxygen is added to the fuel and enables it to burn more rapidly. The tragedy of the rehearsal for the 1967 Apollo moon flight further exemplifies this property. That particular space vehicle utilized a pure oxygen atmosphere. An accidental electrical discharge produced a spark which incinerated the three astronauts. The oxygen didn't burn, but it supported the combustion so that the victims were the fuel.

How then can we detect this property? Should we use a "flameometer" (to distinguish little flames from big flames)? The answer is much simpler. The standard test for the detection of oxygen is a glowing splint. This test is carried out by igniting a wood applicator for a few seconds, then blowing out the flame so that only a glowing ember remains. If this ember is introduced into a high concentration of oxygen, it will burst into flame, clearly demonstrating the property of supporting combustion. This is done in Priestley's experiment. The mercuric oxide is heated and decomposes, depositing the silver mercury on the sides of the test tube. When a glowing splint is introduced into the test tube, it ignites, confirming the formation of oxygen as the other product.

The laboratory method of preparation illustrates another physical property of oxygen: solubility in water. In the laboratory, oxygen is produced by the decomposition of potassium chlorate. It is collected by the displacement of water. This displacement occurs because oxygen is slightly soluble in water. As the oxygen is bubbled into a bottle filled with water, the water quickly becomes saturated with the oxygen. After saturation occurs, the remaining oxygen literally pushes the water out of the collection bottle. (See Figure 6-1.)

FACTORS AFFECTING REACTION RATES

In the laboratory method for the preparation of oxygen, a catalyst is used to increase the rate of the reaction. A variety of methods can be used for this purpose. They are:

- Catalysts.
- Temperature.
- Physical state.
- Concentration.
- Light.
- Pressure.

It is useful to consider all of these, because even if a reaction occurs spontaneously, the rate may be slow to the point of being impractical.

Catalysts

The laboratory method for the preparation of oxygen involves decomposing potassium chlorate ($KClO_3$) by heating it with a catalyst, manganese dioxide (MnO_2). A *catalyst* is defined as a substance which speeds up a chemical reaction yet appears in unchanged form among the products of the reaction. Thus, in the equation:

$$2\ KClO_3 + MnO_2 \xrightarrow{heat} 2\ KCl + 3\ O_2 + MnO_2$$

the MnO_2 appears the same on both sides because it gives nothing of its substance to the reaction. All it does is increase the rate of the reaction. $KClO_3$ decomposes at 420°C without a catalyst. When it is mixed with MnO_2, the decomposition temperature is reduced to 270°C. Thus, this catalyst increases the rate of reaction by lowering the amount of energy necessary for the reaction to occur. Catalysts do not cause reactions; they alter the reaction rates.

If adding the MnO_2 to both sides of the equation appears to be too confusing, an alternate method is to write the catalyst over the arrow. This shows that it participates in the reaction without being affected by it.

$$2\ KClO_3 \xrightarrow[heat]{MnO_2} 2\ KCl + 3\ O_2$$

Temperature

There is a direct proportion between temperature and the speed of a chemical reaction. An increase in temperature increases the speed of reactions and a decrease in temperature decreases the speed of reactions.

For example, if a piece of magnesium ribbon is ignited in a bunsen flame, it burns with a bright white light and produces a white ash. This is expressed as

$$2\ Mg + O_2 \longrightarrow 2\ MgO + light$$

If you examine an old piece of the same type of magnesium ribbon, you will notice that the surface is dull and has a white deposit. This deposit has a strong resemblance to the white ash produced by burning magnesium, because it is exactly the same substance. Magnesium oxide is produced under the ordinary conditions of exposing the metal to the surrounding air. However, this occurs at a very slow rate. Burning the magnesium also illustrates another chemical property of oxygen: it reacts with many other substances slowly at ordinary temperatures but very rapidly at high temperatures.

Physical state

Physical state refers to the size of the particles of the reacting substances. This can influence physical as well as chemical changes. Consider the various grades of sugar:

Type of sugar	Appearance
Raw sugar	Large crystals
Table sugar	Granular solid
Confectionary sugar	Fine powder
Bar sugar	Very fine powder

When ordinary table sugar is mixed with iced tea, most of it seems to fall to the bottom of the glass. Even though you may stir it several times, the majority of it does not dissolve. This dilemma may be resolved by using a finer grade of sugar. One might observe, then, that little pieces react faster than large chunks. The underlying principle is that the smaller the particle size, the larger the surface area. This principle applies also to chemical change. In the laboratory preparation of oxygen, manganese dioxide is much more finely divided than potassium chlorate. The directions for performing this preparation usually include the words, "Take 8 grams of finely powdered potassium chlorate... ." If the experimenter assumes that "finely powdered" means as it comes from the manufacturer, he may encounter some difficulty. The potassium chlorate should be ground with mortar and pestle so that its granules are more compatible in size with the particles of manganese dioxide. When this procedure is followed, the reaction proceeds smoothly.

Concentration

The rate of a chemical reaction is proportional to the molecular concentration of the reacting substances. The greater the concentration, the faster the reaction. The lesser the concentration, the slower the reaction.

Light

Many chemical reactions are caused or accelerated by light. These are called *photochemical reactions*. Smog (smoke + fog) is a good example of this type of reaction. Suspended particles from the exhaust of internal combustion engines react with sunlight to produce this familiar form of air pollution. Photochemical reactions also have applications to embalming. In the past, arterial fluids were shipped in clear bottles. More manufacturers are currently switching to tinted bottles because of the problem of photochemically accelerated polymerization (Chapter 15) of formaldehyde.

Another problem involves the embalming of a jaundiced remains. Disorders of the liver are often accompanied by the deposition of yellow bile pigments throughout the body (jaundice). High concentrations of formaldehyde will change these yellow bile pigments to green. (See the discussion of hemoglobin, bilirubin, and biliverdin in Chapter 19.) Therefore, special arterial fluids are used in the preparation of a jaundiced remains.

However, even when special chemicals are used, a photochemical reaction is possible. If an embalmed remains is exposed to ordinary fluorescent lights, the remains will turn bright green within a matter of a few hours. The reason for this change is the lack of one component of visible light in ordinary fluorescent lamps. This condition may be avoided by the use of "color corrected" fluorescent lights which do not lack this component of light. In fact the color-corrected lights will produce a photochemical reaction resulting in a pink tint of the skin.

Pressure

Pressure has very little effect upon chemical reactions other than those involving gases. Reactions between gaseous reactants are accelerated by an increase in pressure and slowed by a decrease in pressure.

FORMS OF OXYGEN

Besides as a diatomic molecule, oxygen can exist in other forms. When an element exists in two or more different forms, each with its own physical and chemical properties, it is called *allotropic*. There are three allotropes of oxygen, represented by the following formulas:

O_3	O_2	O
Ozone	Molecular oxygen	Nascent oxygen
(unstable)	(stable)	(unstable)

Ozone is prepared by passing a high-voltage electrical discharge through oxygen. This is represented by the following equation:

$$3\,O_2 \xrightarrow{\text{electricity}} 2\,O_3$$

The physical properties of ozone are

○ Pale blue-colored gas.
○ Penetrating odor.

The "clean" aroma that you may notice immediately following an electrical storm is caused by ozone. The chemical properties of ozone are:

○ More active chemically than oxygen, but less stable.
○ Readily decomposes, liberating nascent oxygen:

$$O_3 \longrightarrow O_2 + O$$

Ozone's bleaching and deodorizing qualities have been known for many years. Its high oxidizing ability is responsible for these qualities. Ozone has been used in treating both drinking water and waste water, in disinfecting swimming pools, and in home air "purifiers." However, its uses are limited because of both its toxic nature and its inherent instability.

Ozone is effective in the oxidation of odors. Therefore it qualifies as a true *deodorant* because it actually destroys the odor. By contrast, *reodorants* are masking or perfuming agents and merely cover up the odors. Reodorants are discussed in subsequent chapters.

CHAPTER SUMMARY

○ Oxygen:
Symbol, O.
Formula, O_2.
Atomic weight, 16.
Molecular weight, 32.
Oxidation number, -2.

○ Physical properties of oxygen:
Colorless, odorless, tasteless gas.
Heavier than air.
Slightly soluble in water.
Can be liquefied and solidified by extreme pressure and cooling.
○ Chemical properties of oxygen:
Reacts with many other substances slowly at ordinary temperatures but rapidly at high temperatures.
Reacts with many metallic and non-metallic elements, forming oxides.
Supports combustion.
Acts as an oxidizing agent.
○ Factors influencing the speed of chemical reactions:
Catalysts.
Temperature.
Physical state.
Concentration.
Light.
Pressure.

Oxygen is an allotropic element which exists in three forms: O, O_2, and O_3. Ozone (O_3) has a number of distinctive physical and chemical properties. The properties most important to embalming are those of bleaching, disinfecting, and deodorizing.

QUESTIONS

1. Define: burning, oxide, oxidation, reduction, oxidizing agent, reducing agent, catalytic agent.

2. List three physical properties of oxygen.

3. List three chemical properties of oxygen.

4. Write balanced equations for:

(a) The historical method for preparing oxygen.

(b) The laboratory method for preparing oxygen.

(c) The preparation of oxygen by the electrolysis of water.

(d) The oxidation of magnesium.

(e) The oxidation of carbon.

5. List the names and formulas of the allotropic forms of oxygen.

6. List four factors which influence the speed of chemical reactions.

7. Distinguish between the terms deodorant and reodorant.

8. In each of the following, identify what is oxidized and what is reduced. Tell what substance is the oxidizing agent and what is the reducing agent.

(a) $2 \text{ Mg} + O_2 \longrightarrow 2 \text{ MgO}$

(b) $2 \text{ KCl} \longrightarrow 2 \text{ K} + Cl_2$

(c) $\text{Zn} + \text{S} \longrightarrow \text{ZnS}$

(d) $2 \text{ Fe}^{+3} + 2 \text{ I}^- \longrightarrow 2 \text{ Fe}^{+2} + I_2$

Water is the most abundant compound on earth. In the previous chapter we discussed the properties of oxygen, one of the constituent elements of water. Hydrogen, the other constituent element of water, is the topic of this chapter.

FACTS ABOUT HYDROGEN

Oxygen is the most abundant element on earth, but hydrogen is the most abundant element in the universe. There is very little free hydrogen in the atmosphere. Most hydrogen occurs in the combined state and may be found in acids, bases, water, plant and animal tissues, and natural gases. The

PHYSICAL PROPERTIES

The physical properties of hydrogen are:

- ○ Colorless, odorless, and tasteless gas.
- ○ Lighter than air—the lightest gas known.
- ○ Slightly soluble in water.

Comparing hydrogen with oxygen shows some interesting similarities as well as differences. Both hydrogen and oxygen are colorless, odorless, and tasteless gases. Therefore, like oxygen, a chemical property must be used in order to test for the presence of hydrogen. Like oxygen, hydrogen is slightly soluble in water. Hydrogen, then,

Chapter 7
HYDROGEN

free form of hydrogen exists in the earth's crust and is released in the gases of volcanic eruptions. Tissue gas, the post-mortem manifestation of gas gangrene, is largely free hydrogen gas.

Chemically, hydrogen has the symbol H and the molecular formula H_2. Like oxygen, hydrogen is a homonuclear diatomic molecule. Hydrogen has an atomic number of one, an atomic weight of one, and a usual oxidation number of plus one except when combined to itself.

may also be collected by the displacement of water. Oxygen is heavier than air, but hydrogen is lighter than air. The molecular weight of O_2 is 32 while that of H_2 is two.

In addition to being light, hydrogen is highly diffusible. *Diffusibility* is a property of gases that, because of their highly energetic state, allows them to move through other substances. For instance, if a bottle of embalming fluid is spilled at one end of a room, the odor is soon noticed in all parts of the room. Since the gases in embalming fluid are also heavier than air, let us examine something more comparable in weight to hydrogen. Helium has an atomic weight of four. Its mass is approximately twice that of diatomic hydrogen. If a toy balloon, filled with helium, is released in a small room, it will float to the ceiling. Within a day or two the balloon will shrink and sink to the floor. Why? Helium gas diffuses into the surrounding atmosphere through the membranous skin of the balloon. If this phenomenon occurs so rapidly with helium, try to picture what would happen with a hydrogen filled balloon.

CHEMICAL PROPERTIES

The chemical properties of hydrogen are:

   ○ Burns with a hot, blue flame, forming water.
   ○ Does not support combustion.
   ○ Acts as a reducing agent.

The name *hydrogen* describes the first of its chemical properties. The name means "water producer" or "water former." This property is expressed by the following equation:

$$2 H_2 + O_2 \longrightarrow 2 H_2O$$

The description "burns with a hot, blue flame forming water," is somewhat misleading because, depending on the amount of oxygen present, this reaction usually takes the form of an explosion. The most famous exhibition of this property was the Hindenburg Disaster of 1937. If helium diffuses through the tight membrane of a toy balloon, try to imagine an airship approximately two to three football fields in length containing 6.7 million cubic feet of hydrogen. One small spark of static electricity was reported to have been the cause of this cataclysmic chemical reaction.

The second chemical property of hydrogen is that it does not support combustion. This is an interesting contrast to oxygen. Hydrogen burns but does not support combustion, whereas oxygen supports combustion but does not burn. This means that pure hydrogen will extinguish a full flame. However, do not take this to mean that hydrogen can be used in fire extinguishers. Since this gas is both lighter than air and highly diffusible, to control and contain a large quantity of it is very difficult under normal atmospheric conditions.

The third property of hydrogen is its action as a reducing agent. The relationship between oxidation and reduction was introduced in Chapter 6. Recall the (b) parts of the definitions for oxidation and reduction. Oxidation is the removal of hydrogen from a substance. Conversely, reduction is the addition of hydrogen. Hydrogen acts as a reducing agent when it is added to a substance. Consider a procedure used commercially to produce methyl alcohol. This compound can be formed by applying heat and pressure to a mixture of carbon monoxide and hydrogen in the presence of a catalyst.

$$CO + 2 H_2 \xrightarrow{\text{catalyst}} CH_3OH$$

Since carbon monoxide gains hydrogen, it is reduced. Hydrogen gas is the reducing agent.

The definition of oxidation as removal of hydrogen from a substance is demonstrated by a method for the preparation of formaldehyde. Passage of methyl alcohol over hot copper metal produces formaldehyde and water.

$$\underset{\text{methyl alcohol}}{2 CH_3OH} + O_2 \longrightarrow \underset{\text{formaldehyde}}{2 HCHO} + 2 H_2O$$

In this reaction methyl alcohol is oxidized, since it loses hydrogen. Oxygen undergoes reduction, since it gains the hydrogen. Methyl alcohol is the reducing agent and oxygen is the oxidizing agent.

The loss of hydrogen by reducing agents occurs in many biological oxidation-reduction reactions. As our bodies break down ingested foods, these molecules frequently lose hydrogen ions and electrons, which in turn are accepted by very large molecules which act as oxidizing agents. One of these oxidizing agents is a large organic compound, nicotinamide adenine dinucleotide, symbolized by NAD^+. (See Chapters 18 and 21.) A generalized oxidation-reduction reaction involving NAD^+ in biological systems is:

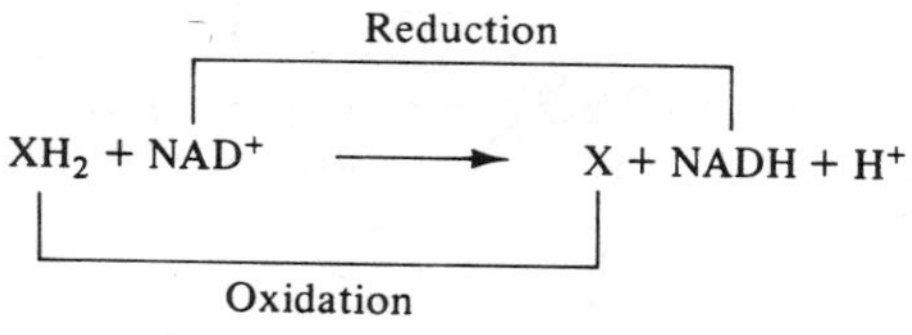

XH_2 is the reducing agent and NAD^+ is the oxidizing agent.

Many examples of these types of reactions are given in this book's biochemistry section. An additional example that students often find of interest is the first step in the breakdown of ethyl alcohol. The reaction is:

$$CH_3CH_2OH + NAD^+ \longrightarrow$$
$$CH_3CHO + NADH + H^+$$

By losing hydrogen to NAD^+, ethyl alcohol is a reducing agent which is oxidized to acetaldehyde. Subsequent reactions convert acetaldehyde to waste products of carbon dioxide and water.

PREPARATION OF HYDROGEN

Methods for the preparation of hydrogen include both a commercial method and two procedures that can be done in the laboratory.

Commercial method

Hydrogen is prepared commercially by the electrolysis of water. This is shown in the following equation:

$$2 H_2O \xrightarrow{\text{electricity}} 2 H_2 + O_2$$

Exactly the same method is used to prepare oxygen.

Laboratory methods

The standard method to prepare hydrogen in the laboratory is based on one of the chemical properties of acids. Common acids used in the laboratory contain hydrogen. Some examples of inorganic acids are hydrochloric acid (HCl), sulfuric acid (H_2SO_4), nitric acid (HNO_3), and phosphoric acid (H_3PO_4). The property of acids important in the preparation of hydrogen involves a concept called the *electrochemical series* or the *activity series*. This series is a list of the metallic elements in order of their chemical activity. The more active metals are listed first, the less active last. Table 7-1 gives the activity series of some of the important

Table 7-1 Activity series of metallic elements

Potassium
Calcium
Sodium
Magnesium
Aluminum
Zinc
Chromium
Iron
Nickel
Tin
Lead
Hydrogen
Copper
Mercury
Silver
Platinum
Gold

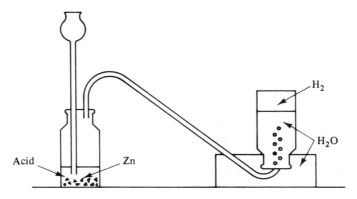

Figure 7-1   Apparatus for preparation of hydrogen

metallic elements. The property of acids that applies to the activity series is: All the elements above hydrogen in the series displace hydrogen from dilute acids. All the elements below hydrogen in the series do not displace hydrogen from dilute acids.

The application of this principle is the basis for the fourth type of chemical reaction: *single replacement*. Since this type of reaction is explained by the principle of displacement, it is called *single displacement* as well. The standard laboratory method for preparation of hydrogen reacts zinc with dilute hydrochloric acid. This is expressed by the following equation:

$$Zn + 2\ HCl \longrightarrow ZnCl_2 + H_2$$

In this reaction zinc (a metal above hydrogen in the activity series) displaces hydrogen from a dilute solution of hydrochloric acid. Note that free hydrogen is written with a subscript 2, since it is a homonuclear diatomic molecule. The reaction is called single replacement because zinc replaces the hydrogen as the metallic part of the compound. Zinc chloride forms as a product.

All metals above hydrogen in the series displace it from inorganic acids. Other exam-

ples are:

$$2\ Al + 3\ H_2SO_4 \longrightarrow Al_2(SO_4)_3 + 3\ H_2$$

and

$$Pb + 2\ HNO_3 \longrightarrow Pb(NO_3)_2 + H_2$$

Figure 7-1 is a diagram of the laboratory apparatus for the generation and collection of hydrogen gas. Since hydrogen is lighter than air, collected bottles are placed mouth downward. Compare to oxygen (Figure 6-1), where collected bottles can be mouth upward, since oxygen is heavier than air.

All the reactions between metals and dilute acids are oxidation-reduction reactions. To understand this, again consider the definitions of these processes.

Oxidation	Reduction
(a) Addition of oxygen	(a) Loss of oxygen
(b) Loss of hydrogen	(b) Addition of hydrogen
(c) Loss of electrons	(c) Gain of electrons
(d) Increase in oxidation number	(d) Decrease in oxidation number

If these definitions are applied to

$$Zn + 2\ HCl \longrightarrow ZnCl_2 + H_2$$

definitions (a) give no information, since oxygen is not part of the reaction. Addition of oxygen is a specific type of oxidation, but not all oxidations involve oxygen. Since the first oxidation processes studied by chemists did, the name "oxidation" was used. Today, oxidation has a much broader meaning.

At first glance it may seem that definitions (b) identify the oxidation and reduction processes. Since hydrogen is displaced from HCl, we might think it is being oxidized. For this definition of oxidation to apply, the other reactant must gain hydrogen. Zinc does not gain hydrogen, so the assignment of what substance undergoes oxidation and what substance undergoes reduction cannot be based on definitions (b).

The definitions that do correctly tell what is oxidized and what is reduced are (c) and (d). They define oxidation and reduction in the broadest sense, since they emphasize the electronic structure of matter. Before zinc reacts with hydrochloric acid, it has neither gained nor lost electrons. After it reacts and forms zinc chloride, two of its electrons are pulled away from it by the chlorine atoms. Since chlorine is more electronegative than zinc, the electrons in each bond between zinc and one chlorine are pulled toward chlorine. The oxidation number of zinc in the compound is $+2$. If we apply either definition (c) or (d), zinc has been oxidized. We must see if the corresponding definitions of reduction apply to the other reactant, HCl. In this compound, chlorine pulls the single electron of hydrogen away from its nucleus. After displacement by zinc, two hydrogen atoms form a diatomic molecule of hydrogen gas. In this form each hydrogen has an oxidation number of zero. There is equal sharing by each atom of the pair of electrons in the bond. Since each hydrogen atom has in a sense gained an electron in going from hy-

drochloric acid to its molecular form, hydrogen is reduced.

In general, whenever a metal displaces hydrogen from a dilute acid by a single-replacement reaction, the metal is oxidized and the hydrogen of the acid is reduced. In trying to identify the oxidized and reduced parts of the reaction between zinc and hydrochloric acid, three facts about oxidation-reduction are demonstrated. First, not all oxidations involve oxygen. Second, the loss of hydrogen by a compound does not automatically mean that oxidation has occurred. Third, correct application of the definitions of oxidation as the loss of electrons and reduction as the gain of electrons (remember LEO GERs) will always identify the oxidized and reduced substances. Another way to express this defines oxidation as an increase in oxidation number and reduction as a decrease in oxidation number.

Another feature of the activity series is based on a chemical property of water. As the top of the series is approached, the metals displace hydrogen not only from dilute acids but also from water. Very active metals such as potassium, calcium, and sodium actually reduce water, liberating free hydrogen. Consider the following equation:

$$2\ Na + 2\ HOH \longrightarrow 2\ NaOH + H_2$$

The metals that react with water in this manner must be packed in a substance such as kerosene. There is enough moisture present in human skin and in the surrounding air to support a violent reaction when these metals are present. Owing to the explosive characteristic of the reaction between the very active metals and water, this method is not routinely used to prepare large quantities of hydrogen. However, it may be used to demonstrate both the properties of hydrogen and the action of certain metals on water.

CHAPTER SUMMARY

○ Hydrogen:
Symbol, H.
Atomic weight, 1.
Formula, H_2.
Molecular weight, 2.
Oxidation number, $+1$.

○ Physical properties of hydrogen:
Colorless, odorless, tasteless gas.
Lighter than air.
Slightly soluble in water.

○ Chemical properties of hydrogen:
Burns with a hot, blue flame, forming water.
Does not support combustion.
Acts as a reducing agent.

The electrochemical series, also called the activity series, is a list of metallic elements in order of their chemical activity. All the elements above hydrogen in the series displace hydrogen from dilute acids. The type of chemical reaction that describes this displacement is called single replacement. Some very active metals such as potassium, calcium, and sodium also displace hydrogen from water. In both of these displacement reactions, the metal is oxidized and hydrogen is reduced.

QUESTIONS

1. Write balanced chemical equations representing two different methods by which hydrogen may be produced in the laboratory.

2. Compare and contrast two physical and two chemical properties of hydrogen and oxygen.

3. Define reduction. Write a balanced chemical equation illustrating each one of the four approaches to this definition.

4. Complete and balance the following equations. If no reaction occurs, write NR on the products side:

(a) $Zn + H_2SO_4 \longrightarrow$
(b) $Ag + HNO_3 \longrightarrow$
(c) $Pt + HCl \longrightarrow$
(d) $Al + H_3PO_4 \longrightarrow$
(e) $Ca + HOH \longrightarrow$
(f) $Mg + HCl \longrightarrow$
(g) $K + HOH \longrightarrow$

5. In each of the following identify what substance is oxidized and what substance is reduced. What is the oxidizing agent and what is the reducing agent?

(a) $2 H_2 + O_2 \longrightarrow 2 H_2O$

(b) $CH_3OH + NAD^+ \longrightarrow HCHO + NADH + H^+$

(c) $H_2 + Cl_2 \longrightarrow 2 HCl$

(d)
$$\begin{matrix} COO^- \\ | \\ C{=}O \\ | \\ CH_3 \end{matrix} + NADH + H^+ \longrightarrow \begin{matrix} COO^- \\ | \\ HCOH \\ | \\ CH_3 \end{matrix} + NAD^+$$

(e) $Mg + H_2SO_4 \longrightarrow MgSO_4 + H_2$

(f) $2 K + 2 HOH \longrightarrow 2 KOH + H_2$

The elements hydrogen and oxygen were discussed in the last two chapters. Reaction between these elements produces water, the most important inorganic compound in biological systems.

FACTS ABOUT WATER

Oxygen is the most abundant element on earth. Water is the most abundant compound. It covers about three-fourths of the earth's surface, is present in the air as water vapor, and is found in all plant and animal tissue. The human body consists of about 70% water. Bacterial cells contain about 85% water. The formula for water is H_2O or, more correctly, HOH, which emphasizes its structure. Water is a bent molecule in which

PHYSICAL PROPERTIES

The physical properties of water are:

- Colorless, odorless, tasteless liquid.
- Freezes at 0°C and boils at 100°C at standard atmospheric pressure.
- Heat of fusion: 80 calories/gram.
- Heat of vaporization: 540 calories/gram.
- Specific heat: 1 calorie/gram/°C.
- Very good solvent for many substances; known for this reason as the "universal solvent."

HYDROGEN BONDING

Physical properties of water such as boiling point, melting point, heat of vaporization,

Chapter 8
WATER

two atoms of hydrogen are covalently bonded to one atom of oxygen. The bond angle is 105 degrees.

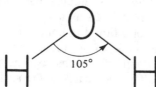

The molecular weight of the compound is 18.

heat of fusion, and specific heat have abnormally high values. Consider the boiling point of water in comparison to that of H_2Te, H_2Se, and H_2S. (See Table 8-1.) Since Te, Se, S, and O are all in Group VI of the periodic table, the compounds formed from them with hydrogen are expected to show similar trends in physical properties. As the molecular weights decrease, the boiling points of H_2Te, H_2Se, and H_2S also decrease.

Table 8-1 Boiling points of compounds of Group VI and hydrogen

Compound	Molecular weight (g)	Boiling point (°C)
H_2Te	129.62	−2.2
H_2Se	80.98	−41.5
H_2S	34.08	−60.7
H_2O	18.02	100.0

Water, having the lowest molecular weight of the four compounds, is expected to boil at a temperature less than −60.7°C. Obviously water does not follow this trend. Why not?

Boiling point has been defined as the temperature at which a substance changes from the liquid state to the gaseous state. Water boils at a higher temperature than predicted because attractive forces between individual liquid molecules must be broken before boiling can occur. Owing to polarity the hydrogen atom in every water molecule is slightly positive and the oxygen is slightly negative. Attractive forces occur between the hydrogen on one water molecule and an oxygen on another molecule. These attractive forces are called *hydrogen bonds*. (See Figure 8-1.) They are about 5% as strong as a normal covalent bond. In addition to existing between hydrogen and oxygen, hydrogen bonds also form between hydrogen and nitrogen and between hydrogen and fluorine. Hydrogen bonds involving nitrogen and oxygen are extremely important in the structure of proteins. (See Chapter 19.)

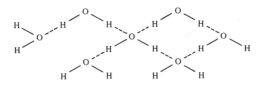

Figure 8-1 Hydrogen bonds

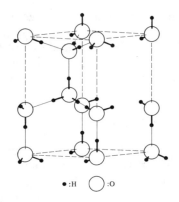

●:H ◯ :O

Figure 8-2 Open framework of ice

Water boils at a higher temperature than is expected because energy must be added to break the hydrogen bonds before water molecules are free to make the transition from liquid to gas. These bonds also account for the value of the heat of vaporization of water. Water has the highest heat of vaporization of any known liquid. The specific heat, the melting point, and the heat of fusion of water are also unusually high because of hydrogen bonds.

Water molecules in the solid state are held together in a special arrangement by hydrogen bonds. (See Figure 8-2.) This open framework of ice explains why ice is less dense than liquid water. Upon melting, the open structure of ice collapses. As a result more molecules of liquid water fit into the space occupied by the ice.

Another property of water with an unusually high value due to hydrogen bonding is *surface tension*. All liquids have a surface tension. It is defined as a force that causes the surface of a liquid to contract. Molecules within the bulk of a liquid are attracted equally in all directions by neighboring molecules. The molecules at the surface of a liquid are attracted only downward or side-

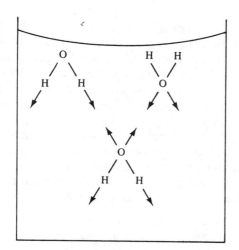

Figure 8-3 Surface tension of water

ways. As a result the surface contracts. (See Figure 8-3.)

The surface tension in water is high compared to that in other compounds. Molecules within the liquid are attracted equally in all directions by hydrogen bonds. Those at the surface experience an unbalanced pull into the liquid, since they cannot hydrogen bond with the air above the surface. Its high surface tension allows water to support a steel needle on its surface. Its surface tension also causes water to form spherical droplets at the end of a medicine dropper. Water will, however, spread out on a clean glass surface, because glass is a polar substance. Likewise it curves upward at the walls of a glass graduated cylinder, forming a *meniscus*.

Surface tension is an important phenomenon in embalming because it also occurs at interfaces of solutions and cell membranes. This interferes with diffusion of embalming chemicals from the capillaries into the tissues. To alleviate this problem, surface-tension-reducing agents are usually incorporated into embalming fluids.

CHEMICAL PROPERTIES

The chemical properties of water are:

1. Very stable substance. Water is thermally stable. If heated to temperatures near 2000°C, decomposition is minimal.

2. Chemically reacts with active metals to liberate hydrogen. (See Chapter 7.) The equations for these changes are:

$$2\,Na + 2\,HOH \longrightarrow 2\,NaOH + H_2$$
$$2\,K + 2\,HOH \longrightarrow 2\,KOH + H_2$$

3. Reacts with some metallic oxides to form bases:

$$CaO + HOH \longrightarrow Ca(OH)_2$$

4. Reacts with some nonmetallic oxides to form acids:

$$CO_2 + HOH \longrightarrow H_2CO_3$$

5. Forms hydrates.
6. Enters into hydrolysis reactions.

Chemical property 2 was discussed in the previous chapter. Properties 3 and 4 will be more fully illustrated after the definitions of acids and bases are presented in Chapter 10. Properties 5 and 6 will be discussed in the last chapter of this general chemistry section. Water, then, represents the pivotal point of this section. From here we can look backward to the properties of its constituent elements, oxygen and hydrogen. We can also look forward to a number of both physical and chemical changes involving water. Among these are solutions, ionization, and hydrolysis. Water is a key factor in both the decomposition of the human body after death and the attempt to arrest this process—the embalming operation.

PREPARATION OF WATER

Since water is the most abundant compound in nature, we need not prepare it. However, it is always necessary to purify water. "Pure" water has a variety of definitions, each one determined by the use for which the water is intended. Therefore, there are different standards for laboratory water, drinking water, and recreational water. The primary vehicle for embalming chemicals is water. As a result, anything that may be dissolved in this water could have an effect on the process of embalming.

HARDNESS IN WATER

Hard water contains certain minerals in solution which destroy the cleansing action of soap. Soft water does not contain these minerals in sufficient amounts to destroy the cleansing action of soap. The minerals in question are calcium, magnesium, and sometimes iron(II). Hardness in water is divided into two classes:

○ Temporary hardness.
○ Permanent hardness.

Temporary hardness can be removed by boiling and is due to the presence of the bicarbonate salts of calcium and magnesium.

○ $Ca(HCO_3)_2$—calcium bicarbonate.
○ $Mg(HCO_3)_2$—magnesium bicarbonate.

Boiling the water containing these salts produces a decomposition reaction which converts these soluble substances into insoluble substances.

$$Ca(HCO_3)_2 \xrightarrow{heat}$$
soluble in water

$$CaCO_3 \quad + H_2O + CO_2$$
insoluble in water

The white deposits found around bathtub and sink faucets are evidence of this reaction in everyday life. When very hot water is run through these outlets, the heat decomposes the bicarbonates dissolved in the water. As a result, the insoluble carbonates are deposited on the fixtures.

Permanent hardness cannot be removed by boiling. Some other method, such as the addition of chemicals, must be used. Permanent hardness is caused by the chloride and sulfate salts of calcium and magnesium.

○ $CaCl_2$—calcium chloride.
○ $CaSO_4$—calcium sulfate.
○ $MgCl_2$—magnesium chloride.
○ $MgSO_4$—magnesium sulfate.

There are several methods of removal.

Removal of hardness by adding sodium carbonate (washing soda)

The chemical reaction for this method is

$$CaCl_2 \quad + Na_2CO_3 \longrightarrow$$
soluble in water

$$CaCO_3 + 2 NaCl$$
insoluble in water

The double-replacement reaction which occurs converts the soluble calcium chloride into the insoluble calcium carbonate.

Use of soap to remove hardness

Hard water, by definition, destroys the cleansing action of soap. This happens because soap chemically reacts with the hard-water minerals to form a deposit called curd. Since the formation of curd effectively removes the minerals from the water, the use of soap qualifies as a method for softening water. The main drawback of this method is its lack of economy. A certain portion of the

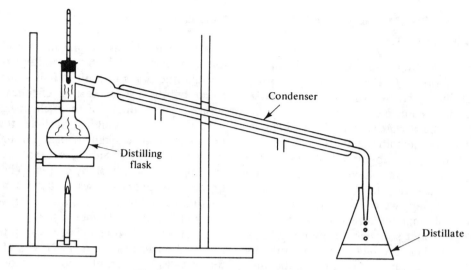

Figure 8-4 Apparatus for distillation

soap is used by the dissolved minerals before the remainder of the soap is able to function as a cleansing agent.

Use of ion-exchange systems

Manufacturers of water-softening devices usually include in their advertising some statement regarding the savings on soap that the consumers of their product will experience. It has already been shown that hard water uses a certain proportion of the soap. Softened water will not use this soap. Most water softeners contain some kind of an ion-exchange system, in which hard-water ions such as calcium are exchanged for soft-water ions such as sodium. In many instances the ions are exchanged on a medium called a *resin*. The resin is composed of thousands of plastic beads which are charged with sodium ions. When hard water passes over the resin, the calcium ions displace the sodium ions and stick to the resin. The sodium ions are eluted from the resin and pass into the solution.

An ion-exchange system, then, does not remove minerals from water by filtration. Instead, it "swaps" one type of metallic ion for another type. Understanding this concept is important, because there is a great deal of controversy about the connection between an abundance of sodium in the environment and health-related problems. It is well known that persons with certain disorders of the heart are placed on low-sodium diets. Whether or not the amount of sodium placed into water by water-softening devices is enough to aggravate these disease conditions is a question yet to be resolved.

Distillation

This process consists of the vaporization and condensation of water. (See Figure 8-4). All the substances that cause hardness in water are water soluble. When water is vaporized, these substances remain in the distillation vessel. Thus, distillation is the fourth method for the removal of hardness in water.

RELATIONSHIP OF HARD WATER TO EMBALMING

The presence of ionized calcium in the blood is very important in the blood-clotting process. It has been shown that hard water contains ionized calcium salts. Therefore the use of very hard water should be avoided as a diluent for embalming fluid. The use of water containing an abnormally large amount of these salts favors blood coagulation and interferes with the blood drainage process. Since most tap water is unsoftened, the majority of manufacturers of embalming fluids have water softeners or anticoagulants included in their product lines. The mechanisms of these various agents will be discussed in subsequent chapters.

CLASSES OF IMPURITIES IN WATER

The substances which cause hardness in water represent the first class of impurities in water: soluble solids. The other classes of impurities in water are:

- ○ Insoluble solids.
- ○ Bacteria.
- ○ Gases.

PURIFICATION METHODS

Distillation

This process of vaporization and condensation represents the most efficient method of purifying water. In addition to soluble solids, distillation removes insoluble solids and some bacteria. Gases with a lower boiling point than water, such as oxygen, carbon dioxide, ammonia, and chlorine, cannot be removed. They condense in the distillate.

Filtration

This method consists of the physical removal of particles which are too large to pass through the pores in a filter. It is sometimes aided by the use of certain chemical substances. The addition of these chemicals will have the effect of building particles that are normally small enough to pass through the pores of a filter into substances that are large enough to be held back by a filter. When this process is applied to water that is heavily contaminated with bacteria, the resultant product is called a *biological floc.*

Another method associated with filtration is called *carbon adsorption*. This is also referred to as "carbon filtration"—incorrectly, because the mechanism is adsorption rather than filtration. *Adsorption* is a phenomenon by which certain substances adhere or "stick" to the surfaces of other substances. Elemental carbon possesses this property. If a form of carbon called "activated charcoal" is used in conjunction with filters, gases and color can be removed from water. However, these impurities are removed because they stick to the surface of the carbon, not because they are physically held back by the size of the pores in the filter. Activated charcoal is a very finely ground preparation of carbon. In Chapter 6 we saw that one of the factors which will increase the speed of a chemical or physical reaction is the physical state. Finely divided substances react more rapidly than larger granules because of an increase in surface area. Activated charcoal provides a large amount of surface area for the adsorption of both gases and substances which produce color in water.

Boiling

This purification method has traditionally been used to remove bacteria from water. Most vegetative forms of bacteria are killed after five minutes of exposure to boiling temperatures. Boiling also removes gases and some soluble solids (see previous discussion of temporary hardness in water).

Aeration

This process consists of spraying water into the air. It removes gases and oxidizable organic matter, which sometimes impart an unpleasant odor or taste to the water. Many wastewater treatment facilities use aeration as an intermediate step in the purification of sewage.

Chlorination

The ability of chlorine to destroy odors and arrest putrefaction attracted attention soon after its discovery in 1774. Chlorine and chlorine compounds have since become the most widely used of the chemical disinfectants, having universal application for treating both water supplies and wastewater effluent. Calcium hypochlorite was first used for water disinfection in the United States in 1908. Within ten years it was adopted in over a thousand cities. Calcium hypochlorite has an available chlorine content of around 35%, but loss occurs even when it is stored in tight drums. Except in emergencies the use of this compound has been abandoned owing to deterioration in quality, the complexity of equipment needed, the difficulty of preparation and application, odors produced, and its corrosive action. Relatively stable hypochlorite powders such as HTH and Perchloron, with available chlorine content of around 70%, were subsequently developed.

Liquid chlorine was first manufactured in 1910, and the apparatus needed for its application came into use in 1913. Direct feed of the gas is used occasionally, but solution feed by first dissolving the gas in water is more common.

The widespread acceptance of chlorine as the disinfectant of choice in the process of the purification of drinking water and wastewater appears to be due to its ability to maintain a residual. This residual constitutes an extra margin of safety in the case of accidental recontamination of the purified water.

CHAPTER SUMMARY

Water, a colorless, odorless, tasteless substance, is the most abundant compound on earth. The values of many of its physical properties are related to hydrogen bonding. This special intermolecular attractive force occurs between hydrogen and the electronegative elements of oxygen, nitrogen, and fluorine.

Owing to its abundance, we need not prepare water. There are, however, various criteria for the purity of water. Four classes of impurities are soluble solids, insoluble solids, bacteria, and gases. Purification methods discussed are distillation, filtration, boiling, aeration, ion-exchange resins, and the addition of chemicals including chlorine.

The most significant impurities in water for the embalmer are those substances that cause hardness in water, since they promote blood coagulation. The two types of hardness in water are temporary hardness and permanent hardness. Temporary hardness can be removed by boiling, whereas other methods must be used to remove permanent hardness. They include the addition of chemicals such as washing soda and soap, the use of ion-exchange resins, and distillation.

QUESTIONS

1. Define: vehicle, pure water, hydrogen bonding, surface tension, distillation.

2. Name the classes of impurities in water.

3. What is meant by "hard" water?

4. Classify hard water according to the types of impurities in water.

5. What are the two classes of hard water?

6. What is the significance of hard water in the embalming process?

7. Name five methods of purification of water. What types of impurities are removed by these methods? What types are not?

8. What is an ion-exchange system? What is the relationship between the use of ion-exchange systems and certain health-related problems?

9. Distinguish between ordinary filtration and carbon filtration.

10. Explain how the properties of water support the statement, "Water is the most important inorganic compound in biological systems."

In an earlier chapter we divided matter into elements, compounds, and mixtures. In everyday living experiences, as well as in the embalming laboratory, we frequently use mixtures. A special type of mixture is a *solution*. Familiar solutions are air, carbonated beverages, embalming fluid, salt water, and brass.

TYPES AND COMPONENTS OF SOLUTIONS

Homogeneous mixtures of two or more substances are called *true solutions*. The components of a solution can be elements or compounds. They also can be gases, liquids, or solids. In a *gaseous solution*, at least one gas is dissolved in another. When gases are placed

familiar and important aqueous solution is embalming fluid. Some of its typical components are formaldehyde (a gas), glycerol (a liquid), and sodium chloride (a solid). They are dissolved in water, forming a homogeneous mixture. Liquid solutions are the most frequently used solutions in a chemistry laboratory.

Another type of solution is a *solid solution*, also known as an *alloy*, defined as a metallic substance that is composed of two or more metallic elements. In these solids the components are randomly dispersed throughout each other. Examples are brass, bronze, stainless steel, and sterling silver. Their components are listed in Table 9-1. Both stainless steel and bronze are used in construction of caskets.

Chapter 9
SOLUTIONS

in a container, they mix in all proportions. Accordingly, any mixture of gases is homogeneous and fulfills the definition of a true solution. Air is the most common gaseous solution. If a gas, liquid, or solid is dissolved in a liquid, a *liquid solution* is formed. The dissolving of salt in water and of iodine in alcohol are liquid solutions. The latter is referred to as a *tincture*. If the liquid is water, the solution is an *aqueous solution*. A

In these examples we have referred to dissolving and dispersing substances in one another. The usual terms for the components

Table 9-1   Composition of alloys

Alloy	Components
Brass	Copper and zinc
Bronze	Copper, tin, and sometimes zinc
Stainless steel	Iron, chromium, and nickel
Sterling silver	Copper and silver

of a solution are solute and solvent. The *solute* is the substance that is dissolved and the *solvent* is the substance that does the dissolving. Another somewhat easier way to define these terms is to consider the solute as the part of a solution present in the lesser amount, and the solvent as the part of a solution present in the greater amount. In aqueous solutions, water is the solvent. In discussing embalming fluids, a synonym for solvent is *vehicle*.

SOLUBILITY

An important property of a specific solute-solvent pair is solubility. To understand this concept, imagine yourself in the laboratory adding a solid solute A to a liquid solvent B. As A is added, you see it dissolving. However, after a certain amount has been added, it will no longer dissolve. This suggests that there is a limit to the amount of A that can be dissolved in a given quantity of B. This limit is A's *solubility* in B. Solubilities are usually expressed in grams of solute per 100 grams of solvent and are evaluated at a specific temperature (25°C). For example, the solubility of sodium chloride in water is 36 g/100 g H_2O at 25°C. A solution that contains all the solute the solvent can hold at a given temperature is described as *saturated*.

What factors influence solubility? The most significant is the nature of the solute and solvent. If a solute is to dissolve in a solvent, they must be similar in structure or in electrical properties. This idea is expressed by the statement frequently used in chemistry: "Like dissolves like." For example, water is a good solvent for salts such as sodium chloride, but water is not a good solvent for iodine. Water and salts are alike in that they are polar molecules. Iodine in contrast is a nonpolar molecule.

What is meant by polar and nonpolar? In a *polar* molecule there are regions of positive and negative charges. All ionic compounds are polar, and those covalent compounds in which there is unequal sharing of electrons are polar. Since sodium chloride is ionic and water is polar covalent, salt dissolves in water. *Nonpolar* molecules are formed by covalent bonding with equal sharing of electrons in the bonds. All homonuclear diatomics and most organic compounds are nonpolar. Since iodine (I_2) is nonpolar, it will not dissolve in polar water molecules. Likewise, oil and grease, which are organic nonpolar molecules, will not dissolve in water.

Another factor that influences solubility is *temperature*. The solubility of gases in liquids is decreased by an increase in temperature. Boiled water tastes flat, since boiling decreases the solubility of air in the water. Similarly, if carbonated beverages are left uncapped in a warm room for several hours, they lose their characteristic taste, owing to the decreased solubility of carbon dioxide. A third consequence of temperature's influence on solubility is that the procedure of hot-water embalming is less efficient than room-temperature embalming. The lower solubility of formaldehyde gas in embalming fluids at elevated temperatures results in low formaldehyde concentrations in these fluids.

There is no general rule for the effect of temperature on the solubility of liquids and solids in liquids. To predict the effect of temperature, the energetics of a dissolving process must be considered. Recall that an exothermic process is one in which heat is liberated and an endothermic process is one in which heat is absorbed. Equations for (1) exothermic dissolving processes and (2) endothermic dissolving processes are written:

(1)   solute + solvent $\rightleftarrows$ solution + heat
(2)   solute + solvent + heat $\rightleftarrows$ solution

In the first case the addition of heat shifts the reaction in the backward direction, decreasing the solubility. In the second case the addition of heat shifts the reaction forward, favoring the formation of solution. Therefore, for those solute-solvent pairs that undergo exothermic dissolving processes, solubility is increased by lowering the temperature. For endothermic dissolving processes, solubility can be increased by raising the temperature.

A third factor affecting solubility is *pressure*. Its influence is limited to gases. The solubility of all gases is increased as the partial pressure of the gas above the solution is increased. The concentration of carbon dioxide in carbonated beverages depends on the pressure of carbon dioxide in the gaseous phase above the liquid. When a bottle of champagne is opened, this pressure decreases, causing the carbon dioxide solubility to decrease. Consequently, bubbles of gas escape.

CONCENTRATION TERMS

The concentration of a solution may be expressed qualitatively or quantitatively. Two qualitative terms are dilute and concentrated. They are used in contrast. A *dilute* solution contains a relatively small amount of solute, while a *concentrated* solution contains a relatively large amount of solute. Another group of qualitative terms is unsaturated, saturated, and supersaturated. A *saturated* solution contains all the solute the solvent is able to hold at a certain temperature and pressure. A solution that has not reached saturation is *unsaturated*. A *supersaturated* solution contains more of the solute than the solvent is normally able to hold. Supersaturated solutions are difficult to prepare and to maintain.

The terms dilute and unsaturated should not be considered synonymous. For example, a saturated solution of sodium chloride contains 36 grams in 100 grams of water. If a solution contains 30 grams of $NaCl/100$ grams of water, it is unsaturated and concentrated. If it contains 5 grams of $NaCl/100$ grams of water, it is unsaturated and dilute.

Some quantitative terms to express the concentrations of solutions are percentage, ratio, index, and the chemical term of molarity.

Percentage

This may be expressed as a percent by weight or a percent by volume. When formaldehyde gas is dissolved in water, the resulting solution, called formalin, is 37% formaldehyde by weight and 40% formaldehyde by volume.

Ratio

Some concentrations are expressed as the weight of solute to the weight of solution. A common concentration for the disinfectant $HgCl_2$ is $1:1000$.

Index

This term is used by embalmers to express the concentration of formaldehyde in an embalming fluid. The definition of *index* is the number of grams of pure formaldehyde gas in 100 milliliters of solution. The index of an arterial fluid is classified as low if it is 5–15, medium if 16–24, and high if 25–36. A 20 index fluid contains 20 grams of formaldehyde gas in every 100 milliliters of solution.

Molarity

This is a purely chemical term for expressing the concentration of a solution. A 1 molar solution contains one mole of solute in one liter of solution. How many grams are in

Table 9-2   Molar weights (grams)

Elements		Compounds	
Na	22.99	H_2O	18.02
Cu	63.55	HCl	36.46
Ca	40.08	HCHO	30.03
C	12.01	H_2	2.02
Fe	55.85	O_2	32.00
K	39.10	NaCl	58.45

one mole? If the atomic weight of a substance is expressed in grams or if the molecular weight of a compound is expressed in grams, these weights are one mole. One mole of sodium is 22.99 grams and one mole of hydrogen chloride is 36.46 grams. Other molar weights are listed in Table 9-2.

A solution that contains 36.46 grams of HCl in one liter of solution is a 1 molar solution. A 1 molar NaCl solution is made by dissolving 58.45 grams of this salt in enough water to form one liter of solution. A formaldehyde solution with an index of 20 is 6.7 molar. This value of molarity is obtained by the following calculation:

1. Index 20 = 20 grams of HCHO in 100 ml of solution.

2. Molarity $(M) = \dfrac{\text{moles of HCHO}}{\text{liters of solution}}$

3. Moles of HCHO
$$= \frac{\text{grams of HCHO}}{\text{molar weight of HCHO}}$$
$$= \frac{20 \text{ grams}}{30 \text{ grams/mole}}$$
$$= 0.67$$

4. Liters of solution $= \dfrac{100 \text{ ml}}{1000 \text{ ml/liter}}$
$$= 0.1$$

5. Substitution of quantities calculated in steps 3 and 4 into step 2:

$$M = \frac{0.67 \text{ moles}}{0.1 \text{ liter}} = 6.7$$

We will not devote much time to molarity because embalmers generally use the index system for expressing concentrations.

PROPERTIES OF SOLUTIONS

Since solutions are homogeneous mixtures of two or more substances, their properties may be different from those of the individual substances. For example, a solution containing a nonvolatile substance as solute boils at a higher temperature and freezes at a lower temperature than does the pure solvent of the solution. A solution of sodium chloride and water has a higher boiling point than pure water. The boiling-point elevation is proportional to the concentration of the solution. Analogously, a solution shows a freezing-point depression in contrast to the freezing point of the pure solvent. The most common application of this property of solutions is the practice of adding antifreeze to the water in a radiator to prevent the water from freezing in the winter.

Elevation of the boiling point and depression of the freezing point are physical properties of solutions. Another physical property is stability of the solution when filtered. Since true solutions are homogeneous, the solute cannot be removed by filtration. Similarly the solute will not separate from the solution while standing.

A fourth property of solutions is *diffusion*. When the components of a solution are initially added to one another, regions of unequal concentration may result. To attain a uniform concentration throughout the solution, particles move from regions of higher concentration to lower concentration. This movement is diffusion. The rate of diffusion is influenced by such factors as temperature, pressure, and molecular weight of the diffusing substance.

A type of diffusion important to living systems is osmosis. Concisely defined, *osmosis* is diffusion through membranes. Consider two aqueous solutions of different concentrations separated by a membrane through which only solvent particles can pass. Such a membrane is described as *semipermeable*. In order to equalize the concentrations on both sides of the membrane, there will be a net flow of water from the solution of *lower solute concentration* to the solution of *higher solute concentration*. The diffusion of the water is from a region of higher water concentration to one of lower water concentration. This movement of the solvent through the membrane can be prevented by application of pressure to the solution with the higher solute concentration. The pressure to prevent osmosis from a given solution is its *osmotic pressure*.

In reference to osmosis certain terms are used to compare concentrations. Two solutions of equal concentration are described as *isotonic*. If two solutions are of different concentrations, the terms *hypertonic* and *hypotonic* are used. If solution A is more concentrated than solution B, then A is hypertonic to B and B is hypotonic to A. The prefixes *iso*, *hyper*, and *hypo* are frequently used throughout science to express *same*, *more*, and *less* respectively. In biology courses you may have heard these prefixes. Membranes of red blood cells allow ions and other small molecules in addition to solvent molecules to pass in and out of the cell. Flow in and out of the cell can be altered by surrounding the cells with solutions other than what is normal to a living organism. Then the cells may shrink or swell.

Placing a red blood cell in a hypertonic solution causes it to shrink. This process, called *crenation*, results from the net flow of water from inside the cell to outside. Similarly if a red blood cell is placed in a hypotonic solution, the net flow of water is from outside the cell to inside. The cell swells and may burst, resulting in hemolysis.

Cell size is not affected if a red blood cell is placed in an isotonic solution. Physiological saline and blood-sugar solution are both isotonic to the contents of red blood cells. The first is 0.9% sodium chloride and the second is a 5.5% glucose solution.

When a body with normal moisture content is embalmed, the injected embalming fluid should be slightly hypotonic to the contents of the tissues. In this way the fluid will pass through the membranes and inside the tissues. If isotonic fluids are used, the rate of flow into the tissues will be too slow to prevent decomposition. One of the products of the reaction between formaldehyde and proteins is water. Following this reaction, tissue contents become hypotonic to their surroundings and water flows into the capillaries. Based on osmotic principles, the initial fluid injected into edematous bodies for embalming should be slightly hypertonic in order to bring water out of the tissues. Similarly fluids that are more hypotonic than those used on normal-moisture-content bodies are recommended for dehydrated bodies.

COLLOIDS AND SUSPENSIONS

All that has been discussed so far in this chapter applies to true solutions. Another name for a true solution is a *crystalloid*. When solutes and solvents are mixed together, two other solutionlike systems can be formed: colloids and suspensions. Some examples of *colloids* are protoplasm, blood plasma, soap solution, egg white solution, mayonnaise, and smoke. *Suspensions* are mixtures such as milk of lime, milk of magnesia, and clay and water. The major distinguishing factor of true solutions, colloidal solutions, and suspensions is particle size. In a true solution the particle size is less than one nanometer, which equals 0.000000001 meter. Suspensions have a particle size of 100 nanometers or more. In between the

Table 9-3   Properties of true solutions, colloids, and suspensions

True solutions	Colloids	Suspensions
1. Particle size < 1 nanometer	Particle size 1 to 100 nanometers	Particle size ≥ 100 nanometers
2. Invisible	Visible with electron microscope	Visible to unaided eye
3. Particles pass through filters and membranes	Particles pass through filters but not membranes	Particles do not pass through filters or membranes
4. Molecular movement	Brownian motion	Move only by force of gravity
5. Particles do not settle out	Particles do not settle out	Particles settle out on standing

particle size of true solutions and suspensions is the colloidal state.

The characteristics of the three types of solutions are listed in Table 9-3. All differences are related to the particle sizes. Colloids have many interesting properties. A notable quality of colloids is Brownian movement. Particles in colloids move randomly, owing to their bombardment by solvent molecules. You can observe this type of motion by watching dust particles dance in a sunbeam or in light from a movie projector.

Colloidal particles can be separated from true solution (crystalloid) particles by the process of *dialysis*. Certain natural membranes such as found in animal kidney tubules allow small ions and molecules, but not larger colloidal particles, to diffuse through them. This selective diffusion is dialysis.

In the kidney small molecules that are metabolic waste products diffuse across the membranes of tubules and form urine. These same waste products can be removed from a person's blood by the use of an artificial kidney machine. Arterial blood is pumped through cellophane tubing surrounded by an aqueous solution. In the solution are ions at the normal concentration of blood plasma. Since cellophane is permeable to small ions

and molecules but not to colloidal protein particles, waste products diffuse from the blood into the solution. The important colloidal proteins remain in the blood. Also during the dialysis process other blood components are regulated to a normal level. Ions such as Na^+, K^+, Cl^- flow through the cellophane from the external solution to the blood or from the blood to the external solution, depending on the region of higher concentration. Following purification and ionic adjustment, the blood reenters the person through the venous system.

CHAPTER SUMMARY

True solutions are homogeneous mixtures of two or more substances. The components of a solution are the solute and the solvent. There may be more than one solute in a solution.

In a saturated solution the solvent contains all the solute it can dissolve at a specific temperature and pressure. This limit is the solubility of the solution. It expresses quantitatively the maximum number of grams of solute in a given volume of solvent. Solubilities are influenced by the nature of the solute and of the solvent, by temperature, and by pressure.

Qualitative terms to express the concentration of a solution are dilute or concentrated, and unsaturated, saturated, or supersaturated. Quantitative concentration terms are percentage, ratio, index, and molarity.

Solutions have different physical properties than those of their components. Examples are elevation of the boiling point and depression of the freezing point in comparison to the pure solvent. Other properties of solutions are stability when filtered and diffusion. An important type of diffusion with respect to biological systems is osmosis, defined as diffusion through membranes. The control of osmosis by using hypotonic, hypertonic, and isotonic solutions is an important consideration in choosing embalming fluids for a specific procedure.

In addition to true solutions, other solutionlike systems are colloids and suspensions. The major distinguishing factor among these three is particle size. Special characteristics of colloids are Brownian movement and dialysis, the process of separating colloidal particles from true solutions.

QUESTIONS

1. Define: alloy, tincture, solubility, dilute, saturated, diffusion, osmosis.

2. Calculate the molarity of a 36 index arterial embalming fluid.

3. Convert to percentage a solution of mercuric chloride that has a ratio concentration of 1 : 1000.

4. Calculate the index of a 3.5 molar embalming fluid.

5. Identify each of the following as a property of a true solution, colloid, or suspension.

(a) Exhibits Brownian movement.

(b) Will pass through both filters and membranes.

(c) Particles are visible to the unaided eye.

(d) Particles will pass through filters but not through membranes.

(e) Particles possess molecular movement.

(f) Particles are larger than 100 nm in diameter.

6. When heat is applied to a solution, particles of solute precipitate from solution. Does this solute dissolve by an exothermic or endothermic process? Explain.

7. Give examples of the following solute-solvent combinations:

Solute ↓	Solvent → Solid	Liquid	Gas
Solid			
Liquid			
Gas			

8. Identify the following substances as polar or nonpolar: water, iodine, sodium chloride, chlorine, and kerosene.

9. Give two examples of each of the following: crystalloid, colloid, and suspension.

10. List three solvents and six solutes found in embalming fluids.

11. Water has been called the universal solvent. What types of substances will not dissolve in water?

12. Using Table 9-2, calculate the molarity of a solution that contains 29.22 grams of NaCl in 500 ml of solution.

The four fundamental types of inorganic compounds are acids, bases, salts, and oxides. In Chapter 2 we defined an oxide as a compound formed from two elements, one of which was oxygen. Examples are Na_2O, Fe_2O_3, and MgO. In this chapter we discuss the nature of acids, bases, and salts. They are the most common types of solutes found in solutions. In biological systems their concentrations are extremely regulated, since they control many physiological processes.

SELF-IONIZATION OF WATER

Acids and bases are normally used dissolved in water. An important characteristic of water that relates to acids and bases is its *self-ionization*.

positive hydrogen of another. If the molecules collide forcefully, the positive hydrogen in the form of an ion can be pulled from its molecule.

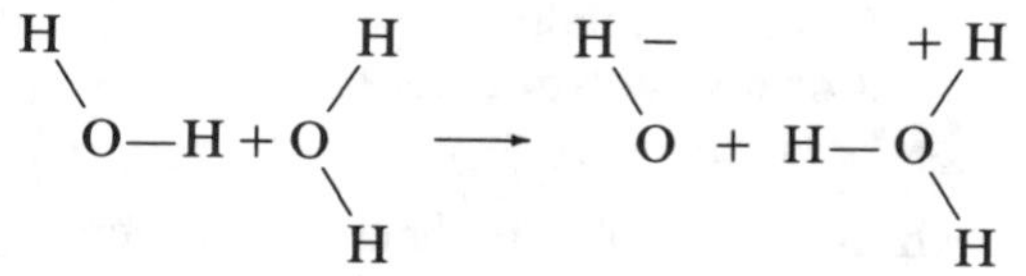

$$\underset{H}{\overset{H}{\diagdown}} O-H + \underset{H}{\overset{H}{\diagdown}} O \longrightarrow \underset{H}{\overset{H-}{\diagdown}} O + H - \underset{H}{\overset{+H}{\diagup}} O$$

The hydrogen leaves behind its electron, so the products of this reaction are a hydroxide ion, OH^-, and a hydronium ion, H_3O^+. Once formed, they may collide to reform two molecules of water. This process is represented by a chemical equation using arrows in both the forward and backward directions.

$$HOH + HOH \rightleftarrows OH^- + H_3O^+$$

Chapter 10
ACIDS, BASES, SALTS, AND IONIZATION

As water molecules collide with one another, there is the possibility that a hydrogen ion from one water molecule will transfer to another water molecule. The polarity of water is the basis for this chemical change. We have already seen that the negative oxygen of one water molecule attracts the

The number of hydronium ions and of hydroxide ions in a volume of pure water is low. At room temperature each has a concentration of 1×10^{-7} moles per liter. The effect of acids and bases on these concentrations is the basis of one way of defining acids and bases.

DEFINITIONS OF ACIDS AND BASES

There are three concepts by which acids and bases are defined. They are:

- Arrhenius theory
- Bronsted-Lowry theory
- Lewis theory

Each is named for the person or persons whose work is responsible for the formulation of the concept.

ARRHENIUS THEORY

This theory was developed in 1887 by Svante Arrhenius, a Swedish chemist. He said that acids are substances that dissociate (break apart) in an aqueous solution to yield hydrogen ions. An example is the very common acid, hydrogen chloride.

$$HCl \longrightarrow H^+ + Cl^- \qquad \text{(aq. soln.)}$$

The Arrhenius definition of a base is a substance that dissociates in an aqueous solution to yield hydroxide ions. A common Arrhenius base is sodium hydroxide.

$$NaOH \longrightarrow Na^+ + OH^- \qquad \text{(aq. soln.)}$$

Arrhenius was not aware of the self-ionization of water. Today we know that hydrogen ions (bare protons) do not exist alone in water. We think of them as being attracted to water molecules, forming hydronium ions. A modification of the Arrhenius definition says acids dissociate in aqueous solution to yield hydronium ions. Actually since water self-ionizes, acids increase the hydronium-ion concentration of water. Likewise, bases increase the hydroxide-ion concentration of water.

Table 10-1 gives a list of frequently used acids and some of their characteristics. The information in the table illustrates several methods of classification of acids. The usual

Table 10-1 Common laboratory acids

Name	Formula	% Dissociation[a]
Strong acids		
Hydrochloric	HCl	92
Hydrobromic	HBr	92
Nitric	HNO_3	92
Sulfuric	H_2SO_4	60
Moderate acids		
Phosphoric	H_3PO_4	27
Sulfurous[b]	H_2SO_3	20
Weak acids		
Acetic	$HC_2H_3O_2$	1.3
Boric	H_3BO_3	0.01
Carbonic[b]	H_2CO_3	0.2
Nitrous[b]	HNO_2	1.5

[a]Based on 0.1 molar acids at room temperature.
[b]Unstable.

ways acids are classified are by:

- Number of hydrogens.
- Number of elements.
- Strength.

Number of hydrogens

Those acids that yield one hydrogen per molecule in solution are called *monoprotic*. An example is hydrochloric acid, HCl. Acids that dissociate into more than one hydrogen are *polyprotic*. These are more specifically described as *diprotic* and *triprotic*. Sulfuric acid, H_2SO_4, is diprotic and phosphoric acid, H_3PO_4, is triprotic.

One aspect of this classification is confusing to beginning students of chemistry. When the formula for an acid is written, it cannot be assumed that all the hydrogens are acidic. When a hydrogen is described as *acidic*, it means that the hydrogen dissociates in aqueous solution. Consider the formula of acetic acid, $HC_2H_3O_2$. Although one molecule has four hydrogens, only one of them, the one expressed first in the formula, is acidic. Acetic acid is monoprotic. A certain amount of "chemical experience" is needed to always correctly analyze a compound for acidic hydrogens. After we study organic acids in Chapter 16, the reason acetic acid is monoprotic will be understood. We can classify all the other acids in Table 10-1 as monoprotic or polyprotic by counting the number of hydrogens.

Number of elements

Acids that are composed of hydrogen and one other element are *binary* or *hydro-acids*.

Acids that contain oxygen in addition to hydrogen and another nonmetallic element are *ternary* or *oxy-acids*.

The commonly used naming system for acids is based on their being binary or ternary. Binary acids derive their name from the element other than hydrogen. Their names always begin with the prefix *hydro-* and end with the suffix *-ic*. Examples are:

- HCl hydro-chlor-ic
- H_2S hydro-sulfur-ic
- HBr hydro-brom-ic
- HF hydro-fluor-ic

The names of ternary acids are derived from the element other than hydrogen and oxygen and end with the suffix *-ic*. Examples of ternary acids are:

- H_2SO_4 sulfur-ic acid
- H_3PO_4 phosphor-ic acid
- HNO_3 nitr-ic acid
- $HClO_3$ chlor-ic acid

If the same three elements form more than one ternary acid, the acid with the lower number of oxygen atoms ends with the suffix *-ous*. Some examples are:

- H_2SO_3 sulfur-ous acid
- H_3PO_3 phosphor-ous acid
- HNO_2 nitr-ous acid
- $HClO_2$ chlor-ous acid

Table 10-2   Acids of halogens

Formula[a]	Name
HXO	Hypochlorous, hypobromous, hypoiodous
HXO_2	Chlorous, bromous, iodous
HXO_3	Chloric, bromic, iodic
HXO_4	Perchloric, perbromic, periodic

[a]X represents the appropriate halogen.

Acids of the halogens can also exist as compounds containing one more oxygen than the *-ic* acid and one less oxygen than the *-ous* acid. These are distinguished by *per-* and *hypo-* prefixes.

The names and formulas for the possible acids of chlorine, bromine, and iodine are listed in Table 10-2.

Strength

On the basis of strength, acids are classified as strong, moderate, and weak. The strength of an acid is determined by its percent dissociation in aqueous solution. Acids yielding a relatively large number of hydrogen ions in solution are *strong*. Table 10-1 lists hydrochloric, hydrobromic, nitric, and sulfuric as strong acids. The usual way to represent strong acids is to use an arrow only in the forward direction in the equation showing the dissociation of the acid. The equation for nitric acid is written as

$$HNO_3 \longrightarrow H^+ + NO_3^-$$

If an acid yields a relatively small number of hydrogen ions in solution, it is *weak*. Examples are acetic acid, boric acid, carbonic acid, and nitrous acid. Their dissociations are written in equation form with an arrow in both the forward and backward direction. The equation for dissociation of acetic acid is

$$HC_2H_3O_2 \rightleftarrows H^+ + C_2H_3O_2^-$$

Other acids are described as *moderate*, since their percent dissociation is neither as high nor as low as those acids traditionally called strong and weak. Common moderate acids are phosphoric acid and sulfurous acid. Equations for the dissociations of these acids are written with arrows in both directions.

Three of the acids listed in Table 10-1 are also described as *unstable*. What does this mean? Carbonic acid and sulfurous acid are formed by the dissolving of carbon dioxide and sulfur dioxide in water. Reactions for the formations of these acids are

$$CO_2 + H_2O \rightleftarrows H_2CO_3$$

and

$$SO_2 + H_2O \rightleftarrows H_2SO_3$$

In both cases the acid that is formed may participate in two processes: (1) dissociation into a hydrogen ion and a negative ion, which shows its acidic properties, and (2) decomposition into water and the corresponding oxide, owing to its instability. For carbonic acid,

$$H_2CO_3 \rightleftarrows H^+ + HCO_3^-$$

and

$$H_2CO_3 \rightarrow H_2O + CO_2$$

Similar equations may be written for H_2SO_3. For both acids decomposition occurs to a greater extent than dissociation, hence their description as unstable acids.

The third unstable acid is the weak acid nitrous acid. It is usually prepared by the acidification of salts containing the nitrite ion, NO_2^-. Like the other unstable acids it can dissociate into a hydrogen ion and nitrite ion or decompose. In aqueous solution it decomposes to nitric acid and gaseous nitric oxide:

$$3\ HNO_2 \rightleftarrows HNO_3 + H_2O + 2\ NO$$

COMMON AQUEOUS BASES

Table 10-3 lists frequently used bases and their characteristics.

Like those of acids, the strengths of bases in aqueous solutions are determined by the percent dissociation of the compounds into positive ions and hydroxide ions. Four strong bases are listed in Table 10-3. Each consists of a metallic element combined with the hydroxide ion. Their names are formed from the name of the metallic element followed by the word hydroxide. Two of these strong bases, sodium hydroxide and potassium hydroxide, are also caustic substances. Both of them are very soluble in water. In the form of concentrated solutions they cause severe burns to the skin. However, this caustic nature can be used to advantage in an embalming procedure. Sodium hydroxide and potassium hydroxide as 10% solutions are used to remove sloughed skin in burn cases. In contrast, the other two strong bases, calcium hydroxide and magnesium hydroxide, have very low solubilities in water and are not caustic. They are classified as strong, since the small amount that does dissolve dissociates approximately 100 percent.

One weak base, aqueous ammonia, is listed in Table 10-3. It is formed by the dissolving

Table 10-3 Common laboratory bases

Name	Formula	% Dissociation
Strong bases		
Sodium hydroxide	NaOH	$> 90^a$
Potassium hydroxide	KOH	$> 90^a$
Calcium hydroxide	$Ca(OH)_2$	$\cong 100^b$
Magnesium hydroxide	$Mg(OH)_2$	$\cong 100^b$
Weak bases		
Aqueous ammonia	NH_3	$\cong\ 1^c$

[a]Based on 0.1 molar solutions at room temperature.
[b]Saturated solution.
[c]Dissociation process is $NH_3 + H_2O \rightleftarrows NH_4^+ + OH^-$.

of ammonia gas, NH_3, in water followed by the ionization

$$NH_3 + H_2O \rightleftarrows NH_4^+ + OH^-$$

The products of this reaction are the ammonium ion and the hydroxide ion. Since the ionization produces relatively few numbers of hydroxide ions, aqueous ammonia is a weak base.

PROPERTIES OF AQUEOUS ACIDS AND BASES

Since acids dissociate in aqueous solutions to produce the hydrogen ion, they will have a common set of properties related to the presence of this ion. Likewise, the properties of bases are related to the formation of hydroxide ions in solution.

Properties of acids

The word "acid" is derived from the Latin word *acidus* meaning "sour." The first property of acids states this observation.

1. Acids in solution taste sour. The familiar sour taste of citrus fruit is due to citric acid. Vinegar has a characteristic sour taste since it is a dilute solution of the organic acid, acetic acid.

2. Acids change blue litmus to red. Litmus is a compound described as an indicator. Substances which are one color in the presence of an acid and another color in the presence of a base are used to experimentally distinguish between acids and bases; the general name for such compounds is *indicator*. In addition to litmus, another frequently used indicator is phenolphthalein. It is used as a colorless solution which remains colorless in the presence of an acid.

3. Dilute acids react with metals above hydrogen in the electrochemical series, liberating hydrogen gas. (See Chapter 7.)

4. Acids react with bases to form water and a salt. This is a most important reaction in chemistry and is called *neutralization*. It is so named because by the reaction of an acid and a base, the hydrogen ion of the acid combines with the hydroxide ion of the base, forming water. In this way, the acidic nature (H^+) of the acid is neutralized by the basic nature (OH^-) of the base. Consider the reaction between hydrochloric acid and sodium hydroxide:

$$HCl + NaOH \rightarrow HOH + NaCl$$

The driving force behind this neutralization reaction is the formation of water. Whenever the constituents of water, H^+ and OH^-, are brought together in a reaction, water forms. In addition, in the reaction between hydrochloric acid and sodium hydroxide, the negative chloride ion from the acid joins with the positive sodium ion from the base. The product, sodium chloride, is classified as a salt. The definition of a salt is a compound formed between a positive ion other than H^+ and a negative ion other than OH^-. The properties of salts are discussed later in this chapter.

Neutralization reactions fit in the general class of reactions that were previously described as double replacement. Other examples of acid-base neutralizations are

$$HNO_3 + KOH \longrightarrow HOH + KNO_3$$
$$HC_2H_3O_2 + NaOH \longrightarrow$$
$$HOH + NaC_2H_3O_2$$
$$H_2SO_4 + 2\,KOH \longrightarrow 2\,HOH + K_2SO_4$$

In each of these reactions the products are described as water and a salt.

5. Acids react with carbonates and bicarbonates, liberating carbon dioxide and

forming a salt. Carbonates are compounds in which the negative part is the radical CO_3^-. Similar to carbonates are bicarbonates, compounds in which the negative radical is HCO_3^-. The reaction between an acid and a carbonate or a bicarbonate can be broken down into two parts. If sodium carbonate and sulfuric acid are reacted, the first step is a double-replacement reaction. The products are carbonic acid and sodium sulfate:

$$Na_2CO_3 + H_2SO_4 \longrightarrow H_2CO_3 + Na_2SO_4$$

Since carbonic acid is unstable, it decomposes into carbon dioxide and water. This decomposition is the second step of the reaction between sodium carbonate and sulfuric acid. Overall the reaction is

$$Na_2CO_3 + H_2SO_4 \longrightarrow CO_2 + H_2O + Na_2SO_4$$

If several drops of dilute sulfuric acid are added to sodium carbonate, which is a white solid, bubbles form. The formation of bubbles during a chemical reaction indicates the production of a gas. In this case, the gas is carbon dioxide and the other products of the reaction are water and the salt sodium sulfate.

If sodium bicarbonate reacts with sulfuric acid, the two steps of the reaction are

$$2\ NaHCO_3 + H_2SO_4 \longrightarrow 2\ H_2CO_3 + Na_2SO_4$$
$$2\ H_2CO_3 \longrightarrow 2\ H_2O + 2\ CO_2$$

The overall reaction is

$$2\ NaHCO_3 + H_2SO_4 \longrightarrow 2\ H_2O + 2\ CO_2 + Na_2SO_4$$

If an acid is spilled, sodium bicarbonate is sometimes poured on the area to "neutralize" the effects of the acid. Sodium bicarbonate is commonly called baking soda. It is used in baking along with an acidic substance to liberate carbon dioxide, which causes cakes and other baked goods to "rise."

6. Acids react with sulfites forming sulfur dioxide and a salt. Sulfites are compounds that contain the radical SO_3^-. The reaction between an acid and a sulfite compound is analogous to that between an acid and a carbonate. As with carbonates, acids first react with sulfites, producing an unstable compound which then decomposes. The reaction between sulfuric acid and sodium sulfite is

$$H_2SO_4 + Na_2SO_3 \longrightarrow H_2SO_3 + Na_2SO_4$$
$$H_2SO_3 \longrightarrow H_2O + SO_2$$

The overall reaction is

$$H_2SO_4 + Na_2SO_3 \longrightarrow H_2O + SO_2 + Na_2SO_4$$

Properties of bases

Another term associated with bases is *alkali*. This word may be derived from the Arabian word *al-qaliy*, meaning "ashes." It could also be derived from the Arabian word *al-kali*, meaning "the plant." Ancient peoples observed that bitter substances they called *alkali* were found in ashes of the saltwort plant.[1] The first property of bases states this observation.

1. Solutions of bases have a bitter, metallic taste.
2. Solutions of bases feel slippery.
3. Bases change red litmus to blue. If a few drops of the colorless indicator phenolphthalein are added to a base, the color changes to pink.
4. Bases react with acids, forming salts and water. Several examples of acid-base neutralization reactions were previously written in this chapter. A neutralization that may not appear to exactly fit the rules is that of

---

[1] Harry Wain, *The Story Behind the Word*, 1958. Courtesy of Charles C Thomas, Publisher, Springfield, Illinois.

aqueous ammonia, NH_3, by an acid. The equation is

$$NH_3 + HCl \longrightarrow NH_4Cl$$

The product of the reaction is only a salt, ammonium chloride, and no water. If it is remembered that the basicity of NH_3 is due to its reaction in water, forming the products $NH_4^+ + OH^-$, then a more typical acid-base neutralization can be written for ammonia:

$$NH_4^+ + OH^- + HCl \longrightarrow HOH + NH_4Cl$$

Either of these last two equations correctly represents the neutralization of ammonia.

BRONSTED-LOWRY THEORY

A second theory of acids and bases was proposed in 1923 by Johannes Bronsted and Thomas Lowry. This theory extends the definitions of acids and bases to include as bases substances other than metallic hydroxides. According to the Bronsted-Lowry theory, an acid is a *proton donor* and a base is a *proton acceptor*. When hydrogen chloride dissolves in water, a proton is donated by hydrogen chloride to water:

$$HCl + HOH \longrightarrow H_3O^+ + Cl^-$$

Hydrogen chloride is the acid; water, which accepts the proton, is the base. In the reaction between ammonia and water, ammonia accepts a proton from water:

$$NH_3 + H_2O \rightleftharpoons NH_4^+ + OH^-$$

Ammonia is the base and water is the acid, since it donates the proton. If the backward reaction for this equation is considered, the ammonium ion is the acid and the hydroxide ion is the base.

Ammonia (NH_3) and the ammonium ion (NH_4^+) differ only by a proton. When the only difference between two substances is a

Table 10-4 Conjugate acid-base pairs

Acid	Base
HCl	Cl^-
$HC_2H_3O_2$	$C_2H_3O_2^-$
NH_4^+	NH_3
H_3O^+	H_2O
H_2O	OH^-

proton, they are called a *conjugate acid-base pair*. Several of these pairs are shown in Table 10-4.

The conjugate base of an acid is always determined by removing one proton from the acid. The conjugate acid of a base is the base plus a proton.

Water appears in Table 10-4 as both an acid and a base. If the reactions that were previously written between hydrogen chloride and water and ammonia and water are compared, this same duality of the acidic-basic nature of water is demonstrated. When water is in the presence of a substance like HCl, with a stronger tendency than its own to donate protons, water is a base. If water is with ammonia, which has a stronger tendency than water to accept protons, then water is an acid. Any substance that can act as either an acid or a base is called *amphoteric*. Water is one of the most common and important amphoteric compounds.

From the list of conjugate acids and bases in Table 10-4, we see that the Bronsted-Lowry theory includes more substances as bases than the Arrhenius theory. Two other Bronsted bases are the carbonate ion and the bicarbonate ion. Both of these ions can pull protons from water:

$$CO_3^{-2} + H_2O \rightleftharpoons HCO_3^- + OH^-$$
$$HCO_3^- + H_2O \rightleftharpoons H_2CO_3 + OH^-$$

In these reactions, water acts as a Bronsted-Lowry acid. Solutions containing either the carbonate or bicarbonate ion test in the laboratory as bases.

LEWIS THEORY

In 1923, G. N. Lewis proposed a theory of acids and bases that is more general than either the Arrhenius theory or the Bronsted-Lowry theory. According to Lewis, an acid is any substance that accepts a pair of electrons and a base is any substance that donates a pair of electrons. An example of a Bronsted-Lowry acid-base reaction that also fits the Lewis definition is

$$H:\overset{xx}{\underset{H}{O}}: + H:\overset{xx}{\underset{xx}{Cl}}: \longrightarrow H:\overset{xx}{\underset{H}{O}}:H^+ + :\overset{xx}{\underset{xx}{Cl}}:^-$$

The hydrogen ion from the hydrogen chloride accepts a pair of electrons from the oxygen of the water. Since hydrogen chloride is the electron-pair acceptor, it is a Lewis acid. Water, as the electron-pair donor, is the Lewis base. A covalent bond forms between the hydrogen ion and water molecule, yielding the hydronium ion. Both electrons in the bond were originally with the oxygen. This is different from most covalent bonds in which one electron comes from each of the atoms joined in the bond. To distinguish these two types of covalent bonds, those in which both bonding electrons come from the same atom are called *coordinate covalent bonds*.

A general application of the theory of Lewis is the reaction between magnesium oxide and sulfur trioxide:

$$Mg^{+2}\left[:\overset{xx}{\underset{xx}{O}}:\right]^{-2} + :\overset{\overset{xx}{O}}{\underset{\underset{xx}{O}}{S}}:\overset{xx}{O}: \longrightarrow Mg^{+2}\left[:\overset{\overset{xx}{O}}{\underset{\underset{xx}{O}}{O:S:O}}:\right]^{-2}$$

Magnesium sulfate forms by magnesium oxide's donating a pair of electrons to sulfur trioxide. Magnesium oxide is a Lewis base and sulfur trioxide is a Lewis acid. This reaction demonstrates a general property of oxides: metallic oxides have basic properties and nonmetallic oxides have acidic properties.

ANHYDRIDES

The word anhydride means "without water." Oxides of metals and nonmetals are called *anhydrides*. By reacting with water they form either acids or bases. Typical anhydrides are CO_2, SO_2, Na_2O, CaO, and Fe_2O_3. The first two are oxides of nonmetals. The reactions of these substances with water are

$$CO_2 + H_2O \rightleftharpoons H_2CO_3$$
$$SO_2 + H_2O \rightleftharpoons H_2SO_3$$

In both cases an acid is the product. A property of nonmetallic oxides is that they react with water to form acids. Nonmetallic oxides are called *acid anhydrides*.

In contrast, metallic oxides are *basic anhydrides*. Na_2O, CaO, and Fe_2O_3 react with water by the following:

$$Na_2O + H_2O \longrightarrow 2\ NaOH$$
$$CaO + H_2O \longrightarrow Ca(OH)_2$$
$$Fe_2O_3 + 3\ H_2O \longrightarrow 2\ Fe(OH)_3$$

Aqueous solutions of these metallic oxides test basic with litmus paper.

SALTS

Substances called *salts* are the fourth of the major types of inorganic compounds. In earlier discussions of the properties of acids and bases, the products of several reactions were identified as salts. General equations by which salts are produced are

$$acid + some\ metals \longrightarrow salt + H_2$$
$$acid + base \longrightarrow salt + H_2O$$
$$acid + carbonate \longrightarrow salt + H_2O + CO_2$$
$$acid + bicarbonate \longrightarrow salt + H_2O + CO_2$$

Table 10-5   Examples of salts

Name	Formula
Normal salts	
Sodium chloride	$NaCl$
Sodium sulfate	Na_2SO_4
Sodium phosphate	Na_3PO_4
Ammonium iodide	NH_4I
Aluminum sulfate	$Al_2(SO_4)_3$
Calcium phosphate	$Ca_3(PO_4)_2$
Acid salts	
Sodium bicarbonate	$NaHCO_3$
Sodium bisulfate	$NaHSO_4$
Sodium biphosphate	NaH_2PO_4
Disodium hydrogen phosphate	Na_2HPO_4
Basic salts	
Basic bismuth nitrate	$Bi(OH)_2NO_3$
Basic lead nitrate	$Pb(OH)NO_3$

Salts were defined in an earlier section on acid-base neutralization as compounds formed between a positive ion other than H^+ and a negative ion other than OH^-. In pure form, salts usually exist as crystalline solids at room temperature. Consideration of Table 10-5 demonstrates some of their other properties.

Composition

Salts are composed of ions of metallic elements or the positive ammonium radical (NH_4^+) in combination with one or more ions of a nonmetallic element or a radical. Salts are ionic substances. Those that dissolve in water dissociate into positive and negative ions.

Classification

Salts are classified as normal, acidic, or basic.

A *normal salt* is one in which all the replaceable hydrogen of the corresponding acid has been replaced by a metal. Sodium chloride ($NaCl$) is a normal salt. This compound is formed by neutralization of hydrochloric acid (HCl) by sodium hydroxide ($NaOH$). Since hydrochloric acid is monoprotic, it reacts in a 1-to-1 ratio with sodium hydroxide. Two other normal salts are sodium sulfate (Na_2SO_4) and sodium phosphate (Na_3PO_4). Consideration of the following neutralization reactions shows that these normal salts are formed by reactions of sulfuric acid and sodium hydroxide in a 1-to-2 ratio, and phosphoric acid and sodium hydroxide in a 1-to-3 ratio:

$$H_2SO_4 + 2\ NaOH \longrightarrow 2\ HOH + Na_2SO_4$$
$$H_3PO_4 + 3\ NaOH \longrightarrow 3\ HOH + Na_3PO_4$$

Other normal salts in Table 10-5 are ammonium iodide, aluminum sulfate, and calcium phosphate. None of them contain hydrogen in the negative part of the compound.

An *acid salt* is one in which only part of the replaceable hydrogen of the acid has been replaced by a metal. Acid salts listed in Table 10-5 are $NaHCO_3$, $NaHSO_4$, NaH_2PO_4, and Na_2HPO_4. If one hydrogen of the diprotic acid, carbonic acid, H_2CO_3, is replaced by sodium, the compound formed is sodium bicarbonate. Another less frequently used name for this salt is sodium hydrogen carbonate. Similarly, sodium bisulfate or sodium hydrogen sulfate is derived from sulfuric acid. Since phosphoric acid, H_3PO_4, is triprotic, two acid salts can form from it. Replacement of one hydrogen by sodium yields NaH_2PO_4 which is called sodium biphosphate or monosodium hydrogen phosphate. The other acid sodium salt of phosphoric acid is Na_2HPO_4, disodium hydrogen phosphate.

Salts of the third kind, *basic salts*, contain one or more replaceable hydroxyl ions. Two examples are $Bi(OH)_2NO_3$, basic bismuth nitrate, and $Pb(OH)NO_3$, basic lead nitrate.

Naming of salts

Salts are named according to the type of acid, binary or ternary, from which they are derived. Salts of binary acids are named by giving first the name of the metal that has formed the positive ion followed by the name of the nonmetal ending with the suffix -ide. The same system applies if the positive ion is ammonium, NH_4^+. Salts from binary acids are

- NaCl—sodium chlor-ide
- KBr—potassium brom-ide
- NH_4I—ammonium iod-ide

The names of salts of ternary acids are formed from the name of the metal (or ammonium) and the name of the radical that is associated with the ternary acid. A few salts from Table 10-5 that demonstrate this naming procedure are

- $Al_2(SO_4)_3$—aluminum sulfate
- $Ca_3(PO_4)_2$—calcium phosphate
- $NaHCO_3$—sodium bicarbonate

Hydrolysis

The major chemical reaction of salts is *hydrolysis*. By this reaction, the ions of a salt "break apart" water molecules into H^+ and OH^- ions. Although only certain salts hydrolyze, this reaction is very common to inorganic chemical processes. Understanding hydrolysis by salts is an important step in learning the principles upon which hydrolysis of biochemical compounds is based. A detailed discussion of hydrolysis is given in the next chapter.

IONIZATION

A property that is common to all aqueous acids, aqueous bases, and water-soluble salts is *ionization*. This property is defined as the dissociating of a substance into charged species that may be atoms or groups of atoms. Positive particles that are formed by ionization are called *cations*. Negative ions are referred to as *anions*. The presence of ions in a solution enables it to conduct electricity. Usually electricity is thought of as a stream of electrons that travels through wires made of metallic substances.

How is electricity carried through a solution of ions? Consider placing two pieces of wire in a solution. If the wires are connected through a battery and switch, current flows through the solution when the switch is closed. (See Figure 10-1.) The wires are called *electrodes*. One of the wires becomes electron-rich by the battery's pumping electrons into it. Positive ions in the solution (cations) are attracted to this negative area. The other electrode loses electrons through the wire to the battery and becomes deficient in electrons. Negative ions in the solution (anions) are attracted to this positive electrode. They can give their electrons to the surface of the positive electrode. Likewise, at the other electrode, the cations remove electrons from its

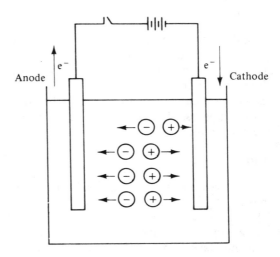

Figure 10-1 Apparatus for electrolysis

surface. The net effect of these processes is formation of a closed circuit between the wires and battery by the solution. The passage of an electric current through a solution is called *electrolysis*. Solutions which allow electrolysis are called *electrolytes*. Since electrolysis depends on ions, substances that dissociate to a large extent in a solution are good conductors of electricity and are called *strong electrolytes*. Water-soluble salts and strong acids and bases are strong electrolytes. Weak acids and bases which dissociate slightly are *weak electrolytes*.

Substances that do not form appreciable numbers of ions in solution are *nonelectrolytes*. Pure water and most organic compounds are nonelectrolytes.

Table 10-6   Relationship of pH to the concentrations of hydrogen and hydroxyl ions

	H$^+$ conc. (M)	pH	OH$^-$ conc. (M)
Acidic	1	0	10^{-14}
	10^{-1}	1	10^{-13}
	10^{-2}	2	10^{-12}
	10^{-3}	3	10^{-11}
	10^{-4}	4	10^{-10}
	10^{-5}	5	10^{-9}
	10^{-6}	6	10^{-8}
Neutral	10^{-7}	7	10^{-7}
Basic	10^{-8}	8	10^{-6}
	10^{-9}	9	10^{-5}
	10^{-10}	10	10^{-4}
	10^{-11}	11	10^{-3}
	10^{-12}	12	10^{-2}
	10^{-13}	13	10^{-1}
	10^{-14}	14	1

pH: HYDROGEN-ION CONCENTRATION

We have seen that common acids dissociate into hydrogen ions in water and that common bases dissociate into hydroxyl ions. We have also seen that pure water at room temperature contains equal concentrations (1×10^{-7} M) of hydrogen ions and hydroxyl ions. Such water is described as *neutral*, since the number of hydrogen ions equals the number of hydroxyl ions. If an acid is added to the water, the hydrogen-ion concentration increases and the solution is no longer neutral. Addition of a base to pure water also destroys neutrality by increasing the hydroxyl-ion concentration. The intensity of the acidity or basicity of a solution is commonly expressed by chemists in terms of pH. This really means the power of the hydrogen-ion concentration. The pH scale is used to evaluate hydrogen-ion concentration between 1 molar and 10^{-14} molar. The mathematical definition of pH is the negative logarithm of the hydrogen ion concentration. Familiarity with logarithms may help in understanding the pH scale, but such knowledge is not absolutely necessary. Understanding of pH can be attained by comparing the hydrogen-ion concentrations and hydroxyl-ion concentrations in solutions of various pH's. (See Table 10-6.)

Important relationships that can be learned by comparing numbers in Table 10-6 are:

1. The product of the hydrogen-ion concentration (symbolized by [H$^+$]) and the hydroxyl-ion concentration (symbolized by [OH$^-$]) in an aqueous solution is always 10^{-14}:

$$[H^+] \times [OH^-] = 10^{-14}$$

This is a statement of a fundamental property of pure water and aqueous solutions. If acid or base is added to pure water, the concentrations of these ions always adjust themselves so their product is constant at 10^{-14}.

2. A neutral solution has a pH of 7. This means [H$^+$] and [OH$^-$] are equal.

Table 10-7 Approximate pH values of common liquids

Liquid	pH value
Human gastric juice	1.0–3.0
Soft drinks	2.0–4.0
Beer	4.0–5.0
Milk	6.0–6.5
Pure water (neutral)	7.0
Blood	7.3–7.5
Embalming fluid	7.3–7.5
Milk of magnesia	10.0–11.0

3. pH values less than 7 represent acid solutions, because in them $[H^+] > [OH^-]$. The intensity of the acidity increases as the pH values decrease.

4. pH values greater than 7 represent basic solutions because in them $[OH^-] > [H^+]$. The intensity of the basicity increases as the pH values increase.

Table 10-7 shows approximate pH values of common liquids. Values of pH do not have to be whole numbers. For example, the pH of blood is 7.3–7.5. It is absolutely necessary that the pH of blood in a living human being be within this narrow range. If the pH changes outside this range, normal bodily functions are altered and death may result. Our bodies have protective mechanisms to keep the pH of blood constant. Substances known as *buffers* are present in the blood to protect against changes in pH. In general, these substances interact with acidic and basic substances that enter the blood, converting them into compounds that the body can excrete.

pH Dependence of formaldehyde

In the same way that the blood must be buffered, it is also necessary to buffer embalming fluids. They have pH values approximately equal to that of blood. Following death the pH of the blood changes from slightly basic to acidic. As decomposition occurs, the pH again becomes basic. As decomposition products accumulate, the basicity increases. It is necessary to restore the pH to its normal range (7.3–7.5) by the injected embalming fluid because the action of formaldehyde is pH dependent. It functions most effectively at pH values approximately the same as those of normal blood. Typical buffers added to embalming fluids are borax, sodium phosphates, and citrates. See the organic chemistry and biochemistry sections for the details of changes in pH after death and the sensitivity of formaldehyde to pH.

CHAPTER SUMMARY

The four fundamental types of inorganic compounds are acids, bases, salts, and oxides. Three concepts that define acids and bases are

- ○ Arrhenius theory
- ○ Bronsted-Lowry theory
- ○ Lewis theory

The Arrhenius theory is the most specific and the Lewis theory the most general.

An Arrhenius acid dissociates in aqueous solutions, yielding hydrogen ions. Hydroxide ions are produced in solutions by dissociation of Arrhenius bases. Both of these dissociation processes affect the self-ionization of water. Arrhenius acids are monoprotic or polyprotic, binary or ternary, and strong, moderate, or weak. Their strength is determined by their degree of dissociation in water. Bases also exist in varying degrees of strength with respect to percent dissociation.

The Bronsted-Lowry theory of acids and bases defines acids as proton donors and bases as proton acceptors. This theory extends the concepts of acids and bases to include other substances in addition to hydroxides as bases.

The most general theory of acids and bases is the Lewis theory. Lewis acids are substances that accept a pair of electrons in a chemical reaction. The substance that donates the pair of electrons is a Lewis base.

Reactions that involve acids, bases, salts, and oxides in aqueous solutions are:

○ Acid + base $\longrightarrow$ salt + HOH.
○ Acid + some metals $\longrightarrow$ salt + H_2.
○ Acid + carbonate or bicarbonate $\longrightarrow$ salt + CO_2 + HOH.
○ Acid + sulfite $\longrightarrow$ salt + SO_2 + HOH.
○ Metallic oxide + HOH $\longrightarrow$ base.
○ Nonmetallic oxide + HOH $\longrightarrow$ acid.

The first reaction, called neutralization, is the most important one of acids and bases. Its products are water, which forms by the combination of H^+ and OH^-, and a salt, which forms from the anion of the acid and the cation of the base. Salts are classified as normal, acidic, or basic. Some salts undergo a reaction called hydrolysis by which they dissociate water into its constituents.

Acids, bases, and water-soluble salts ionize in aqueous solutions. The presence of ions in certain solutions called electrolytes enables them to conduct an electric current.

The concentrations of hydrogen ions and hydroxyl ions in a solution are compared by the pH scale. Values of pH range from 0 to 14. A pH of 7 represents a neutral solution. Acidic solutions have pH values that are less than 7 and basic solutions have pH values that are greater than 7.

QUESTIONS

1. Define: salt, acid salt, buffer, anhydride, ternary acid, amphoteric compound, electrode, cation.

2. Classify the following acids as (1) monoprotic or polyprotic and (2) binary or ternary: hydroiodic acid, sulfuric acid, nitrous acid, chloric acid, and carbonic acid.

3. Write equations showing:
  (a) Self-ionization of water.
  (b) The Arrhenius definition of an acid.
  (c) The Arrhenius definition of a base.
  (d) The Bronsted-Lowry definition of a base.
  (e) The Lewis definition of an acid.

4. What is the difference between a strong acid and a weak acid? Give an example of each. Relate the strength of acids and bases to the ability to conduct an electric current.

5. Complete and balance the following equations:
  (a) $HCl + KOH \longrightarrow$
  (b) $H_2SO_4 + NH_4OH \longrightarrow$
  (c) $NH_3 + H_2O \longrightarrow$
  (d) $Zn + H_2SO_4 \longrightarrow$
  (e) $HC_2H_3O_2 + Ca(OH)_2 \longrightarrow$
  (f) $NaHCO_3 + HCl \longrightarrow$
  (g) $H_2SO_4 + Na_2SO_3 \longrightarrow$
  (h) $K_2O + H_2O \longrightarrow$
  (i) $MgO + H_2O \longrightarrow$
  (j) $CaO + SO_3 \longrightarrow$

6. Complete the following table:

Conjugate acid	Conjugate base
HI	
	$C_2H_3O_2^-$
NH_4^+	
HSO_4^-	
	$H_2PO_4^-$
H_2O	
	Cl^-

7. Classify the following as properties of acidic or basic solutions:
  (a) Feels slippery.
  (b) Tastes sour.
  (c) Changes blue litmus to red.
  (d) Tests pink with phenolphthalein.
  (e) Tastes bitter.

8. Why is a solution with a $pH = 7$ called neutral?

9. An oxide has the general formula XO. When it is dissolved in water, the resulting solution turns red litmus blue. Suggest possible elements from the periodic table for X.

10. Convert the following concentrations to values of pH:
    (a) $H^+ = 10^{-5} M$
    (b) $H^+ = 10^{-11} M$
    (c) $H^+ = 1 M$
    (d) $OH^- = 10^{-6} M$
    (e) $OH^- = 10^{-9} M$

11. Name the following compounds:
    (a) H_3BO_3 (b) $HC_2H_3O_2$
    (c) HNO_3 (d) HF
    (e) HIO_2 (f) $HClO_4$
    (g) $NaOH$ (h) $KHCO_3$
    (i) $CaCl_2$ (j) $(NH_4)_2SO_4$

12. Write formulas for the following compounds:
    (a) Hydronium ion.
    (b) Phosphoric acid.
    (c) Hydrosulfuric acid.
    (d) Hypobromous acid.
    (e) Sodium nitrate.
    (f) Potassium bromide.
    (g) Calcium sulfite.
    (h) Potassium hydrogen sulfate.
    (i) Monosodium hydrogen phosphate.
    (j) Magnesium hydroxide.

We have seen that water is the focal point of the chemistry of decomposition and embalming. In Chapter 9 we discussed the physical aspects of water, focusing on solutions. This chapter is the study of two chemical properties of water: the formation of hydrates and hydrolysis reactions.

HYDRATES

A *hydrate* is a compound in which there is a chemical union between water and the molecules of certain substances. The physical appearance of a hydrate is crystalline. The water held in the chemical union is called the "water of crystallization." When the formula

Table 11-1 gives examples of some commonly encountered hydrates. From the formulas in the table we see that the water of crystallization not only varies from one hydrate to another, but also may vary within the same substance. Such substances are termed *partly anhydrous* and *fully hydrated*. Anhydrous literally means "without water." This term usually refers to a chemical compound after the water of crystallization has been removed. This may be accomplished by heating, which breaks the chemical bond and releases the water of crystallization. The process of removing the water of crystallization from a compound is called *dehydration*. For example:

Chapter 11
HYDRATES AND HYDROLYSIS

is written for a hydrate, the chemical bond is represented by a dot connecting the hydrated substance to its water of crystallization.

Hydrates have varying amounts of water of crystallization. This amount is expressed by a *coefficient number* attached to the formula for water. For example, hydrated copper sulfate is written

$$CuSO_4 \cdot 5\ H_2O$$

$$\overbrace{CuSO_4 \cdot 5\ H_2O \xrightarrow{\text{heat}} CuSO_4 + 5\ H_2O\uparrow}^{\text{Dehydration}}$$

Hydrated copper sulfate (bright blue crystals)	Anhydrous copper sulfate (grey powder)	Water vapor

When copper sulfate crystals are heated, the water of crystallization is released as water

Table 11-1 Examples of hydrates

Formula	Chemical name	Common name(s)
$Na_2CO_3 \cdot 10\,H_2O$	Sodium carbonate	Washing soda Sal soda
$CuSO_4 \cdot 5\,H_2O$	Copper sulfate	Blue vitriol Blue stone
$MgSO_4 \cdot 7\,H_2O$	Magnesium sulfate	Epsom salts
$Na_2B_4O_7 \cdot 10\,H_2O$	Sodium tetraborate	Borax
$(CaSO_4)_2 \cdot H_2O$	Calcium sulfate	Plaster of Paris
$CaSO_4 \cdot 2\,H_2O$	Calcium sulfate	Gypsum

vapor. The product, anhydrous copper sulfate, loses its crystalline form and appears as a powdery grey substance. This may also be classified as a decomposition reaction, since there is only one reactant but two products. Reformation of the blue crystals will occur if water is added to the anhydrous copper sulfate.

Setting of plaster of Paris

Some hydrates are capable of having two different waters of crystallization and thus appearing in two distinct physical forms. This occurs with calcium sulfate, which in its partly anhydrous form, $(CaSO_4)_2 \cdot H_2O$, is called plaster of Paris, and in its fully hydrated form, $CaSO_4 \cdot 2\,H_2O$, is known as gypsum. The reaction occurs by the addition of water, as follows:

$$(CaSO_4)_2 \cdot H_2O + 3\,H_2O \longrightarrow$$
Plaster of Paris

$$2\,CaSO_4 \cdot 2\,H_2O$$
Gypsum

This hydration reaction may be classified as a synthesis reaction, since there are two reactants and only one product. Upon initial observation this equation does not appear to be balanced. This emphasizes the importance of understanding that the dot represents a true chemical bond. Thus gypsum, $CaSO_4 \cdot$

$2\,H_2O$, is one substance, and the coefficient 2 multiplies everything in that expression. Therefore, $2\,CaSO_4 \cdot 2\,H_2O$ means $2\,CaSO_4$ and $2 \times 2\,H_2O$ or $4\,H_2O$. If the equation is done in diagram form, the point is better illustrated.

$$CaSO_4 - H_2O - CaSO_4 + H_2O \longrightarrow$$

with H_2O above and H_2O below the $+H_2O$.

Plaster of Paris   Water

$$H_2O - CaSO_4 - H_2O$$
$$H_2O - CaSO_4 - H_2O$$
Gypsum

In plaster of Paris, two molecules of calcium sulfate are bonded together by one molecule of water. In gypsum, the calcium sulfate becomes fully hydrated and each calcium sulfate molecule binds two molecules of water.

Plaster of Paris has traditionally been used in the embalming operation as a method of closing the back of the skull in the case of a cranial autopsy. When the plaster of Paris hardens into gypsum, it provides a seal for the cut edges of bone, over which the scalp is then sutured. Although this method has largely been supplanted by the use of calvaria clamps, it is still used in cases where trauma to the cranial bones necessitates a matrix in which the broken pieces may be reassembled. Plaster of Paris is also the hardening agent in solid autopsy compounds. It is used as a dehydrating agent and effectively removes water from the viscera to which it is applied. The action of plaster of Paris under these circumstances has generated the term "hardening compounds," which is commonly used by embalmers when referring to solid autopsy compounds.

Special types of hydrates

Certain hydrates have the ability to attract additional water, whereas others will spontaneously release their water of crystallization to the surrounding air. Embalming terminology designates substances which have an affinity for water as *hydrophilic* (water-loving). Chemists use the word *hygroscopic* (*hygro* is Greek for moisture) when referring to hydrates that are able to attract additional water. Hygroscopic is a very general word applying to many forms of substances (solids, liquids, and gases) which readily absorb moisture.

Certain hydrates have the ability to absorb enough moisture from the air under ordinary atmospheric conditions to dissolve. The process involved is called *deliquescence*. The word "dissolve," in this case, implies that the hydrate is a solid. Therefore, sulfuric acid, a liquid, may be described as hygroscopic but not deliquescent. Calcium chloride ($CaCl_2 \cdot 2\ H_2O$), however, may be described as both hygroscopic and deliquescent. When calcium chloride is exposed to the air it will eventually dissolve. As a result this deliquescent substance is routinely applied to unpaved, rural roads during the summer months in order to control the production of dust by passing vehicles. "Putting chloride on the roads" is a much more efficient and economic procedure than the practice of applying oil or tar. Calcium chloride is a normal component of hard water (see Chapter 9 on water) and therefore more acceptable to the environment when it is eventually washed off these roads by rain. Oil and tar are not miscible with water and have detrimental effects on vegetation. In addition to dust control, calcium chloride may also be used as a de-icer. When applied to pavement in cold weather it will both attract enough water to dissolve and depress the freezing point of the resultant solution. By this process ice formation is inhibited. (See the discussion of solutions in Chapter 10.)

Deliquescent substances may be used in caskets as mold inhibitors. Mold growth on the face and hands of the remains is commonly observed in bodies that have been exhumed. The reason is the common occurrence of mold spores in the surrounding air. Mourners at a funeral are the unintentional source of these spores. When the casket is closed, these spores, together with the moist surrounding air, are trapped within the casket. Two important elements supporting mold growth are moisture and darkness. Therefore, it is not surprising that this growth routinely occurs in the absence of a mold inhibitor. Deliquescent substances remove moisture from the air, eliminating one of the key factors which support mold growth. For this reason these substances are referred to as mold inhibitors rather than mold killers (fungicides).

Some hydrates behave in an opposite manner and give up their water of crystallization to the surrounding air. These substances are called *efflorescent*. Sodium carbonate, $Na_2CO_3 \cdot 10\ H_2O$, is a good example of an efflorescent substance. Sodium carbonate usually appears as a dry powder, since it readily loses its water of crystallization to the air under ordinary atmospheric conditions. Both deliquescent and efflorescent substances must be kept in tightly sealed containers in order to maintain their hydrated forms.

HYDROLYSIS

Hydrolysis is a process by which water is split by other compounds. The constituents of water are then introduced into the products of the reaction. This process was previously cited (Chapter 10) as the principal chemical property of the salts. Take, for example, the hydrolysis reaction of copper sulfate:

$$CuSO_4 + 2\ HOH \longrightarrow Cu(OH)_2 + H_2SO_4$$

Hydrolysis is a double-replacement reaction. It may be identified by a number of factors. First, water appears on the reactant side of the equation. Second, water is written as HOH rather than H_2O in order to emphasize that the *reacting* constituents of water are H^+ and OH^-. By way of contrast, hydrogen and oxygen are the *elemental* constituents of water. Third, the products of a hydrolysis reaction are an acid and a base. This presents an interesting dilemma, because we have previously stated that acids and bases neutralize each other and produce a salt and water. Since the reverse seems to be going on here, more information about the acid and base is necessary. Neutralization occurs between acids and bases of similar strengths. In other words:

strong acid + strong base $\longrightarrow$ salt + water

moderate acid + moderate base $\longrightarrow$
                               salt + water

weak acid + weak base $\longrightarrow$ salt + water

In a hydrolysis reaction the acid and the base must be of different strengths. We will discuss two possibilities:

salt + water $\longrightarrow$ strong acid + weak base

salt + water $\longrightarrow$ weak acid + strong base

How can you tell which is which? The simplest detection method is a pH indicator such as litmus paper. The salt is reacted with the water. The resultant "solution" is then spotted on litmus paper with a glass stirring rod. The stronger of the two species will predominate and bring about the change in the indicator. The remainder of the two new substances is then judged to be weak. Reexamining the hydrolysis of copper sulfate:

$$CuSO_4 + 2\ HOH \longrightarrow \underset{\text{copper}}{Cu(OH)_2} + \underset{\text{sulfuric}}{H_2SO_4}$$
$$\underset{\text{hydroxide}}{} \quad \underset{\text{acid}}{}$$

Litmus reaction

red $\longrightarrow$ red

blue $\longrightarrow$ red

A change of litmus from blue to red is termed an acid reaction. Therefore, sulfuric acid is judged to be a strong acid. Since hydrolysis reactions produce acids and bases of different strengths, the copper hydroxide is the weak base.

Strengths of acids and bases are determined by the amount of their respective hydrogen and hydroxyl ions that are dissociated when they are in solution. The relative values of these strengths are listed as *dissociation constants*, which may be obtained from a handbook of chemistry and physics. The student has a third alternative in judging the relative strengths of the products of a hydrolysis reaction: memorization of a list of the more common strong and weak acids and bases (see Chapter 10).

The second possible result of a hydrolysis reaction is a strong base and a weak acid.

Consider the hydrolysis of sodium carbonate:

$$Na_2CO_3 + 2\ HOH \longrightarrow 2\ NaOH + H_2CO_3$$

sodium   carbonic
hydroxide   acid

Litmus reaction

red $\longrightarrow$ blue

blue $\longrightarrow$ blue

The results of the litmus test indicate a basic reaction. Sodium hydroxide is a strong base. Carbonic acid is a weak acid (see Chapter 10).

There is a third possibility: no reaction. The chemical property of salts that applies is specifically worded, "*Some* salts undergo hydrolysis." This implies that some salts do *not* undergo hydrolysis. Take, for example, what happens when sodium chloride is dissolved in water:

$$NaCl + HOH \longrightarrow Na^+ + Cl^- + HOH$$

Table salt dissolves in water. This is a physical change rather than a chemical change. The equation illustrates that ionization takes place. However, hydrolysis does not take place. Let us write a proposed equation for the hydrolysis of sodium chloride.

$$NaCl + HOH \longrightarrow NaOH + HCl$$

Sodium   Water   Sodium   Hydrochloric
chloride   hydroxide   acid
                   (strong base) (strong acid)

This expression shows that if we attempt to write a hydrolysis reaction for sodium chloride, the products will be a strong acid and a strong base. This cannot occur, because strong acids and strong bases neutralize each other to form salts and water. Remember that hydrolysis produces acids and bases of *different* strengths. In fact, this provides the

student with a procedure to check if hydrolysis of an unknown salt does, in fact, occur. For example, determine whether or not sodium sulfate undergoes hydrolysis.

$$Na_2SO_4 + 2\ HOH \longrightarrow H_2SO_4 + 2\ NaOH$$

Sodium   Water   Sulfuric   Sodium
sulfate   acid   hydroxide
                   (strong acid) (strong base)

Since a strong acid and a strong base are produced, hydrolysis of sodium sulfate does not occur. Let us contrast this with the hydrolysis of copper(II) chloride.

$$CuCl_2 + 2\ HOH \longrightarrow Cu(OH)_2 + 2\ HCl$$

Copper(II) Water   Copper   Hydrochloric
chloride   hydroxide   acid
                   (weak base)   (strong acid)

Hydrolysis of copper(II) chloride does occur because the products are an acid and a base of different strengths.

At first glance, hydrolysis of salts seems to be very far afield from the processes of embalming and decomposition. In reality it is not. Hydrolysis is the single most important factor in the initiation of decomposition. At the inorganic level, salts split water to form acids and bases of different strengths. In the human remains, proteins, carbohydrates, and fats are split into amino acids, monosaccharides, and fatty acids and glycerin by the action of water and enzymes. It is important to realize that water *chemically* reacts with these substances rather than merely *physically* dissolving them. An understanding of simple inorganic hydrolysis, then, is integral to the appreciation of the more complex biochemical hydrolysis which is the key to the decomposition of the unembalmed human remains.

CHAPTER SUMMARY

The formation of hydrates and hydrolysis reactions are two important chemical properties of water. Hydrates are compounds in which certain molecules are held in a special chemical union with water when they crystallize. This water is called the "water of crystallization" and may vary not only from compound to compound, but also within the same compound under a variety of different conditions. There are two special types of hydrates. Those which are capable of absorbing additional water are called deliquescent. Those which spontaneously give up their water of crystallization to the surrounding atmosphere under ordinary conditions are called efflorescent. Two hydrates that have special applications to mortuary science are calcium chloride and calcium sulfate.

Hydrolysis is a process whereby water is split by other substances, and the constituents of water are introduced into the products of the reaction. Some salts undergo hydrolysis. If hydrolysis occurs, the products are a strong acid and a weak base or a strong base and a weak acid. Understanding hydrolysis of inorganic salts is the first step in learning the mechanisms of decomposition of the human body following death.

QUESTIONS

1. Define: hydrate, water of crystallization, anhydrous, dehydration, hydrolysis.

2. Name and give the function of two hydrates which may be used in the embalming process.

3. What are the primary storage requirements of hydrates?

4. Write balanced hydrolysis equations for the following salts (if no hydrolysis occurs, write N.R. on the products side of the reaction): copper(II) nitrate, sodium tetraborate, sodium bromide, calcium sulfite, and potassium sulfate.

5. What is the significance of hydrolysis to the embalmer?

6. Using the following experimental results, determine if three unknown substances A, B, and C are deliquescent, efflorescent, or hygroscopic. When placed on a watch glass and exposed to the air the following changes in physical properties of the unknowns occur:

Substance	Initial properties	Properties after one day
A	Grey powder	Grey powder with blue specks
B	White crystals	Clear solution
C	White crystals	White powder

Section II
ORGANIC CHEMISTRY

The first section of this book centered on the basic rules of chemistry. The vocabulary of chemistry, which uses symbols, formulas, and equations, should no longer be foreign to you. Although you have never seen an atom or a proton or an electron, you now know how to communicate about them with others. You have also become familiar with the fundamental states of matter: gas, liquid, and solid. Using your new knowledge, you have examined the chemical and physical properties of common substances such as hydrogen, oxygen, and water and of the fundamental types of inorganic compounds of acids, bases, salts, and oxides.

organic compounds exist, either as natural substances or as materials synthesized by man.

NATURE OF ORGANIC CHEMISTRY

Organic chemistry is that branch of chemistry which deals with carbon compounds. It was originally thought that organic compounds could be produced only by living plant or animal organisms. Wöhler's synthesis of urea in 1828 disproved this theory; however, the name organic chemistry has been retained. There are certain essential differences between organic and inorganic chemistry, as listed next.

Chapter 12
INTRODUCTION

We are now ready to study the second major division of chemistry: organic chemistry. If you look around, you can probably observe many organic chemical compounds. Your clothes, the paper in this book, and any wood or plastic in furniture are all organic compounds. The gasoline in your car, the fuel used to heat your home, and any medication you have recently taken are also most likely organic in nature. Totally, millions of

Inorganic chemistry	Organic chemistry
1. Molecules are relatively small.	1. Molecules are relatively large.
2. Molecules are ionizable.	2. Molecules are non-ionizable.
3. Reactions involve a major change in the molecule.	3. Reactions involve a change in only a small part of the molecule.
4. Reactions occur instantaneously.	4. Reactions take place slowly.
5. Four types of compounds.	5. At least eight types of compounds.

PROPERTIES OF CARBON

The properties and reactions of organic compounds are ultimately the function of the elements of which they are made. Let us examine some of the characteristics of the element carbon.

Combining capacity

Carbon has a combining capacity of four. The electronic configuration of carbon, $1s^2 2s^2 2p^2$, shows four valence electrons in its outermost shell. The property of carbon that it forms four bonds is graphically represented by a dash (—) drawn vertical, horizontal, or at an angle to its chemical symbol:

$$-\overset{|}{\underset{|}{C}}-$$

It may, therefore, combine with four univalent (needs one electron to fill its outermost shell) atoms (e.g., H):

$$H-\overset{\overset{\displaystyle H}{|}}{\underset{\underset{\displaystyle H}{|}}{C}}-H$$

two divalent atoms (e.g., O):

$$O=C=O$$

two univalent atoms and one divalent atom:

$$H-\overset{\overset{\displaystyle H}{|}}{C}=O$$

and one univalent and one trivalent (e.g., N) atom:

$$H-C\equiv N.$$

The carbon-to-carbon bond

Carbon has a great tendency to combine with itself to form large molecules. Carbon may be bound to adjacent carbon atoms by one, two, or even three bonds. However, three is the limit. Carbon has a

$$-\overset{|}{\underset{|}{C}}-\overset{|}{\underset{|}{C}}- \qquad -\overset{|}{C}=\overset{|}{C}- \qquad -C\equiv C-$$

combining capacity of four, but the maximum number of bonds between two adjacent carbon atoms is three. When carbon bonds to itself or to other atoms, it shares its electrons. Therefore, organic compounds have covalent bonds.

Organic chemistry also involves other elements in addition to carbon. The three most commonly found are nitrogen, oxygen, and hydrogen. Together with carbon, these four elements make up over 96% of the weight of the human body.

FUNCTIONAL GROUPS

Combining capacities are easy to remember in organic chemistry, since they are one, two, three, and four: hydrogen, 1; oxygen, 2; nitrogen, 3; carbon, 4. The essential compounds are combinations of these elements and are organized into eight groups. These groups are identified by what are called *characteristic* or *functional groups*. The eight basic functional groups are:

1. Hydrocarbons $\quad -\overset{|}{\underset{|}{C}}-$

2. Alcohols $\quad -OH$

3. Aldehydes $\quad -\overset{\overset{\displaystyle H}{|}}{C}=O$

4. Acids $\quad -\overset{\overset{\displaystyle O}{\|}}{C}-OH$

5. Ketones $\quad -\overset{\overset{\displaystyle O}{\|}}{C}-$

6. Esters $\quad -\overset{\displaystyle O}{\overset{\|}{C}}-O-$

7. Ethers $\quad -O-$

8. Amines $\quad -NH_2$

Two things are evident from the previous list. First, the element nitrogen appears in only one of the eight compounds. This means that organic chemistry deals with essentially three elements instead of four. Second, the list does not illustrate a complete compound but instead, a radical (radicals were previously discussed in inorganic compounds). An organic compound is actually composed of two radicals, the *functional group* which identifies the compound as to general type (alcohol, aldehyde, etc.) and the *alkyl group* which identifies the specific substance (wood alcohol or grain alcohol, formaldehyde or glutaraldehyde). This is why the functional groups are drawn with open bonds. The open bonds indicate where the other part of the compound (the "R" group) will attach. As a result, general formulas have been con-

structed using a combination of the functional group and the "R" group. (See Table 12-1.)

You will notice the absence of the hydrocarbons in the previous list. The reason for this is that the hydrocarbons are used for alkyl groups. The hydrocarbons must first be named before the alkyl groups can be identified.

FORMULAS

General formulas are one type of abbreviation used in organic chemistry. Three other types of formulas are commonly employed:

1. *Molecular formulas.* These represent the actual number of each constituent atom in the molecule. For instance, the molecular formula for formaldehyde is CH_2O.

2. *Structural formulas.* These represent the spatial relationship of the constituent atoms to each other. The structural formula for formaldehyde is

$$H-\overset{\displaystyle H}{\overset{|}{C}}=O.$$

3. *Line formulas.* These are used to conserve space over structural formulas and are nothing more than condensations of them. The line formula for formaldehyde is $HCHO$.

These three types of formulas will be routinely used throughout the rest of this text, as will modifications and combinations of the basic themes.

CHAPTER SUMMARY

Organic chemistry is the study of certain carbon compounds. Carbon, which has a combining capacity of four, bonds to itself

Table 12-1 Names and formulas of fundamental organic compounds

Name	Functional group	General formula
Alcohol	$-OH$	ROH
Aldehyde	$-\overset{\displaystyle H}{\overset{\|}{C}}=O$	RCHO
Acid	$-\overset{\displaystyle O}{\overset{\|}{C}}-OH$	RCOOH
Ketone	$-\overset{\displaystyle O}{\overset{\|}{C}}-$	RCOR
Ester	$-\overset{\displaystyle O}{\overset{\|}{C}}-O-$	RCOOR
Ether	$-O-$	ROR
Amine	$-NH_2$	RNH$_2$

and other atoms such as hydrogen, oxygen, and nitrogen by covalent bonds. Although there are millions of organic compounds, they can be classified into eight fundamental classes on the basis of. functional groups. Both the chemical and physical properties of an organic compound are determined by the structure of the functional group. General formulas, molecular formulas, and line formulas express the composition of organic compounds.

QUESTIONS

1. How many bonds are associated with every carbon atom in an organic compound?

2. What type of bond links carbon to itself and to other atoms?

3. State three differences between organic and inorganic chemistry.

4. Name and draw the eight essential functional groups.

5. List all the functional groups that:
   (a) Do not contain carbon.
   (b) Do not contain oxygen.
   (c) Contain carbon.
   (d) Contain oxygen.
   (e) Contain nitrogen.
   (f) Have one open bond.
   (g) Have two open bonds.
   (h) Have three open bonds.
   (i) Have four open bonds.

6. Give the general formula for each one of the essential types of organic compounds.

7. List the three types of formulas commonly used in organic chemistry.

8. Identify the following compounds by functional group:

(a) $CH_3 - \overset{\displaystyle H}{\underset{\displaystyle OH}{\overset{|}{\underset{|}{C}}}} - CH_3$

(b) $CH_3CH_2CH_2\overset{\displaystyle O}{\overset{\|}{C}}OH$

(c) $CH_3CH_2CH_3$

(d) $CH_3\overset{\displaystyle O}{\overset{\|}{C}}H$

(e) $CH_3\overset{\displaystyle O}{\overset{\|}{C}}CH_2CH_3$

(f) $CH_3CH_2\overset{\displaystyle O}{\overset{\|}{C}}H$

(g) $CH_3\overset{\displaystyle O}{\overset{\|}{C}} - O - CH_2CH_3$

(h) $CH_3 - O - CH_2CH_3$

(i) $\underset{\displaystyle OH}{\underset{|}{CH_2}}CH_2\underset{\displaystyle OH}{\underset{|}{CH_2}}$

(j) $H - \overset{\displaystyle O}{\overset{\|}{C}} - \overset{\displaystyle O}{\overset{\|}{C}} - H$

The hydrocarbons are organic compounds containing only hydrogen and carbon as constituent elements. In general, the hydrocarbons are obtained from natural gas and petroleum. Natural gas consists largely of methane (CH_4) but also contains small quantities of other hydrocarbons. Most of the other hydrocarbons are obtained from petroleum by fractional distillation according to their boiling points:

$< 70°C$:   Petroleum ether
$85–200°C$:   Gasoline
$200–300°C$:   Kerosene
$> 300°C$:   Lubricating oils

The physical state of the hydrocarbons depends on the length of the carbon chain.

be joined together by one, two, or three bonds (see Chapter 12). This provides the basis for one method of classification.

Alkanes

Hydrocarbons in which carbons are joined together by single bonds are called *alkanes*. They are named according to the number of carbon atoms in the chain and an *-ane* suffix. The number of carbon atoms are named according to the following:

1 –	Meth	6 –	Hex
2 –	Eth	7 –	Hept
3 –	Prop	8 –	Oct
4 –	But	9 –	Non
5 –	Pent	10 –	Dec

Chapter 13
HYDROCARBONS

○ C to C_4 are gases.
○ C_5 to C_{17} are liquids.
○ C_{18} and higher are solids.

HYDROCARBONS

Hydrocarbons are the simplest of the organic compounds containing only two elements, hydrogen and carbon. Adjacent carbons may

Thus:

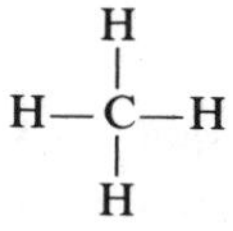

$$
\begin{array}{c}
H \\
| \\
H - C - H = CH_4 = \text{methane} \\
| \\
H
\end{array}
$$

$$
\begin{array}{c}
H \quad H \\
| \quad | \\
H - C - C - H = C_2H_6 = \text{ethane} \\
| \quad | \\
H \quad H
\end{array}
$$

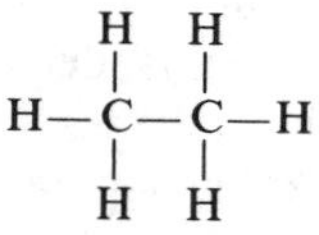

$$H-\underset{\underset{H}{|}}{\overset{\overset{H}{|}}{C}}-\underset{\underset{H}{|}}{\overset{\overset{H}{|}}{C}}-\underset{\underset{H}{|}}{\overset{\overset{H}{|}}{C}}-H = C_3H_8 = propane$$

$$H-\underset{\underset{H}{|}}{\overset{\overset{H}{|}}{C}}-\underset{\underset{H}{|}}{\overset{\overset{H}{|}}{C}}-\underset{\underset{H}{|}}{\overset{\overset{H}{|}}{C}}-\underset{\underset{H}{|}}{\overset{\overset{H}{|}}{C}}-H = C_4H_{10} = butane$$

$$H-\underset{\underset{H}{|}}{\overset{\overset{H}{|}}{C}}-\underset{\underset{H}{|}}{\overset{\overset{H}{|}}{C}}-\underset{\underset{H}{|}}{\overset{\overset{H}{|}}{C}}-\underset{\underset{H}{|}}{\overset{\overset{H}{|}}{C}}-\underset{\underset{H}{|}}{\overset{\overset{H}{|}}{C}}-H = C_5H_{12} = pentane$$

There is a fixed ratio between carbon and hydrogen in alkanes that can be expressed by a type formula: C_nH_{2n+2}. This formula can be used to predict the number of hydrogens in any alkane, provided the number of carbons is known. The next member of the series has six carbons. Therefore, application of the formula $C_6H_{2(6)+2} = C_6H_{14}$ shows that there are 14 hydrogen atoms in hexane. Drawing the structure proves this hypothesis:

$$H-\underset{\underset{H}{|}}{\overset{\overset{H}{|}}{C}}-\underset{\underset{H}{|}}{\overset{\overset{H}{|}}{C}}-\underset{\underset{H}{|}}{\overset{\overset{H}{|}}{C}}-\underset{\underset{H}{|}}{\overset{\overset{H}{|}}{C}}-\underset{\underset{H}{|}}{\overset{\overset{H}{|}}{C}}-\underset{\underset{H}{|}}{\overset{\overset{H}{|}}{C}}-H = C_6H_{14} = hexane$$

Alkanes are also called *saturated hydrocarbons* because single bonds between adjacent carbon atoms allow attachment of the maximum number of hydrogen atoms.

Alkyl groups

It was previously mentioned that organic compounds are actually composed of two radicals, a functional group and an alkyl group. The *alkyl* or "R" group is derived from the alkanes. Whereas alkanes are expressed as C_nH_{2n+2}, the alkyl group has as its type formula C_nH_{2n+1}. The elimination

of one hydrogen atom allows a point of attachment for a functional group and the number name (meth, eth, prop, etc.) now acquires a *-yl* (from alk*yl*) name ending in place of the *-ane* name ending. Thus:

Meth*ane*	CH_4	becomes	meth*yl*	CH_3
Eth*ane*	C_2H_6	becomes	eth*yl*	C_2H_5
Prop*ane*	C_3H_8	becomes	prop*yl*	C_3H_7
But*ane*	C_4H_{10}	becomes	but*yl*	C_4H_9
Pent*ane*	C_5H_{12}	becomes	pent*yl*	C_5H_{11}

and so on.

Structurally:

Methyl
$$H-\underset{\underset{H}{|}}{\overset{\overset{H}{|}}{C}}-$$

Ethyl
$$H-\underset{\underset{H}{|}}{\overset{\overset{H}{|}}{C}}-\underset{\underset{H}{|}}{\overset{\overset{H}{|}}{C}}-$$

Propyl
$$H-\underset{\underset{H}{|}}{\overset{\overset{H}{|}}{C}}-\underset{\underset{H}{|}}{\overset{\overset{H}{|}}{C}}-\underset{\underset{H}{|}}{\overset{\overset{H}{|}}{C}}-$$

Butyl
$$H-\underset{\underset{H}{|}}{\overset{\overset{H}{|}}{C}}-\underset{\underset{H}{|}}{\overset{\overset{H}{|}}{C}}-\underset{\underset{H}{|}}{\overset{\overset{H}{|}}{C}}-\underset{\underset{H}{|}}{\overset{\overset{H}{|}}{C}}-$$

Pentyl
$$H-\underset{\underset{H}{|}}{\overset{\overset{H}{|}}{C}}-\underset{\underset{H}{|}}{\overset{\overset{H}{|}}{C}}-\underset{\underset{H}{|}}{\overset{\overset{H}{|}}{C}}-\underset{\underset{H}{|}}{\overset{\overset{H}{|}}{C}}-\underset{\underset{H}{|}}{\overset{\overset{H}{|}}{C}}-$$

The bond on the right has been exaggerated to emphasize the point of attachment of the functional group. The basis for naming all organic compounds is very consistent. In the next chapter (alcohols) the simplest alcohol is named by taking the first alkyl group,

$$CH_3 \quad (H-\underset{\underset{\displaystyle H}{|}}{\overset{\overset{\displaystyle H}{|}}{C}}-) \quad methyl$$

and linking it to the alcohol functional group (—OH). The name for this compound is methyl alcohol:

$$H-\underset{\underset{\displaystyle H}{|}}{\overset{\overset{\displaystyle H}{|}}{C}}\boxed{-OH}$$

Alkyl group (methyl) Functional group (alcohol)

Alkyl halides

Alkyl groups may be attached to groups other than the eight basic functional groups. When Group VII (halogen) elements are attached to the alkyl group, substances are formed called *alkyl halides* with the general formula

RX

Alkyl group   Halogen

The simplest of these occurs if one or more of the hydrogen atoms in methane is replaced by chlorine:

$$H-\underset{\underset{\displaystyle H}{|}}{\overset{\overset{\displaystyle H}{|}}{C}}-Cl = CH_3Cl \quad = methyl\ chloride \\ (chloromethane)$$

$$H-\underset{\underset{\displaystyle Cl}{|}}{\overset{\overset{\displaystyle H}{|}}{C}}-Cl = CH_2Cl_2 = methylene\ chloride \\ (dichloromethane)$$

$$H-\underset{\underset{\displaystyle Cl}{|}}{\overset{\overset{\displaystyle Cl}{|}}{C}}-Cl = CHCl_3 \quad = chloroform \\ (trichloromethane)$$

$$Cl-\underset{\underset{\displaystyle Cl}{|}}{\overset{\overset{\displaystyle Cl}{|}}{C}}-Cl = CCl_4 \quad = carbon\ tetrachloride \\ (tetrachloromethane)$$

Chloroform is well known for its anaesthetic properties. Carbon tetrachloride is a common cleaning fluid and may be used as an external solvent for tar, asphalt, and other petroleum-based stains.

Isomers

Another property of alkanes is that they form *isomers*. Two or more substances having the same molecular formula but different structural formulas are isomers.

The first three members of the alkane series have only one form.

$$H-\underset{\underset{\displaystyle H}{|}}{\overset{\overset{\displaystyle H}{|}}{C}}-H \qquad H-\underset{\underset{\displaystyle H}{|}}{\overset{\overset{\displaystyle H}{|}}{C}}-\underset{\underset{\displaystyle H}{|}}{\overset{\overset{\displaystyle H}{|}}{C}}-H$$

Methane   Ethane

$$H-\underset{\underset{\displaystyle H}{|}}{\overset{\overset{\displaystyle H}{|}}{C}}-\underset{\underset{\displaystyle H}{|}}{\overset{\overset{\displaystyle H}{|}}{C}}-\underset{\underset{\displaystyle H}{|}}{\overset{\overset{\displaystyle H}{|}}{C}}-H$$

Propane

Butane, the fourth member of the series, is the first opportunity to generate a new structure.

$$H-\underset{\underset{\displaystyle H}{|}}{\overset{\overset{\displaystyle H}{|}}{C}}-\underset{\underset{\displaystyle H}{|}}{\overset{\overset{\displaystyle H}{|}}{C}}-\underset{\underset{\displaystyle H}{|}}{\overset{\overset{\displaystyle H}{|}}{C}}-\underset{\underset{\displaystyle H}{|}}{\overset{\overset{\displaystyle H}{|}}{C}}-H$$

$$CH_3CH_2CH_2CH_3$$

Normal butane
(*n*-butane)

$$H-\overset{\overset{\displaystyle H}{|}}{\underset{\underset{\displaystyle H}{|}}{C}}-\overset{\overset{\displaystyle H}{|}}{\underset{\underset{\displaystyle H-\overset{\displaystyle |}{\underset{\displaystyle H}{C}}-H}{|}}{C}}-\overset{\overset{\displaystyle H}{|}}{\underset{\underset{\displaystyle H}{|}}{C}}-H$$

$$CH_3CHCH_3CH_3$$

Isobutane

Both the structural formulas and the line formulas show that there is a difference in the two compounds. However, C_4H_{10} is the molecular formula for both normal and isobutane. The term *normal* (*n-*) is used throughout organic chemistry to indicate a straight chain isomer. Any other prefix, such as *iso-*, represents a branched compound.

As we progress to the next member of the series, we find three different forms.

$$C_5H_{12} = pentane$$

$$H-\overset{\overset{\displaystyle H}{|}}{\underset{\underset{\displaystyle H}{|}}{C}}-\overset{\overset{\displaystyle H}{|}}{\underset{\underset{\displaystyle H}{|}}{C}}-\overset{\overset{\displaystyle H}{|}}{\underset{\underset{\displaystyle H}{|}}{C}}-\overset{\overset{\displaystyle H}{|}}{\underset{\underset{\displaystyle H}{|}}{C}}-\overset{\overset{\displaystyle H}{|}}{\underset{\underset{\displaystyle H}{|}}{C}}-H$$

For convenience, we may eliminate the hydrogen atoms and the bonds (other than carbon to carbon) and work with carbon skeletons.

$$C-C-C-C-C \qquad C-\overset{\displaystyle C}{\underset{\underset{\displaystyle C}{|}}{C}}-C-C$$

n-pentane   Isopentane

$$C-\overset{\overset{\displaystyle C}{|}}{\underset{\underset{\displaystyle C}{|}}{C}}-C$$

Neopentane

One way of naming the two additional isomers of pentane uses the prefixes *iso-* and *neo-*. However, in order to reduce the amount of memorization of names of compounds that we must do, a more systematic approach was formulated. This other system, called the IUPAC System, is used worldwide by chemists. It originated at a conference called the International Union of Pure and Applied Chemists. By using it, chemists everywhere are able to communicate effectively.

For alkane hydrocarbons the IUPAC rules are very simple.

1. Find the longest carbon chain.
2. Number the carbons.
3. Locate and name any alkyl groups attached to the longest chain.

The first form of pentane presents no problem:

$$C-C-C-C-C$$

is simply called *pentane*. Taking the second form:

$$C-\overset{\displaystyle C}{\underset{\underset{\displaystyle C}{|}}{C}}-C-C$$

the longest carbon chain is four.

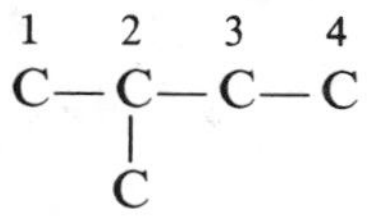

```
 1   2   3   4
 C — C — C — C
     |
     C
```

or

```
     2   3   4
 C — C — C — C
     |
     C
     1
```

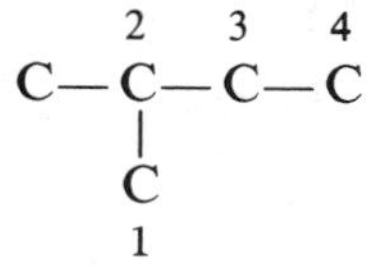

No matter how we rearrange the numbers, the longest chain is four. The name for a hydrocarbon with four carbons with adjacent carbons joined by single bonds is *butane*. Thus, the base name for

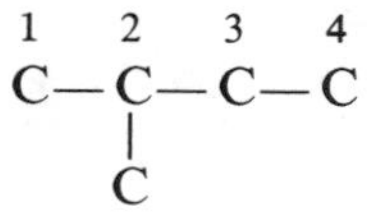

```
 1   2   3   4
 C — C — C — C
     |
     C
```

is butane. There is a methyl (CH$_3$) alkyl group attached to the number 2 carbon of the butane molecule. Thus,

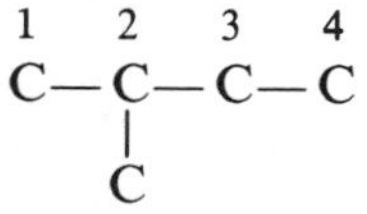

```
 1   2   3   4
 C — C — C — C
     |
     C
```

could be named 2-*methyl butane*. It is not really necessary to include the number 2 in the name of this compound. Naming it methyl butane is sufficient. If we were asked to draw the structure of methyl butane, the only one that we could draw has the methyl group on the second carbon from either end.

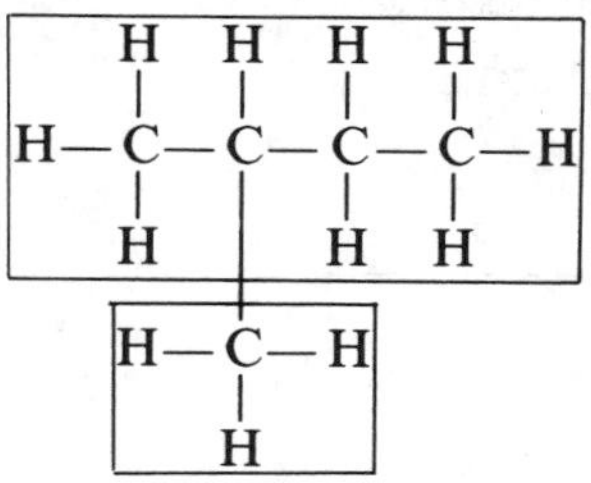

```
     H   H   H   H
     |   |   |   |
 H — C — C — C — C — H     Butane
     |   |   |   |
     H       H   H
     |
 H — C — H                Methyl
     |
     H
```

The other form, C — C — C, is named in a
                    |
                    C
(with C at top), is named in a similar fashion. (1) The longest carbon chain is three. (2) There are two methyl (CH$_3$) groups attached to the middle carbon. Therefore, the name is dimethyl propane.

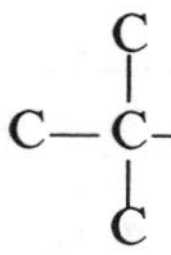

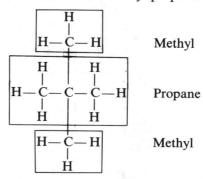

H—C—H	Methyl
H—C—C—C—H	Propane
H—C—H	Methyl

With the isomers of C$_6$H$_{14}$, in addition to locating and naming any branched alkyl groups, their positions must be also indicated by numbers. For example, the name of

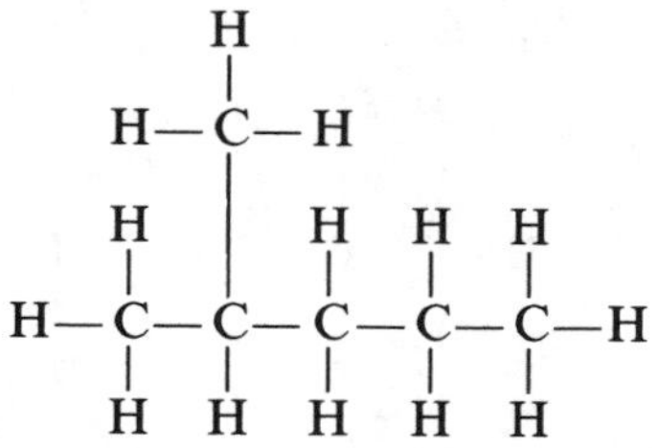

```
         H
         |
     H — C — H
     H   |   H   H   H
     |   |   |   |   |
 H — C — C — C — C — C — H
     |   |   |   |   |
     H   H   H   H   H
```

is 2-*methyl pentane*. The number 2 must be included in the name in order to distinguish this compound from 3-*methyl pentane*, which has the following structure:

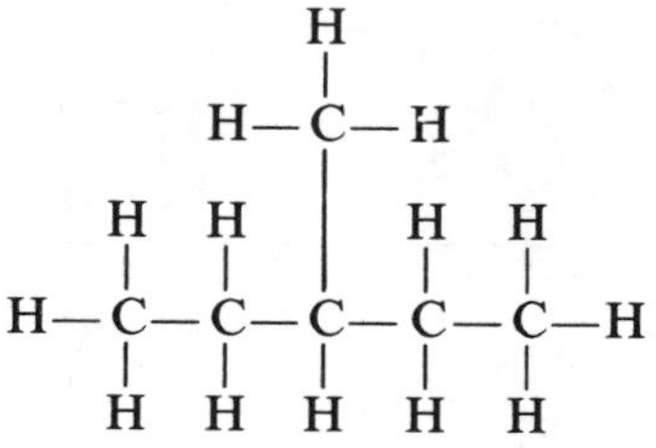

```
             H
             |
         H — C — H
     H   H   |   H   H
     |   |   |   |   |
 H — C — C — C — C — C — H
     |   |   |   |   |
     H   H   H   H   H
```

Table 13-1 Isomers of C_6H_{14}

Structural formula	Line formula

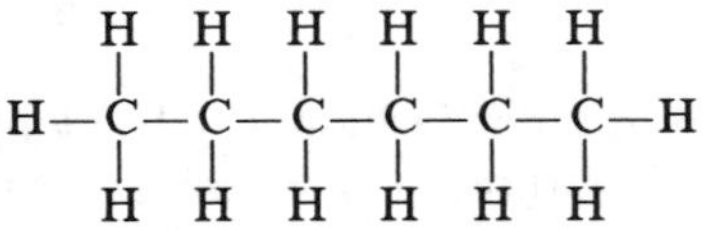

$$\begin{array}{c}
\text{H} \quad \text{H} \quad \text{H} \quad \text{H} \quad \text{H} \quad \text{H} \\
| \quad\; | \quad\; | \quad\; | \quad\; | \quad\; | \\
\text{H—C—C—C—C—C—C—H} \\
| \quad\; | \quad\; | \quad\; | \quad\; | \quad\; | \\
\text{H} \quad \text{H} \quad \text{H} \quad \text{H} \quad \text{H} \quad \text{H}
\end{array}$$

$CH_3CH_2CH_2CH_2CH_2CH_3$

n-hexane

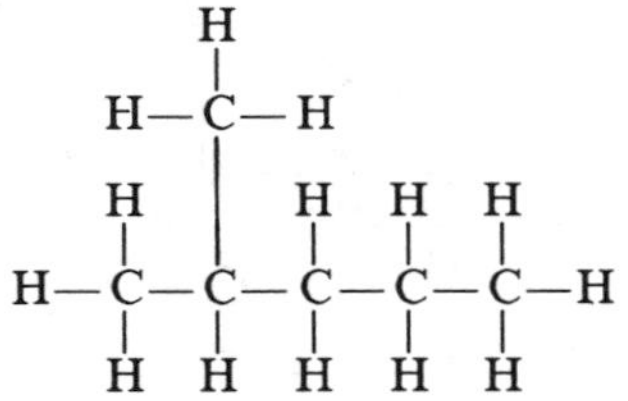

$$\begin{array}{c}
\text{H} \\
| \\
\text{H—C—H} \\
\\
\text{H} \quad\;\; | \quad\; \text{H} \quad \text{H} \quad \text{H} \\
| \quad\; | \quad\; | \quad\; | \quad\; | \\
\text{H—C—C—C—C—C—H} \\
| \quad\; | \quad\; | \quad\; | \quad\; | \\
\text{H} \quad \text{H} \quad \text{H} \quad \text{H} \quad \text{H}
\end{array}$$

$CH_3CHCH_3CH_2CH_2CH_3$

2-methyl pentane

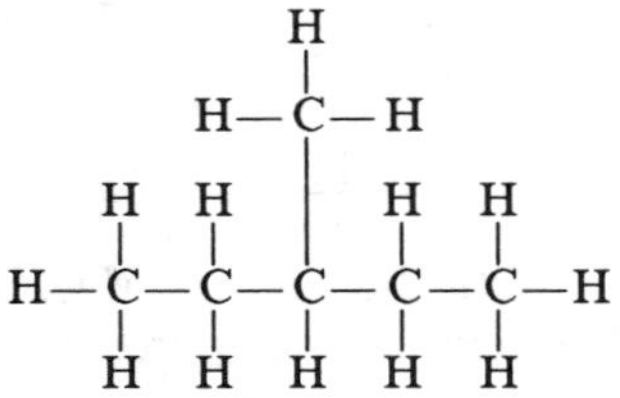

$$\begin{array}{c}
\text{H} \\
| \\
\text{H—C—H} \\
\\
\text{H} \quad \text{H} \quad\; | \quad\; \text{H} \quad \text{H} \\
| \quad\; | \quad\; | \quad\; | \quad\; | \\
\text{H—C—C—C—C—C—H} \\
| \quad\; | \quad\; | \quad\; | \quad\; | \\
\text{H} \quad \text{H} \quad \text{H} \quad \text{H} \quad \text{H}
\end{array}$$

$CH_3CH_2CHCH_3CH_2CH_3$

3-methyl pentane

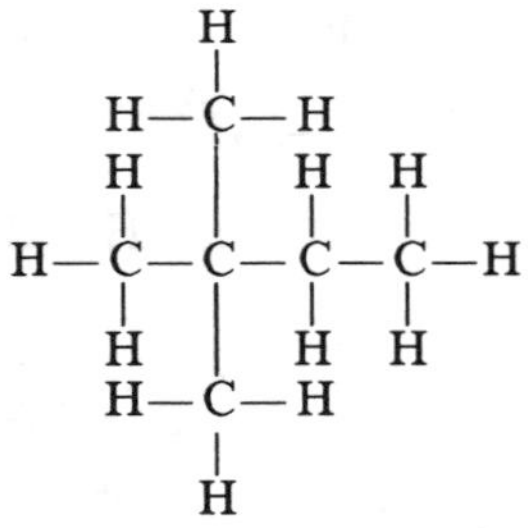

$$\begin{array}{c}
\text{H} \\
| \\
\text{H—C—H} \\
\text{H} \quad\;\; | \quad\; \text{H} \quad \text{H} \\
| \quad\; | \quad\; | \quad\; | \\
\text{H—C—C—C—C—H} \\
| \quad\; | \quad\; | \quad\; | \\
\text{H} \quad\;\; | \quad\; \text{H} \quad \text{H} \\
\text{H—C—H} \\
| \\
\text{H}
\end{array}$$

$CH_3C(CH_3)_2CH_2CH_3$

2,2-dimethyl butane

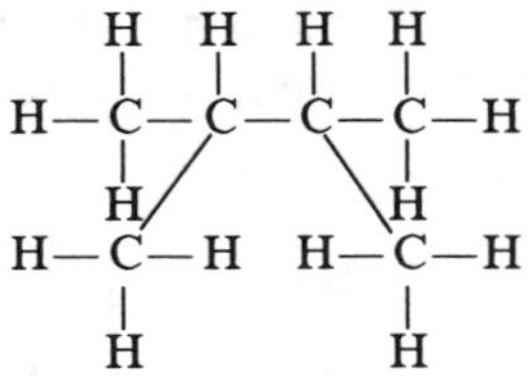

$$\begin{array}{c}
\text{H} \quad \text{H} \quad \text{H} \quad \text{H} \\
| \quad\; | \quad\; | \quad\; | \\
\text{H—C—C—C—C—H} \\
\;\;\; \text{H} \quad\quad\; \text{H} \\
\text{H—C—H} \quad \text{H—C—H} \\
| \quad\quad\quad\;\; | \\
\text{H} \quad\quad\quad\;\; \text{H}
\end{array}$$

$CH_3CHCH_3CHCH_3CH_3$

2,3-dimethyl butane

It is important to remember that the numbers 2 and 3 must be included in each of these names. It would be incorrect to name either compound only methyl pentane, since we could not draw the structure without questioning the location of the methyl group. All the isomers of C_6H_{14} are drawn and named in Table 13-1.

The next member of the series, C_7H_{16}, has nine forms. After this point, the number of isomers increases dramatically:

$C_8 - 18$
$C_9 - 35$
$C_{10} - 75$
$C_{20} - 366,319$

Alkenes

When multiple bonds are present in a carbon chain, the substance is referred to as an *unsaturated hydrocarbon*. It is so called because it contains less hydrogen atoms than it could if only single bonds were present. The simplest unsaturated hydrocarbons contain one double bond in the chain. These are called *alkenes*. The simplest alkene is ethene

C=C. The *eth-* indicates the two carbons, the *-ene* a double bond. Propene, then, is C=C—C. The next member of the series poses an interesting problem. Butene has two possibilities:

C=C—C—C   or   C—C=C—C

The dilemma is resolved by numbering the position of the double bond. The first expression is called 1-butene and the second 2-butene. However, it is important to note that there is only *one* double bond in the expression. If the substance contained *2* double bonds it would be called a *di*ene, *3* double bonds a *tri*ene, and so forth. Thus:

C=C—C=C is named 1,3-butadiene, *not* 1,3-butene.

Alkenes also contain a fixed ratio between carbon and hydrogen atoms. The type formula for this series of compounds is C_nH_{2n}. The first two members of this series are

Ethene or ethylene:

C_2H_4

$$H—\overset{\displaystyle H}{\underset{\displaystyle |}{C}}=\overset{\displaystyle H}{\underset{\displaystyle |}{C}}—H$$

Propene or propylene:

C_3H_6

$$H—\overset{\displaystyle H}{\underset{\displaystyle |}{C}}=\overset{\displaystyle H}{\underset{\displaystyle |}{C}}—\overset{\displaystyle H}{\underset{\displaystyle |}{\underset{\displaystyle H}{C}}}—H$$

Alkynes

Another form of unsaturated hydrocarbons contains a triple bond between adjacent carbon atoms. The first member of this series is ethyne or acetylene H—C≡C—H. The type formula for this series of compounds is C_nH_{2n-2}. Therefore, the formula for the next member of the series is $C_3H_{2(3)-2}$ or C_3H_4,

$$H—C≡C—\overset{\displaystyle H}{\underset{\displaystyle |}{\underset{\displaystyle H}{C}}}—H$$

Again we should take note that alkynes contain only *one* triple bond in the chain. Two triple bonds would constitute a *di*yne and three a *tri*yne. In addition, there must be a spacing of at least one carbon atom to con-

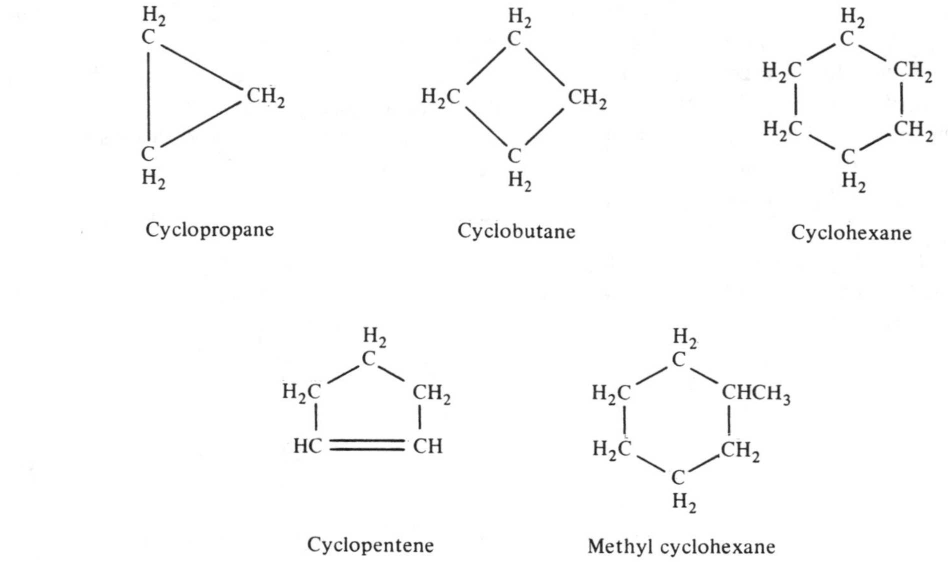

Cyclopropane   Cyclobutane   Cyclohexane

Cyclopentene   Methyl cyclohexane

Figure 13-1   Structures of cyclic hydrocarbons

form with the rule of four bonds per carbon atom. For example: $H-C \equiv C-C \equiv C-H$ would be correct for 1,3-butadiyne but *not* $C \equiv C \equiv C-C$, because the number-2 carbon would have *six* bonds instead of *four*.

Cyclic hydrocarbons

The carbon atoms of all the hydrocarbons that we have discussed were bonded to one another to form chains. They are described as *open-chain compounds*. Hydrocarbons also exist as *ring* or *cyclic* compounds. They are named by adding the prefix *cyclo-* to the name of the corresponding open-chain compound. Both cycloalkanes and cycloalkenes exist. The type formula for *cycloalkanes* is C_nH_{2n} and for *cycloalkenes* is C_nH_{2n-2}. The simplest cycloalkane contains three carbons. It is called *cyclopropane* and has anaesthetic properties. Figure 13-1 shows the structures of some of the cyclic compounds. Notice that

alkyl groups may be substituted for hydrogen atoms as in methyl cyclopentane.

AROMATIC HYDROCARBONS

A major way to classify all organic compounds is as aliphatic or as aromatic. The word aliphatic means "fatty." The alkanes, alkenes, alkynes, and their cyclic derivatives are *aliphatic* compounds. The connection between the word "fatty" and these compounds is that fats contain a hydrocarbon portion which often resembles long-chain alkanes or alkenes. Compounds classified as *aromatic* contain a benzene ring or a system of these rings. These compounds are called aromatic because the first ones discovered had pleasant odors. Examples are vanilla and oil of wintergreen. Since aromatic compounds are widely used and have unique properties, we will study the structure of *benzene*, the parent compound of all aromatics.

Structure of benzene

The molecular formula of benzene is C_6H_6. It is a ring compound. In order for each carbon to have four bonds, chemists who first studied benzene described it as a ring compound with alternating double and single bonds. If we use this description to draw its structure, we are faced with a dilemma. Where do we place the double bonds? Numbering the carbons one through six, there are two possible structures. In structure A the double bonds are between carbons one and two, three and four, and five and six. Structure B has them between carbons two and three, four and five, and six and one. Does it make any difference where we draw them?

Before answering this, let's consider two other pieces of confusing information. First, if the distances between all bonded carbons in benzene are measured, they are equal. This does not fit the picture of alternating double and single bonds. Carbon-to-carbon double bonds are shorter than carbon-to-carbon single bonds. This means that in both structures A and B there should be three carbon-to-carbon bonds of equal length and three others of another length. However, experimental studies measure all six carbon-to-carbon bond lengths as equal. Second, both structures A and B indicate that benzene should react chemically like an alkene.

Experimentally, it does not undergo typical alkene reactions. It would seem that describing benzene as a compound of alternating double and single bonds is not correct.

What structure is consistent with benzene's being a ring compound of formula C_6H_6 with equal carbon-to-carbon bond lengths and undergoing nonalkene reactions? This question was answered by Fredrick August Kekulé, who proposed that benzene is neither structure A nor B, but a hybrid of them. The hybrid consists of six equal carbon-to-carbon bonds that are intermediate in properties between a double and single bond. The structure of the benzene hybrid is represented as

where the ↔ indicates that the molecule's true structure is a blend of what are drawn as two contributing structures. Each of the corners of the hexagons represents a carbon atom bonded to a hydrogen. The only difference between the two structures is the placement of the double bonds which represent electron pairs. Whenever two or more structures that differ only in the position of electrons can be drawn for a compound, that compound has the property of *resonance*. This is a characteristic of all aromatic compounds.

Another way of understanding the structure of benzene is based on the concept of *delocalization* of electrons. Each carbon atom has four valence electrons. Three of them are involved in single bonds. We are interested in the other electron of each carbon. In the whole molecule there are six of these electrons that in structures A and B form the three double bonds. Instead of localizing two of them between carbons one and two, two between carbons three and four, and a pair between carbons five and six in structure A, let's think of the six electrons as free to move throughout the entire molecule. The same description is applied to structure B. The two electrons that were confined in the double bond between carbon one and carbon two may sometimes interact with carbon four or with any other carbon. To show delocalization of electrons, the modern accepted structure of benzene is drawn as

The circle represents electron delocalization, which is a stabilizing factor for the molecule. If the electron that originally was associated with carbon one can only be between carbon one and carbon two, it is attracted to two nuclei. However, if it is delocalized, it can interact with six positive nuclei. Instead of the electron of each carbon belonging only to its original carbon, it now belongs to the entire molecule. To preserve the stability of delocalization, the benzene molecule is rather unreactive. This explains its resistance to react as an alkene. The major reactions of benzene generally occur only under strenuous conditions and involve substituting other atoms for the hydrogens. Since the electrons in the carbon to hydrogen bonds are not part of the delocalization, the molecule retains its aromatic stability.

Physical properties of benzene

At room temperature and one atmosphere pressure, benzene is a colorless liquid that is insoluble in water. It is extremely flammable and should be used with great caution. Its use has been linked to certain blood disorders including some types of leukemia. It is a good organic solvent and the starting material for the synthesis of many widely used compounds. Plastics, synthetic rubbers, pharmaceuticals, and pesticides are a few of the commonly used products that are formed from benzene.

Derivatives of benzene

We have seen that benzene typically undergoes substitution reactions. One or more of its six hydrogens are replaced by other atoms or groups of atoms. We will look at the nomenclature and uses of some monosubstituted and disubstituted benzenes.

If one hydrogen of benzene is replaced, the resulting compound is named as a derivative of benzene. (See Figure 13-2.) Examples are chlorobenzene, nitrobenzene, and ethyl benzene. Some monosubstituted benzenes are known by common names. Important compounds in this classification are toluene (methyl benzene), phenol (hydroxybenzene) and aniline (aminobenzene). Toluene is so named because it can be obtained from the bark of the South American tolu tree. Like benzene, toluene is an extremely good solvent for other organic compounds such as paints and varnishes. It is frequently remembered as the starting material for the explosive TNT (trinitrotoluene). Phenol and aniline contain the alcohol and amino functional groups, respectively. Their properties are discussed in later chapters.

Since all six carbon-to-hydrogen bonds are equivalent in benzene, only one form of each of the monosubstituted benzenes exist. The story is different for the disubstituted benzenes. Three isomers of each exist. Con-

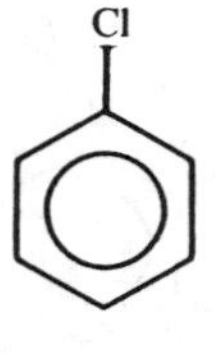

Chlorobenzene    Nitrobenzene 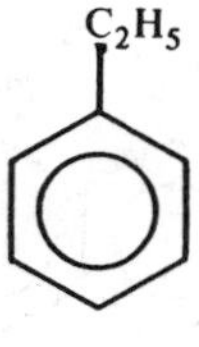   Ethyl benzene

Toluene   Phenol   Aniline
(methyl benzene)   (hydroxybenzene)   (aminobenzene)

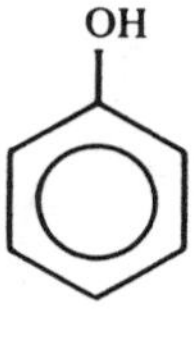

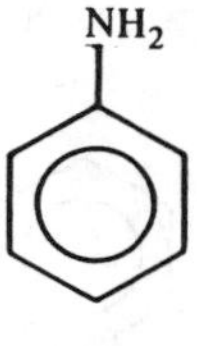

Figure 13-2   Derivatives of benzene

sider the compound *dichlorobenzene*. There are three possible ways to draw its structure.

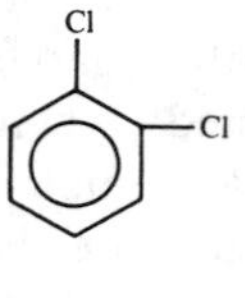

A 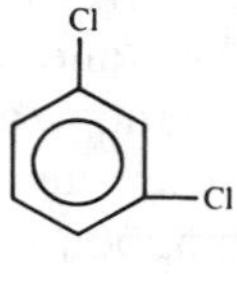   B    C

Each of these represents an individual compound with different properties. To distinguish among them, chemists use a nomenclature with the prefixes: *ortho, meta,* and *para.*

If two substituents on a benzene ring are on adjacent carbons, the compound is the *ortho* isomer. When one carbon separates the positions of the two substituents, the molecule is the *meta* form. Finally, if the substituents are directly across the ring from each other (separated by two carbons), the compound is the *para* isomer. The previ-

ously drawn isomers of dichlorobenzene are named following these rules. Structure A is *ortho* dichlorobenzene, structure B is *meta* dichlorobenzene, and structure C is *para* dichlorobenzene. *Ortho, meta,* and *para* are commonly abbreviated as *o, m,* and *p.* Similarly, three isomers of dimethyl benzene can be drawn. Since the common name for dimethyl benzene is xylene, these compounds are named as

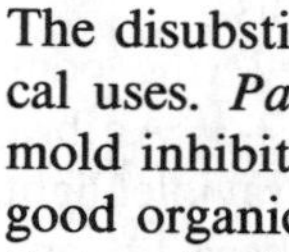

o–xylene 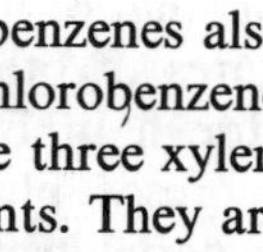   *m*–xylene 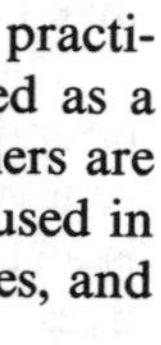   *p*–xylene

The disubstituted benzenes also have practical uses. *Para* dichlorobenzene is used as a mold inhibitor. The three xylene isomers are good organic solvents. They are also used in the synthesis of certain dyes, explosives, and photographic developers.

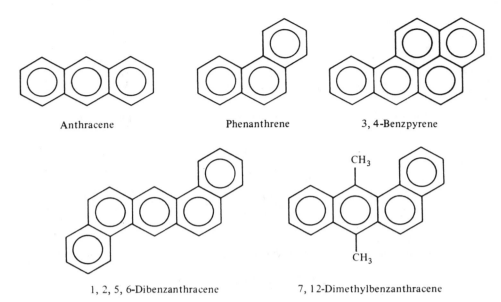

Anthracene Phenanthrene 3, 4-Benzpyrene

1, 2, 5, 6-Dibenzanthracene 7, 12-Dimethylbenzanthracene

Figure 13-3 Fused ring compounds

POLYNUCLEAR AROMATIC HYDROCARBONS

Some aromatic compounds contain two or more fused benzene rings. The simplest of these has the molecular formula $C_{10}H_8$ and is called *naphthalene*. Its structure may be drawn using the Kekulé form of alternating double and single bonds or using the circle to represent electron delocalization.

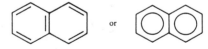

A practical use of naphthalene is as a moth repellant. You would probably recognize its odor as that of moth balls.

The structures of other fused ring compounds are drawn in Figure 13-3. Anthracene, which fluoresces blue in ultraviolet light, is a starting material in the synthesis of some dyes. Also important to the manufacture of dyes is phenanthrene. Its arrangement of three six-membered rings is also found in cholesterol, vitamin D, and the steroid

hormones. The other three compounds shown in Figure 13-3 have been shown to be carcinogenic. They and certain other large aromatic compounds are formed when organic materials are heated to high temperatures. The compound 3,4-benzpyrene is found in cigarette smoke. The other carcinogenic aromatics have been detected in soot in urban environments and in the exhaust of automobile fumes.

SOURCES OF AROMATIC COMPOUNDS

A major source of aromatic compounds is bituminous or soft coal. Bituminous coal consists of layers of six-membered carbon rings. (See Figure 13-4.) The layers are not chemically bonded to one another, which accounts for the "softness" of this coal. If the coal is heated to temperatures near 1200°C in the absence of oxygen, the large coal layers decompose. The products are a nonvolatile residue called coke and smaller

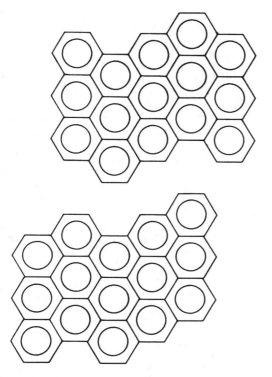

Figure 13-4 Bituminous coal

volatile materials. Collection and condensation of the volatile material yields a tarry material, coal tar. Benzene, toluene, and some polynuclear aromatics can be separated from the coal tar.

There is a great demand by modern-day society for aromatic compounds and their derivatives. To supplement the aromatic compounds produced from coal tar, industry also uses chemical procedures to convert open-chain alkanes into aromatic compounds.

CHAPTER SUMMARY

Hydrocarbons, the simplest of organic compounds, contain only two elements, hydrogen and carbon. The source of hydrocarbons, both open chain and closed chain, is fossil fuels, such as natural gas, petroleum, and coal. Organic chemistry is a science of synthesis, and hydrocarbons represent the starting material for many widely used compounds including anaesthetics, plastics, synthetic rubbers, pharmaceuticals, pesticides, disinfectants, and preservatives. In light of this information, it is readily apparent why the depletion of hydrocarbon sources has such a tremendous impact on every aspect of contemporary living. It is more than an "energy" crisis that we face, because fuel is only one of the many uses for these organic substances.

QUESTIONS

1. Draw structural formulas and line formulas for each of the following compounds: heptane, 2-pentene, 2-butyne, tetrachloroethane.

2. Draw structural formulas for all the isomers of C_7H_{16}. Name them according to the IUPAC system.

3. Define isomer, aliphatic, aromatic.

4. What is the significance of the hydrocarbons to the embalmer?

5. Draw three types of structures used to represent benzene. What does resonance mean?

6. Name the following compounds:

(a) Cl—⬡—Cl   (d) ⬡—CH₃, Cl

(b) ⬡   (e) ⬡—CH₂CH₃, CH₂CH₃

(c) ⬡⬡   (f) H₃C—⬡—CH₃

Two components of the threefold definition of embalming are disinfection and preservation. The alcohols are the first class of organic compounds that function as both disinfectant and preservative agents. This chapter will discuss the aromatic as well as the aliphatic alcohols, with special emphasis on the ones most commonly used in embalming fluids.

Ethers are also discussed in this chapter, since they may be considered to be derivatives of alcohols.

ALCOHOLS

Alcohols are organic compounds containing one or more —OH groups. The alcohols may be considered as derivatives of the hydro-

methods. One method uses the concept that an organic compound is composed of an alkyl group and a functional group. Thus the simplest monohydroxy alcohol is *methyl alcohol*.

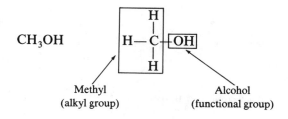

CH_3OH

Methyl
(alkyl group)

Alcohol
(functional group)

In methyl alcohol, one of the hydrogen atoms in methane (CH_4) has been replaced by the alcohol (OH) functional group.

Chapter 14
ALCOHOLS AND ETHERS

carbons in which one or more hydrogen atoms are replaced by —OH groups. Alcohols may be classified according to the number of —OH functional groups they contain.

Monohydroxy alcohols

Alcohols containing only one —OH group are called *monohydroxy alcohols*. These compounds are named according to two different

The second member of the series is ethyl alcohol (C_2H_5OH).

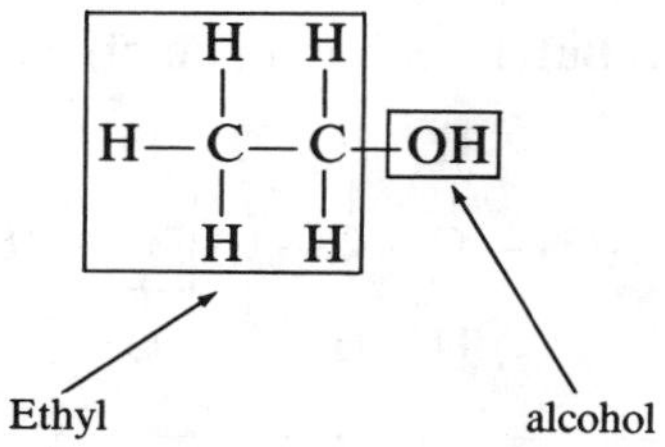

Ethyl   alcohol

The list below demonstrates some other monohydroxy alcohols:

Name	Formula	Structure
n-Propyl alcohol	C_3H_7OH	$H-\overset{\overset{H}{\vert}}{\underset{\underset{H}{\vert}}{C}}-\overset{\overset{H}{\vert}}{\underset{\underset{H}{\vert}}{C}}-\overset{\overset{H}{\vert}}{\underset{\underset{H}{\vert}}{C}}-OH$
n-Butyl alcohol	C_4H_9OH	$H-\overset{\overset{H}{\vert}}{\underset{\underset{H}{\vert}}{C}}-\overset{\overset{H}{\vert}}{\underset{\underset{H}{\vert}}{C}}-\overset{\overset{H}{\vert}}{\underset{\underset{H}{\vert}}{C}}-\overset{\overset{H}{\vert}}{\underset{\underset{H}{\vert}}{C}}-OH$
n-Pentyl alcohol	$C_5H_{11}OH$	$H-\overset{\overset{H}{\vert}}{\underset{\underset{H}{\vert}}{C}}-\overset{\overset{H}{\vert}}{\underset{\underset{H}{\vert}}{C}}-\overset{\overset{H}{\vert}}{\underset{\underset{H}{\vert}}{C}}-\overset{\overset{H}{\vert}}{\underset{\underset{H}{\vert}}{C}}-\overset{\overset{H}{\vert}}{\underset{\underset{H}{\vert}}{C}}-OH$

Another method for naming the monohydroxy alcohols changes the *-e* ending of the corresponding hydrocarbon to *-ol*, as shown in the following list.

Name of hydrocarbon	Name of alcohol
Methane	Methanol (methyl alcohol)
Ethane	Ethanol (ethyl alcohol)
Propane	Propanol (*n*-propyl alcohol)
Butane	Butanol (*n*-butyl alcohol)
Pentane	Pentanol (*n*-pentyl alcohol)

Monohydroxy alcohols are further classified according to the place of attachment of the —OH group as primary, secondary, or tertiary.

Primary alcohols

These are alcohols in which the hydroxyl group is attached to a carbon atom that is joined to only *one* other carbon atom.

Example   *n*-Butyl alcohol (butanol)

$$C_4H_9OH \qquad H-\overset{\overset{H}{\vert}}{\underset{\underset{H}{\vert}}{C}}-\overset{\overset{H}{\vert}}{\underset{\underset{H}{\vert}}{C}}-\overset{\overset{H}{\vert}}{\underset{\underset{H}{\vert}}{C}}-\boxed{\overset{\overset{H}{\vert}}{\underset{\underset{H}{\vert}}{C}}}-OH$$

The carbon to which the —OH group is attached is also joined to two hydrogen atoms but only one other carbon atom.

Secondary alcohols

These are alcohols in which the hydroxyl group is attached to a carbon atom that is joined to *two* other carbon atoms.

Example   Secondary butyl alcohol

$$CH_3CH_2CHOHCH_3 \qquad H-\overset{\overset{H}{\vert}}{\underset{\underset{H}{\vert}}{C}}-\overset{\overset{H}{\vert}}{\underset{\underset{H}{\vert}}{C}}-\boxed{\overset{\overset{H}{\vert}}{\underset{\underset{OH}{\vert}}{C}}}-\overset{\overset{H}{\vert}}{\underset{\underset{H}{\vert}}{C}}-H$$

The carbon to which the OH group is attached is also joined to one hydrogen atom and two other carbon atoms.

Tertiary alcohols

These are alcohols in which the hydroxyl group is attached to a carbon atom that is joined to *three* other carbon atoms.

Example   Tertiary butyl alcohol

$$(CH_3)_3COH \qquad H-\overset{\overset{H}{\vert}}{\underset{\underset{H}{\vert}}{C}}-\boxed{\overset{\overset{H-\overset{\overset{H}{\vert}}{\underset{\underset{}{}}}{C}-H}{}}{\underset{\underset{H-\overset{}{\underset{\underset{H}{}}{C}}-H}{}}{C}}}-OH$$

Note that the key to naming all these structures is the carbon to which the functional group (—OH) is attached, and not the functional group itself. In addition, all three of these structures (butyl alcohol, secondary butyl alcohol, and tertiary butyl alcohol) are isomers because they share the same molecular formula, C_4H_9OH. Tertiary alcohols represent the limit of this sort of rearrangement. In other words, it is not possible to construct a quaternary alcohol, since there would be a total of five bonds on the carbon atom.

Dihydroxy alcohols

These are alcohols containing two —OH groups. They are also sometimes known as *glycols*.

Example   Ethylene glycol

$$CH_2OHCH_2OH$$

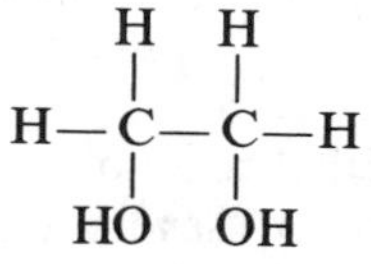

$$H-\overset{\displaystyle H}{\underset{\displaystyle HO}{C}}-\overset{\displaystyle H}{\underset{\displaystyle OH}{C}}-H$$

It is interesting to note that although this compound is named as an alkene, it does *not* have a double bond. The reason is that since organic chemistry is a science of synthesis, compounds are often named according to the substances from which they were made. Consider the following:

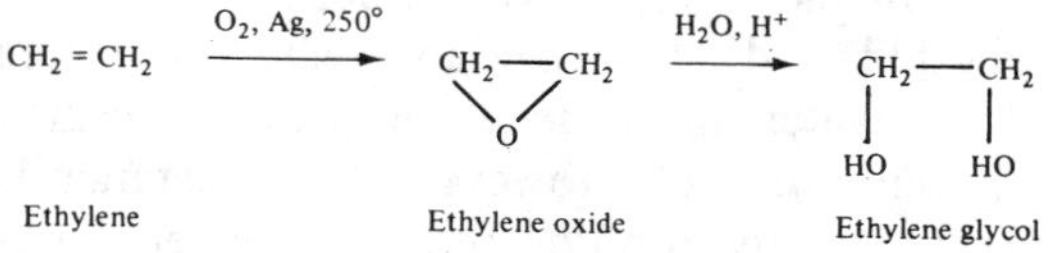

Because of its high boiling point, low freezing point, and high solubility in water, ethylene glycol is used commercially as a coolant for automobile engines (e.g., Prestone). In embalming fluids, glycols represent the simplest class of *humectants* or moisture-retaining agents. As will be pointed out in the next chaper, most formaldehyde gas in aqueous solutions takes the form of methyl-

ene glycol ($CH_2(OH)_2$). The significance of this compound will become more apparent as the role of the methylene group is illustrated in the preservation of tissue protein.

Trihydroxy alcohols

These include alcohols containing three —OH groups. The most common of these is *glycerin* (glycerol), $CH_2OHCHOHCH_2OH$, which is used as both a humectant and a solvent in embalming fluid.

Polyhydroxy alcohols

Alcohols containing more than three —OH groups are included in this category. *Sorbitol*, $CH_2OH(CHOH)_4CH_2OH$, and two of its isomers, *mannitol* and *dulcitol*, are commonly employed in embalming fluids as humectants.

IMPORTANT ALCOHOLS IN EMBALMING

Methyl alcohol (*methanol*), the first member of the series of primary monohydroxy alcohols, is also known as *wood alcohol* because it is produced by a process known as the destructive distillation of wood. *Destructive distillation* involves heating an organic substance (in this case wood) in the absence of air or oxygen and condensing the resulting vapors.

It is extremely important to exclude the oxygen, because the complete oxidation of any organic substance results in the production of carbon dioxide and water. Once methanol has been formed, it can undergo moderate or partial oxidation. It is interesting that about 50% of the fundamental organic compounds are related to each other by the process of oxidation and reduction.

For example:

$$\text{alcohol} \xrightarrow[\text{oxidation}]{\text{partial}} \text{aldehyde} \xrightarrow[\text{oxidation}]{\text{partial}} \text{acid}$$

As a result, methyl alcohol is instrumental in the commercial production of formaldehyde (methanol $\longrightarrow$ methanal).

Let us compare complete and partial oxidation of methyl alcohol. During complete oxidation, it burns with a blue flame, forming carbon dioxide and water.

$$2 CH_3OH + 3 O_2 \longrightarrow 2 CO_2 + 4 H_2O$$

If moderate or cautious oxidation occurs, formaldehyde is produced.

$$2 CH_3OH + O_2 \xrightarrow{Cu} 2 HCHO + 2 H_2O$$

Note that it takes three times as much oxygen to completely oxidize methanol to carbon dioxide and water as it does to produce formaldehyde. This corresponds to the number of steps that it takes to oxidize methanol to CO_2 and H_2O by partial oxidation.

methanol $\xrightarrow{O_2}$ methanal $\xrightarrow{O_2}$

methanoic acid $\xrightarrow{O_2}$ carbon dioxide + water

This process of partial oxidation explains the toxicity of methyl alcohol. If one imbibes wood alcohol, the methanol is partially oxidized to formaldehyde. Theoretically, then, you could embalm yourself without injecting a single blood vessel!

Ethyl alcohol is the second member of the series of primary monohydroxy alcohols. Ethanol (C_2H_5OH) is also called *grain alcohol* because it is produced by the fermentation of carbohydrates.

$$C_6H_{12}O_6 \xrightarrow{zymase} 2 C_2H_5OH + 2 CO_2$$

Like methanol, ethanol burns with a blue flame, forming carbon dioxide and water (complete oxidation).

$$C_2H_5OH + 3 O_2 \longrightarrow 2 CO_2 + 3 H_2O$$

Partial oxidation produces acetaldehyde (ethanal).

$$2 C_2H_5OH + O_2 \longrightarrow 2 CH_3CHO + 2 H_2O$$

Further oxidation produces acetic acid, and eventually carbon dioxide and water. The oxidation and reduction of primary alcohols may be summarized by the following diagram:

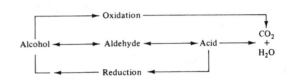

Ethyl alcohol is a good solvent, but because of severe tax restrictions it is used chiefly in the form of denatured alcohol, which is obtainable tax free. *Denatured alcohol* is ordinary ethyl alcohol to which poisonous or ill-tasting substances have been added in order to render it unfit for use as a beverage. In this form, it can be used in industry. Denaturing additives generally will have about the same boiling point as ethyl alcohol so that they cannot be removed even by further distillation. Specially purified methyl and ethyl alcohols which are free from water and other impurities are termed *absolute alcohol*. However, this substance is extremely hydrophilic and must be kept carefully sealed in order to remain free from water that would be absorbed from the surrounding air.

The third member of the series of primary, monohydroxy alcohols is *propanol*, C_3H_7OH. Like its predecessors, *n*-propyl alcohol undergoes oxidation and reduction patterns typical of all the primary alcohols. However, its isomer (isopropyl alcohol) is of special interest. Isopropyl alcohol (rubbing alcohol) is a secondary alcohol. Compare:

$$H-\overset{\overset{\displaystyle H}{|}}{\underset{\underset{\displaystyle H}{|}}{C}}-\overset{\overset{\displaystyle H}{|}}{\underset{\underset{\displaystyle H}{|}}{C}}-\overset{\overset{\displaystyle H}{|}}{\underset{\underset{\displaystyle H}{|}}{C}}-OH$$

$CH_3CH_2CH_2OH$
Normal propyl alcohol

$$H-\overset{\overset{\displaystyle H}{|}}{\underset{\underset{\displaystyle H}{|}}{C}}-\overset{\overset{\displaystyle H}{|}}{\underset{\underset{\displaystyle OH}{|}}{C}}-\overset{\overset{\displaystyle H}{|}}{\underset{\underset{\displaystyle H}{|}}{C}}-H$$

$CH_3CHOHCH_3$
Isopropyl alcohol

Secondary alcohols, upon partial oxidation, yield ketones as shown by the following:

$$H-\overset{\overset{\displaystyle H}{|}}{\underset{\underset{\displaystyle H}{|}}{C}}-\overset{\overset{\displaystyle H}{|}}{\underset{\underset{\displaystyle OH}{|}}{C}}-\overset{\overset{\displaystyle H}{|}}{\underset{\underset{\displaystyle H}{|}}{C}}-H+\tfrac{1}{2}O_2 \longrightarrow$$

$$H-\overset{\overset{\displaystyle H}{|}}{\underset{\underset{\displaystyle H}{|}}{C}}-\overset{\overset{\displaystyle H}{|}}{\underset{\underset{\displaystyle O}{\parallel}}{C}}-\overset{\overset{\displaystyle H}{|}}{\underset{\underset{\displaystyle H}{|}}{C}}-H+H_2O$$

This discussion has demonstrated that four of the eight functional groups are related to each other by oxidation and reduction.

Isopropyl alcohol has many industrial uses, since it is relatively inexpensive and is sold tax free without restriction. Little use is made of it in embalming fluid. However, it is an excellent disinfectant, possessing approximately twice the germicidal strength of ethyl alcohol.

Table 14-1 summarizes the important alcohols utilized in the embalming process.

Table 14-1 Alcohols used in the embalming process

Name	Function
Methyl alcohol	Solvent
	Lowers the freezing point of the fluid
	Formaldehyde antipolymerant
Ethyl alcohol	Solvent
	Lowers the freezing point of the fluid
	Preservative
	Disinfectant
Isopropyl alcohol	Disinfectant
Ethylene glycol	Humectant
Glycerin	Humectant
	Solvent
	Lubricant
	Penetrating agent
	Increases the effectiveness of germicides in solution

PHENOLS

Phenols are derivatives of benzene containing one or more OH groups.

Phenol

They are colorless, crystalline solids that are soluble in water and weakly acidic (pH 6), hence phenol's other name of *carbolic acid*. Phenol has been used as a general disinfectant since the 1860s, when it was discovered to be the active agent in German creosote, a mixture of aromatic hydrocarbons, nitrogen bases, and phenols. This creosote was used as a deodorant in sewage treatment.

Joseph Lister, an English surgeon, hypothesized that if this substance "sweetened" the putrefaction in sewage, it could have some value in stopping postoperative putrefactive infections. He soaked gauze dressings in various concentrations of phenol and applied them to the compound-fracture wounds of his surgical cases. Up to that time, the death rate of postoperative compound-fracture infections exceeded 50%. Lister's technique dramatically reduced these infections to less than 2%. He eventually extended the procedures to soaking surgical ligatures in this compound and is credited with pioneering aseptic surgery. A number of disinfectant compounds are derived from phenol, the most advertised of which bears the name of this pioneer—Listerine.

CRESOLS

Phenols which are derivatives of toluene are called *cresols*. Three isomeric cresols have the formula $C_6H_4OHCH_3$.

Ortho-cresol   Meta-cresol   Para-cresol

A mixture of the three is known as *tricresol*. The cresols have a greater germicidal power than phenol and are somewhat less toxic to humans. Cresols are combined with soap to produce a commercial preparation known as Lysol. One of the highly desirable qualities of a good disinfectant is the ability to work well in the presence of organic matter such as soap. Since many phenolic derivatives

possess this quality, they are extensively used in embalming procedures.

Phenol has been used as a standard for evaluating the efficiency of other germicides. The method, called the *phenol coefficient*, compares the effectiveness of other antiseptics to phenol under identical conditions. The phenol coefficient of phenol is 1. The P.C. of cresols is 2.5, which means that the cresols are 2.5 times as effective as phenol. A germicide with a P.C. of 0.5, therefore, would be one-half as effective as phenol under the same conditions. The main difficulty with this method is that it sets phenol apart as an ideal disinfectant, which, considering its drawbacks of toxicity and causticity to living tissue, is simply not true.

Another problem is that the phenol-coefficient method is only useful in evaluating *phenolic* disinfectants. When it is applied to nonphenolic agents, the results are often erratic. For example, the P.C. of formaldehyde is 1.8, but the P.C. of activated glutaraldehyde is 0.8. The fact that this latter compound has been labeled a "cold chemical sterilant" increases one's skepticism about the use of phenol coefficients. The phenol-coefficient method of evaluation has, for the most part, been abandoned in favor of less arbitrary procedures.

RESORCINOL

This phenolic derivative, with a formula of $C_6H_4(OH)_2$, has a P.C. of 0.4 and is used as an antiseptic. Its structure is

HEXYL RESORCINOL

This compound has a much higher phenol coefficient (46 to 56) than the others we have discussed. It is sometimes known as S.T. 37, which refers to its low surface tension. It is used as a germicide and is commonly found in mouthwashes. Its molecular formula is $C_6H_3(OH)_2C_6H_{13}$ and its structure is

HEXACHLOROPHENE

This compound, described as a halogenated *bis*-phenol, is an extremely effective germicide (P.C. 450) even at low concentrations (2% to 3%) that can be used in conjunction with soap. This once popular germicide was routinely found as a standard component in soaps, deodorants, and toothpastes.

Unfortunately, in concentrations greater than 12% hexachlorophene acts as a neurotoxic agent. As a result, this excellent disinfectant has been withdrawn from general use and may be obtained only by a physician's prescription.

COMPARISON OF ALCOHOLS AS GERMICIDES

Concentration is the most critical factor in considering the disinfectant or preservative action of any of the previously discussed compounds. Ethyl alcohol is most effective as a disinfectant in concentrations of 50% to 70%. In concentrations exceeding 70%, ethanol is actually less effective, since its high affinity for water impedes its ability to penetrate cell membranes at these levels. By way of contrast, glycerin exhibits its best antiseptic qualities in strong solutions. In weak ones, it will actually promote the growth of bacteria!

The use of phenol as a disinfectant varies widely according to its concentrations. In solutions containing 5% phenol, the material has the physical appearance of a reddish-purple liquid and the chemical characteristic of extreme causticity to living tissues. Although it must be handled with protective gloves, it is valuable in bleaching discolorations and also may be used in reducing swollen areas in human remains. This concentration of phenol is available in a number of commercially available preparations and may either be applied by external pack or injected directly into the affected area by hypodermic syringe. When the concentration is reduced to 3%, the solution becomes somewhat less caustic and yet is still effective as an external drying agent. Dropping the concentration to 2% produces a disinfectant that is routinely applied to laboratory table tops in microbiology with a sponge. Gloves are not necessary at this concentration, as there are apparently no adverse effects to the skin. At 1% concentration, this material has been utilized as a mouthwash. This, of course, is the basis for Listerine Antiseptic. However, if you examine the label of this product, you won't find phenol included with the ingredients.

What is listed is a substance called *thymol*.

Thymol

Thymol is another of the phenolic derivatives. This compound signals the beginning of a pattern and a theme that will consistently recur throughout organic chemistry. The theme has many variations, but one idea definitely pervades: the simplest organic substances appear to be the most caustic. When the basic substance is modified either by the addition of carbons in the chain or the substitution of side chains on the essential structure, its caustic or astringent characteristic is substantially reduced *without* loss of germicidal activity. In fact, the germicidal quality seems to increase. Take, for example, the difference in toxicity between methyl and ethyl alcohol, and the increased germicidal activity of isopropyl alcohol over ethyl alcohol. This principle will hold true as we progress through the remaining organic compounds. For instance, formaldehyde is the most astringent of all the aldehydes—thus the case for activated glutaraldehyde as a preservative as well as a disinfectant.

THIOALCOHOLS (MERCAPTANS)

Mercaptans are the sulfur analogs of alcohols. These compounds contain the sulfhydryl group, —SH, instead of the hydroxyl group, —OH. The general formula for the thioalcohols is R—SH. The first four members of the series are

- ○ Methyl mercaptan CH_3SH
- ○ Ethyl mercaptan CH_3CH_2SH
- ○ Propyl mercaptan $CH_3CH_2CH_2SH$
- ○ Butyl mercaptan $CH_3CH_2CH_2CH_2SH$

The presence of sulfur produces obnoxious odors. *Methyl mercaptan* is responsible for the unique odor acquired by normal urine after the ingestion of asparagus. *Ethyl mercaptan* is a tracer substance added to natural gas (which by itself is odorless) in order to make gas leaks more readily detectable. The best-known mercaptan is 3-methyl-1-butanethiol, the scent of the skunk. Many proteins, such as keratin, are rich in both sulfhydryl groups and disulfide bridges (—S—S—). This is manifested by the distinctive disagreeable odor of burning hair and flesh. Mercaptans are routinely present as final products of decomposition and contribute substantially to the accompanying odors.

ETHERS

Ethers are compounds in which two alkyl groups are attached to an oxygen atom. Ethers may be viewed as derivatives of alcohols in which the H of the ROH has been replaced with an alkyl group to form a substance with the general formula of ROR. They may also be considered as derivatives of water in which both hydrogen atoms have been replaced by alkyl groups. An additional expression of the general formula is ROR′, where R′ may or may not be identical with R. It is important to note that, like the ketones, each R group must contain a minimum of a methyl (CH_3) group. If this is not true, the following will result. First, substituting a hydrogen atom for the R:

HO—R′

This effectively converts the substance into an alcohol. Substituting a hydrogen atom for the R′ produces another alcohol:

R—OH

If hydrogens are used in place of both R groups, water is produced:

H—O—H

This verifies our definition of ethers being derivatives of alcohols or water. There are two types of ethers.

Simple ethers

In simple ethers the two alkyl groups are identical. These compounds are named by the alkyl group–functional group method that was introduced in primary monohydroxy alcohols. The first member of the series is

$$H-\overset{\displaystyle H}{\underset{\displaystyle H}{\overset{|}{\underset{|}{C}}}}-O-\overset{\displaystyle H}{\underset{\displaystyle H}{\overset{|}{\underset{|}{C}}}}-H$$

This substance may be called *dimethyl ether*, which indicates that there are two methyl (CH_3) groups attached to the ether functional group (—O—). It may also be called *methyl ether*, since it is known that both R groups must contain a minimum of one carbon atom and the appropriate number of hydrogen atoms. Therefore, if we call a substance methyl ether, we can be assured that the structure contains two methyl groups, even though this is not expressed in the name. In the same manner, the name *octyl ether* is a correct simplification of *dioctyl ether*. The name conveys two ideas. First, the substance is a simple ether. Second, *both* alkyl groups are composed of an octyl radi-

cal (C_8H_{17}). The second member of the series is

$$H-\overset{\displaystyle H}{\underset{\displaystyle H}{\overset{|}{\underset{|}{C}}}}-\overset{\displaystyle H}{\underset{\displaystyle H}{\overset{|}{\underset{|}{C}}}}-O-\overset{\displaystyle H}{\underset{\displaystyle H}{\overset{|}{\underset{|}{C}}}}-\overset{\displaystyle H}{\underset{\displaystyle H}{\overset{|}{\underset{|}{C}}}}-H$$

$$(C_2H_5-O-C_2H_5)$$

This is *diethyl ether* or *ethyl ether*. Under its common name, *ether*, this substance has become widely known for its qualities as a surgical anaesthetic. Although it was used as such for over a century, it has been replaced by other substances because it is highly flammable and has undesirable side effects, including nausea, vomiting, and irritation of the respiratory passages.

Since the simple ethers are chemically inert, they make excellent solvents for organic compounds. As a result, they have sometimes been incorporated in embalming fluid for this purpose. However, because they are highly flammable, a great deal of care must be exercised in their use. Another problem is that upon standing, ethers are oxidized to highly unstable, explosive peroxides.

Mixed ethers

In mixed ethers, the two alkyl groups are different. These compounds are also named by using the alkyl group–functional group method.

Thus:

$$H-\overset{\displaystyle H}{\underset{\displaystyle H}{\overset{|}{\underset{|}{C}}}}-O-\overset{\displaystyle H}{\underset{\displaystyle H}{\overset{|}{\underset{|}{C}}}}-\overset{\displaystyle H}{\underset{\displaystyle H}{\overset{|}{\underset{|}{C}}}}-H$$

Methyl ethyl ether

$$(CH_3OC_2H_5)$$

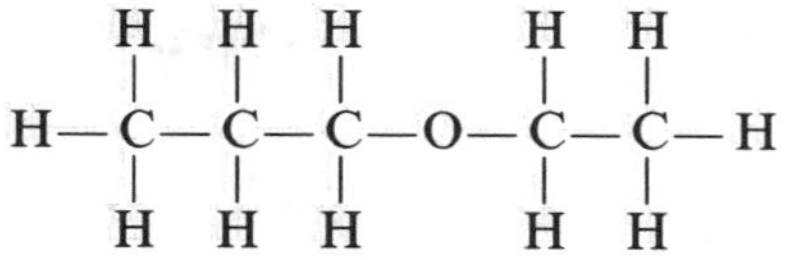

Ethyl propyl ether

$$(C_3H_7OC_2H_5)$$

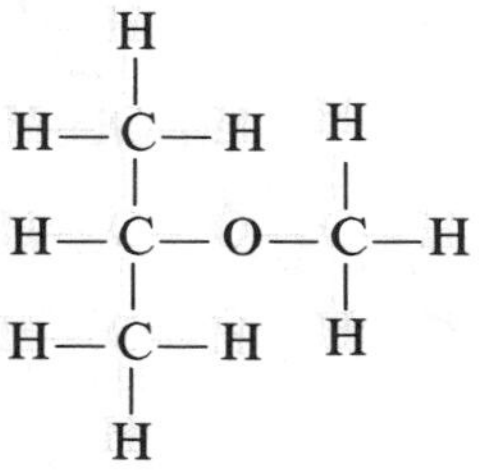

Methyl isopropyl ether

$$(CH_3)_2CHOCH_3$$

The R groups need not be restricted to open-chain hydrocarbons.

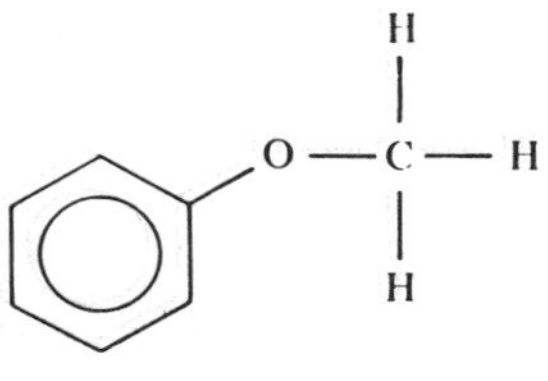

Phenyl methyl ether

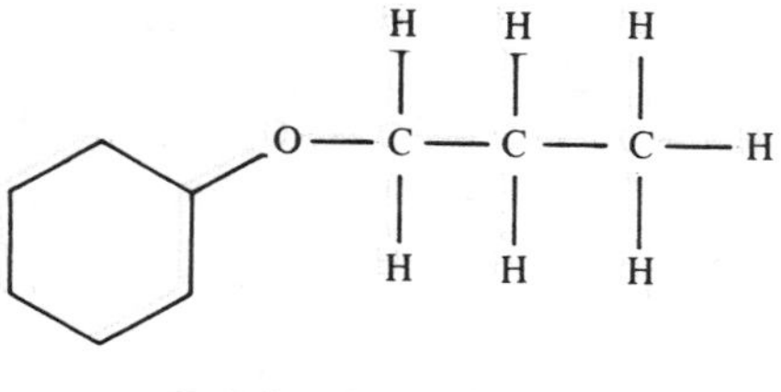

Cyclohexyl propyl ether

CHAPTER SUMMARY

The functional group of the alcohols is the —OH group. Alcohols are classified on the basis of the number and position of this group. This is the same hydroxy group that was introduced in the general chemistry section. In organic compounds, however, the —OH group does not ionize. Nonetheless, this group is significant because it makes part of the alcohol molecule polar, thus keeping the small-chain alcohols soluble in water. This solubility is important because of the uses of alcohols in embalming fluids, which use water as their primary solvent. Many different alcohols are used in embalming for a wide variety of functions, including disinfection, preservation, moisture retention, penetration, lubrication, and solvation.

The functional group of the ethers is —O—. The ethers are related to the alcohols in both structure and function. The related function is solvation. However, since ethers are nonpolar, they serve as solvents for organic substances.

QUESTIONS

1. What is the functional group in alcohols and ethers?

2. Draw structures for the following compounds: ethanol, glycerol, isopropyl alcohol, methylene glycol, phenol, *meta*-cresol, propyl mercaptan, diethyl ether, ethyl isopropyl ether.

3. Distinguish between primary, secondary, and tertiary alcohols. Classify the alcohols in question 2 by this method.

4. Define: humectant, glycol, wood alcohol, grain alcohol, phenol coefficient, simple ether.

5. What are the products of complete oxidation of any organic compound? What

product is produced by partial oxidation of an alcohol? What products form by stepwise reduction of a carboxylic acid?

6. Complete the following equations by drawing structures of the products.

(a) $H-\underset{\underset{H}{|}}{\overset{\overset{H}{|}}{C}}-OH + \frac{1}{2}O_2 \longrightarrow$

(b) Product of (a) $+ \frac{1}{2}O_2 \longrightarrow$

(c) $CH_3-\underset{\underset{}{\overset{OH}{|}}}{C}HCH_3 + \frac{1}{2}O_2 \longrightarrow$

(d) $CH_3-CH_2\overset{\overset{O}{\parallel}}{C}H + \frac{1}{2}O_2 \longrightarrow$

7. Show the significance of the following factors to the germicidal activity of a compound: (a) concentration, (b) number of carbons in compound.

The aldehydes represent the second major class of disinfectants and preservatives commonly found in embalming fluids. "Second," however, refers to the order of discussion and not the order of usage. As a group, aldehydes comprise the largest percentage of disinfectant-preservative chemical agents routinely incorporated into embalming fluids.

Ketones are discussed in this chapter because of their similarity in structure to the aldehydes. The similarity, however, ends there because ketones serve an entirely different function in the embalming process.

ALDEHYDES

Aldehydes are organic compounds containing one or more CHO groups. They are considered to be derivatives of the hydro-

$$
\begin{array}{cc}
\text{H} & \text{H} \\
| & | \\
\text{H}-\text{C}-\text{C}-\text{H} \\
| & | \\
\text{H} & \text{H}
\end{array}
\qquad
\begin{array}{cc}
\text{H} & \text{H} \\
| & | \\
\text{H}-\text{C}-\text{C}=\text{O} \\
| \\
\text{H}
\end{array}
$$

$$
\begin{array}{ccc}
\text{H} & \text{H} & \text{H} \\
| & | & | \\
\text{H}-\text{C}-\text{C}-\text{C}-\text{H} \\
| & | & | \\
\text{H} & \text{H} & \text{H}
\end{array}
\qquad
\begin{array}{ccc}
\text{H} & \text{H} & \text{H} \\
| & | & | \\
\text{H}-\text{C}-\text{C}-\text{C}=\text{O} \\
| & | \\
\text{H} & \text{H}
\end{array}
$$

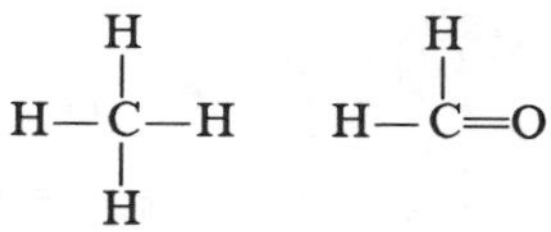

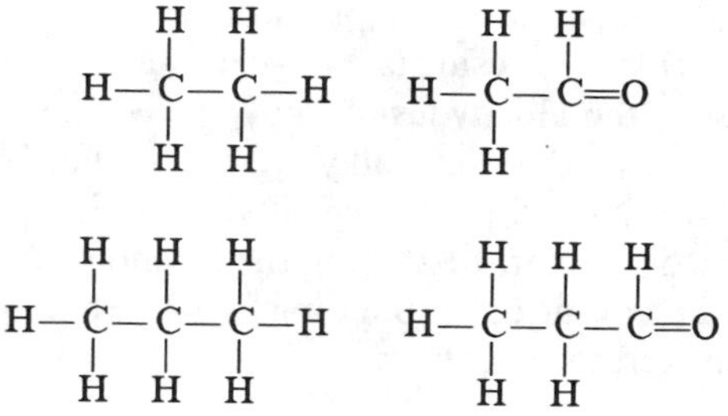

Nomenclature

Since there is a carbon atom in the functional group, aldehydes are *not* named like the alcohols. We have seen that an organic compound is composed of two radicals: an alkyl group and a functional group. The functional group of the alcohols was —OH. The simplest alcohol required a methyl (CH_3)

Chapter 15
ALDEHYDES AND KETONES

carbons in which two hydrogen atoms on the same carbon atom have been replaced by an oxygen atom. Consider the following:

Hydrocarbon	Aldehyde

$$
\begin{array}{cc}
\text{H} & \text{H} \\
| & | \\
\text{H}-\text{C}-\text{H} & \text{H}-\text{C}=\text{O} \\
| \\
\text{H}
\end{array}
$$

group. Some organic compounds with carbon atoms in their functional groups need only a hydrogen atom in the alkyl-group position. Thus, the simplest aldehyde can be expressed as

$$
\text{HCHO} \qquad \left(\begin{array}{c} \text{H} \\ | \\ \text{H}-\text{C}=\text{O} \end{array} \right)
$$

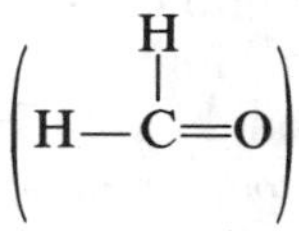

However, if we attempt to do this with the alcohols, the result is H—OH (water). As a result, the aldehydes are not named like the alcohols—that is, alkyl group–functional group. Nonetheless, *one* of the naming systems is similar. In naming the alcohols, the *-e* ending of the corresponding hydrocarbon was changed to *-ol*. Thus:

○ Methane – methanol
○ Ethane – ethanol
○ Propane – propanol

In naming the aldehydes, the *-e* ending of the corresponding hydrocarbon is changed to *-al*. Thus:

○ Methane – methanal
○ Ethane – ethanal
○ Propane – propanal

This naming system also reflects the relationship of the aldehydes to their corresponding alcohols. We have previously defined oxidation (Chapter 6) as the removal of hydrogen as well as the addition of oxygen. The intermediate position of aldehydes between alcohols and acids has been recognized for many years. The name *aldehyde* was originally coined by putting together the first syllables of the three words *al*cohol *de*-prived of *hy*drogen. Thus:

Alcohol	Aldehyde
Methanol	Methanal
Ethanol	Ethanal
Propanol	Propanal

If the alkyl group—functional group method of naming were used, the first member of the series would be methyl aldehyde. If we attempted to generate a formula from this name (taking into consideration that the general formula for the aldehydes is R—CHO), we would have CH_3CHO, which, in fact, is the *second* member of the series,

ethanal. In organic compounds containing a carbon in the functional group, it is always sound procedure to count *all* the carbons in the compound before attempting to name it.

The second method of naming aldehydes is derived from the corresponding acids. Recall the oxidation-reduction relation among alcohols, aldehydes, and acids (Chapter 14).

Although aldehydes are produced by the oxidation of their corresponding alcohols, they may be named as the *reduction products* of their corresponding acids. To make things even more interesting, the acids in question are named according to the source from which they were originally isolated, instead of something more systematic such as the number of carbon atoms in the chain. Take, for example, the first member of the series, which according to the initial naming system is called methanal (HCHO). *Formaldehyde* is the familiar name for this substance. According to its derivation, then, formaldehyde is named as the reduction product of *formic acid*. Formic acid, in turn, comes from ants (Latin *formica*, "ant"). This substance was originally isolated by distilling a quantity of these insects. Discovered by Butlerov in 1859, formaldehyde has remained the primary preservative in arterial embalming fluids. Up to that time, the principal substances in embalming fluids were heavy-metal protein precipitants such as the arsenicals. However, with the emergence of forensic medicine, all heavy metals (e.g., lead, arsenic, mercury) were eventually prohibited by law from inclusion in injectable embalming fluids. Let us examine formaldehyde in detail.

Formaldehyde (methanal)

Formulas:

$$CH_2O \qquad HCHO \qquad H-\overset{\displaystyle H}{\underset{\displaystyle |}{C}}=O$$

The commercial method of preparation of formaldehyde is the partial oxidation of methyl alcohol, carried out by passing methyl alcohol vapors over sheets of hot copper which act as a catalyst. The equation is

$$2 CH_3OH + O_2 \xrightarrow{Cu} 2 HCHO + 2 H_2O$$

Note that this is partial or cautious oxidation, because complete oxidation of any organic substance produces carbon dioxide and water (Chapter 14).

Properties of formaldehyde

1. It is a colorless gas with an irritating odor. Formaldehyde is highly dehydrating and has been shown to have a detrimental effect on the nasal and pharyngeal mucous membranes of those exposed to levels as low as 0.05 parts per million.

2. It is quite soluble in water. Formaldehyde is generally available as *formalin*, an aqueous solution containing 37% formaldehyde gas by weight or 40% by volume. This represents the solubility limit of formaldehyde gas in water. In order to increase the concentration above this level, it is necessary to use an additional solvent such as ethyl alcohol.

The funeral service industry uses an interesting system of expressing formaldehyde concentration in embalming fluids. It is called the index of a fluid. *Index* is defined as the number of grams of pure formaldehyde gas dissolved in 100 milliliters of solution. Since embalming fluids are usually diluted before injection, a calculation must be done to determine the true percentage of formaldehyde in an injected fluid. One 16-ounce bottle of a 36-index arterial embalming fluid mixed in one gallon of water (128 ounces) has an effective formaldehyde concentration of 4.5%.

3. It combines with water, forming methylene glycol:

$$CH_2O + HOH \longleftrightarrow CH_2(OH)_2$$

When in solution in water, most of the formaldehyde is actually in the form of methylene glycol. This substance is very unstable, but it does give rise to the question of the actual source of the methylene (CH_2) group which is instrumental in the cross-linking reaction of embalming preservatives with protein molecules. (See Chapter 19 on proteins.)

4. It is easily oxidized to form formic acid.

$$2 HCHO + O_2 \longrightarrow 2 HCOOH$$

5. It polymerizes to form paraformaldehyde. *Polymerization* is a reaction between molecules of the same kind that produces a substance having a molecular weight approximately a multiple of the original substance. A *polymer* is the product resulting from polymerization. Technically, the term means "many (*poly*) units (*mer*)." This is consistent with the general format of organic chemistry, because, just as many carbon atoms have the tendency to join together forming long chains, many repeating structural units exhibit the same tendency. One of the simplest polymers is Teflon, which is nothing more than repeating units of CF_2 (e.g., $-CF_2-CF_2-CF_2-$).

When formaldehyde polymerizes to form *paraformaldehyde*, it is composed of repeating units of CH_2O. The formula for this polymer is $(CH_2O)_x$, where x is a minimum of eight. The simplest representation of the structure is shown in trioxymethylene $(CH_2O)_3$. In order for the CH_2O unit to combine with itself, the double bond to the oxygen must be broken.

H—C—H, O—C, etc. ring structure

The more CH_2O units that add into the structure, the heavier the molecule becomes, until it precipitates out of solution in the form of large paraffinlike flakes. The phenomenon can be observed in bottles of formaldehyde-based embalming fluid that have exceeded their shelf life or have been subjected to extremes of temperature or light. Polymerization is a natural occurrence in organic compounds. In addition to the factors mentioned above, formaldehyde tends to polymerize when subjected to acid pH. As a result, commercial embalming fluids are buffered to approximately 7.2–7.4 as a preventive measure. Methyl alcohol is routinely included in the composition of arterial embalming fluids as an antipolymerizing agent for formaldehyde. Although paraformaldehyde (paraform) is undesirable in arterial fluids, it is employed as a major preservative in solid autopsy compounds. When used in this situation, the paraform is hydrolyzed by the moisture in the body tissues and releases formaldehyde gas into the adjacent areas.

6. In basic solutions, formaldehyde is unstable. Its reaction with alkaline substances is known as the *Cannizzaro reaction*:

$$2\ CH_2O + NaOH \longrightarrow$$
Formaldehyde   Base

$$HCOONa + CH_3OH$$
Salt   Methanol

Formaldehyde has a very limited pH range. If the surrounding medium becomes too acidic, it polymerizes. If that medium is too alkaline, it decomposes.

7. Formaldehyde reacts with ammonia to form *hexamethylene tetraamine*, commonly known as *urotropin*.

$$6\ CH_2O + 4\ NH_3 \longrightarrow$$
$$(CH_2)_6N_4 + 6\ H_2O$$

Urotropin is neither an open-chain compound nor a ring structure, but instead assumes the following crystalline form:

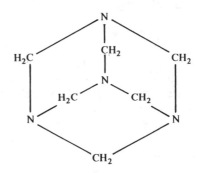

The formation of urotropin demonstrates the affinity of formaldehyde for nitrogen. The end result is the "neutralization" of formaldehyde. Ammonia is the standard nitrogen donor in this reaction, but any source of nitrogen can bring about a similar reaction. This explains the difficulty encountered in embalming a remains with advanced or advancing decomposition. Nitrogen is an important constituent in the structure of protein (see Chapter 19). As protein is progressively hydrolyzed during decomposition, more and more nitrogen becomes exposed, thereby increasing the formaldehyde demand. This means that more formaldehyde above and beyond normal concentrations must be added in order to overcome the elevated threshold generated by decomposition. Thus, recommendations for embalming a remains in the state of advanced decomposition include the injection of a large volume of embalming fluid containing high concentrations of formaldehyde. This is similar to the effect of hard water on soap (see Chapter 8) in that a certain amount of the soap is used in reacting with the hard-water minerals before the remaining portion is able to function as a cleansing agent.

Decomposition is not the only situation that increases formaldehyde demand. Uremic poisoning (urine in the blood) is an example of a pathological condition that produces a similar effect. Urea ($NH_2-\overset{\overset{\displaystyle O}{\|}}{C}-NH_2$) is a form of nonprotein nitrogen that is selectively absorbed and eventually excreted by kidney tissue. It is routinely produced by the liver and represents the means by which the human body can rid itself of excess nitrogen. When renal dysfunction occurs, the urea is not absorbed by the kidney tissues, resulting in dramatic increases of this toxic substance in the circulating blood. When the embalmer opens the blood vascular system, there is a pervasive odor of urine. If special precautions are not taken to flush this contaminated blood from the system, ordinary arterial embalming will be totally ineffective.

8. Formaldehyde cross-links proteins (see Chapter 19 on proteins).

9. It changes the color of the bile pigment bilirubin (yellow) to biliverdin (green). (See Chapter 19.)

Formaldehyde is the first in a series of compounds called *monoaldehydes*. The following table summarizes the names and formulas for the first three members of this homologous series.

Names	Formulas
Methanal (formaldehyde)	HCHO
Ethanal (acetaldehyde)	CH_3CHO
Propanal (propionaldehyde)	CH_3CH_2CHO

Dialdehydes

The *dialdehydes* are organic compounds containing two —CHO groups. Since dialdehydes are also incorporated in embalming fluids, we shall look at the names and formulas for several of the more important members of this group.

Dialdehydes like monoaldehydes are named as the reduction products of their corresponding dicarboxylic acids. The following table shows the relationship between the names.

Dicarboxylic acid	Dialdehyde
Oxalic acid	Glyoxal
Malonic acid	Malonaldehyde
Succinic acid	Succinaldehyde
Glutaric acid	Glutaraldehyde
Adipic acid	Adipaldehyde
Pimelic acid	Pimelaldehyde

Learning the dialdehydes and dicarboxylic acids requires memorization of an additional system of classification. However, the stress involved can be alleviated by the use of the following memory device: Oh My, Such Good Apple Pie. The first letter of each word represents the first letter of each of the first six compounds in the series.

Glyoxal The simplest of the dialdehydes, $(CHO)_2$, further reflects the oxidation-reduction relationship among alcohols, aldehydes, and acids because it contains in its name both the corresponding oxidative product (oxalic acid) and the analogous reductive compound (ethylene glycol), while retaining an *-al* name ending to identify it as an aldehyde.

Ethylene glycol   reduction → Glyoxal   oxidation → Oxalic acid

Glyoxal is comparable in protein coagulability to formaldehyde. However, the resultant yellow color makes its use in embalming fluid undesirable. As stated in Chapter 14, the astringency of organic compounds generally decreases as the length of the carbon chain increases. As a result, the higher dialdehydes have been investigated for possible applications to embalming. The structures for the dialdehydes subsequent to glyoxal are generated by introducing a succession of methylene (CH_2) groups between the two —CHO groups. Thus:

$$O=\overset{\overset{\displaystyle H}{|}}{C}-\overset{\overset{\displaystyle H}{|}}{C}=O \qquad (CHO)_2$$

Glyoxal

$$O=\overset{\overset{\displaystyle H}{|}}{C}-\underset{\underset{\displaystyle H}{|}}{\overset{\overset{\displaystyle H}{|}}{C}}-\overset{\overset{\displaystyle H}{|}}{C}=O \qquad OHCCH_2CHO$$

Malonaldehyde

$$O=\overset{\overset{\displaystyle H}{|}}{C}-\underset{\underset{\displaystyle H}{|}}{\overset{\overset{\displaystyle H}{|}}{C}}-\underset{\underset{\displaystyle H}{|}}{\overset{\overset{\displaystyle H}{|}}{C}}-\overset{\overset{\displaystyle H}{|}}{C}=O \qquad OHC(CH_2)_2CHO$$

Succinaldehyde

$$O=\overset{\overset{\displaystyle H}{|}}{C}-\underset{\underset{\displaystyle H}{|}}{\overset{\overset{\displaystyle H}{|}}{C}}-\underset{\underset{\displaystyle H}{|}}{\overset{\overset{\displaystyle H}{|}}{C}}-\underset{\underset{\displaystyle H}{|}}{\overset{\overset{\displaystyle H}{|}}{C}}-\overset{\overset{\displaystyle H}{|}}{C}=O \qquad OHC(CH_2)_3CHO$$

Glutaraldehyde

Glutaraldehyde has been found to have the best application to embalming. Two percent activated glutaraldehyde has proved to be not only a good preservative but also an excellent germicide. In fact this compound has been described as a "cold chemical sterilant." The term "activated" refers to the addition of a sodium bicarbonate buffer which stabilizes the pH of the resulting solution at approximately 7.2. Like formalde-

hyde, glutaraldehyde operates best at this pH and exhibits the tendency to polymerize in more acidic solutions. The one drawback is that once the solution has been activated, it has an effective shelf life of only 14 days. However, this problem is circumvented by incorporating glutaraldehyde into embalming fluid in an inactive state. When this fluid is ready to be used in an embalming operation, the glutaraldehyde is activated by the addition of another chemical called a *coinjection*, which contains the buffer.

The manifestations of preservation by glutaraldehyde are quite a bit different from those of formaldehyde. Glutaraldehyde is much less astringent and dehydrating than formaldehyde. As a result, tissue preserved in this manner is not as hard as formaldehyde-treated tissue and retains much more of its original texture. An illustration of the mechanism of glutaraldehyde cross-linked protein as compared to formaldehyde cross-linked protein is given in Chapter 19.

Cyclic aldehydes

The low-molecular-weight aldehydes have harsh, irritating odors. As the molecular weight increases, the odors become more fragrant. Aromatic aldehydes are used as reodorants (perfuming agents) in embalming fluids.

Some examples are:

CHO

Benzaldehyde
(almonds)

$$CH=CH-\overset{\overset{\displaystyle H}{|}}{C}=O$$

Cinnamaldehyde
(cinnamon)

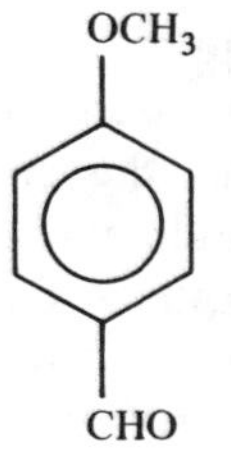

Anisaldehyde
(anise)

KETONES

Ketones are derivatives of hydrocarbons containing one or more carbonyl ($>C=O$) groups. The carbonyl group is common to both aldehydes and ketones. We may distinguish between aldehydes and ketones by the position of the CO group.

If the $C=O$ is placed at the end of a carbon chain, the compound is an aldehyde. If this group is not on the end of the chain, the compound is a ketone. For example:

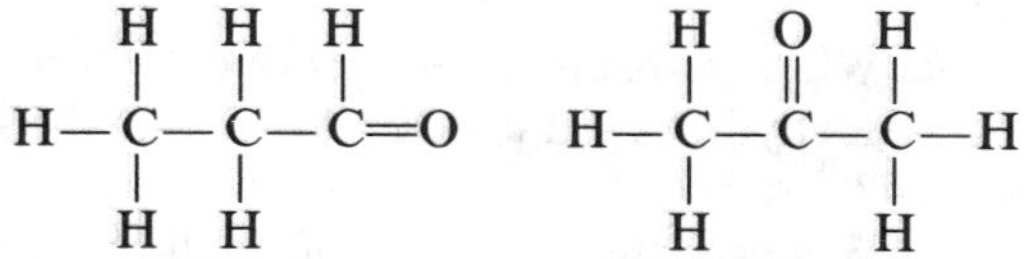

The structures are distinct. The aldehyde is expressed as CH_3CH_2CHO, while the ketone is CH_3COCH_3. However, the molecular formula for both these compounds is the same: C_3H_6O. Since isomers are defined as compounds having the same molecular formulas but different structural formulas, homologous aldehydes and ketones may be considered to be isomers of each other.

The general formula for the ketones is RCOR or RCOR'. The purpose of the R' is to indicate that one of the alkyl groups may be different from the other. There are two methods for naming the ketones. The first method names the compound according to the R or alkyl groups which are attached to the functional group:

Formula for ketone	Name of ketone
CH_3COCH_3	Dimethyl ketone
$CH_3COC_2H_5$	Methyl ethyl ketone
$C_2H_5COC_2H_5$	Diethyl ketone

Note that the name ketone reflects the name of the CO functional group and the other name represents the alkyl groups. Note also that, unlike the aldehydes, the ketones contain a *minimum* alkyl group of CH_3. If, instead, a hydrogen atom is placed in either R position of a ketone, the following occurs:

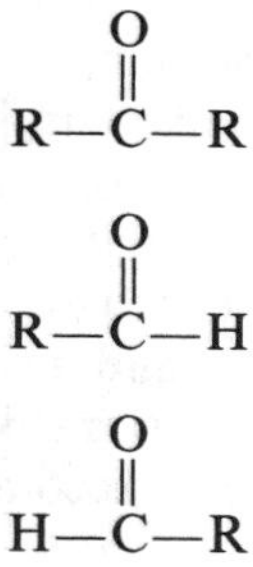

The incorrect use of a hydrogen atom in this situation results in moving the carbonyl group to the end of the carbon chain. Thus, we have produced an aldehyde instead of a ketone.

In the second method for deriving the name of a ketone, the *-e* ending of the corresponding hydrocarbon is changed to *-one*. Take note that, in this method, *all* the carbons in the compound are counted, including the one in the functional group.

Name of hydrocarbon	Name of corresponding ketone	Formula for corresponding ketone
Propane	Propanone	CH_3COCH_3
Butane	Butanone	$CH_3COC_2H_5$
Pentane	Pentanone	$C_2H_5COC_2H_5$

We saw in Chapter 14 that ketones are prepared by the oxidation of secondary alcohols. *Propanone*, CH_3COCH_3, the simplest ketone, is produced by the oxidation of isopropyl alcohol, $CH_3CHOHCH_3$. Also called *dimethyl ketone* and *acetone*, this is the most important ketone as far as the embalmer is concerned. It is an excellent solvent which will dissolve most organic substances yet is completely miscible with water. It is sometimes incorporated into embalming fluids as a solvent, but it could cause problems because it will dissolve plastic and is thereby contraindicated for use with plastic hoses or plastic machine parts. Acetone is most valuable in embalming as an external solvent for removal of road tar or bandage adhesive from the surface of the skin.

Acetone is produced in small quantities by normal body metabolism. If carbohydrate metabolism is impaired, it accumulates, and its distinctive odor can be detected on the breath. Acetone on the breath and in the urine may be indicative of diabetes mellitus, since accelerated lipid metabolism accompanies this disease.

Methyl ethyl ketone

Another commonly encountered solvent is methyl ethyl ketone. This substance may be an active ingredient in nail polish remover.

CHAPTER SUMMARY

Both monoaldehydes and dialdehydes represent the largest proportion of disinfectant-preservative chemicals currently utilized in the embalming procedure. Formaldehyde is the most widely used monoaldehyde, and glutaraldehyde is the most popular dialdehyde. Cyclic aldehydes are aromatic and are used as reodorants in embalming fluids.

Ketones, especially acetone, are used as external solvents for the removal of petroleum-based stains, such as road tar or asphalt, and bandage adhesive from the surface of the skin.

QUESTIONS

1. Define: polymerization, formalin, monoaldehyde, dialdehyde.

2. Give five physical and five chemical properties of formaldehyde.

3. State the principal reason why glyoxal is not used in arterial embalming fluids.

4. The well-known reaction between formaldehyde and ammonia suggests what practical use for ammonia in mortuary practice?

5. What substance is produced when formaldehyde is oxidized? When it is reduced?

6. What is the function of each of the following in embalming fluids: formaldehyde, glutaraldehyde, benzaldehyde, acetone.

7. What substance is produced when glutaraldehyde is oxidized? When it is reduced?

8. How does the presence of an excess concentration of nitrogen interfere with the embalming operation?

Chapters 14 and 15 showed the structural relationships among alcohols, aldehydes, and acids. This chapter not only completes that sequence but also ties in the concept of neutralization. Organic salts, the neutralization products of carboxylic acids, function as buffers, water-conditioning agents, and anticoagulants in embalming fluids. The formation of esters illustrates another aspect of neutralization. Esters are used in embalming fluids as perfuming or masking agents for the less-pleasant odors of the alcohols and aldehydes.

STRUCTURE OF ORGANIC ACIDS

Organic acids are compounds containing one or more —COOH groups. This functional group is called a *carboxyl* group because it is

general formula for the acids is usually abbreviated RCOOH. The organic acids are classified according to the number of carboxyl groups they contain.

MONOCARBOXYLIC ACIDS

These compounds contain one —COOH group. This class of acids is also known as *fatty acids*, since they occur naturally in fats and oils.

Two general methods are used in naming these acids.

1. In deriving the name for a certain acid, the *-e* ending of the corresponding hydrocarbon is changed to *-oic*. This is shown in Table 16-1.

Like the aldehydes, the organic acids contain a carbon atom in their functional group.

Chapter 16
CARBOXYLIC ACIDS AND ESTERS

a combination of the carbonyl, CO, and hydroxyl, —OH, groups on the same carbon atom:

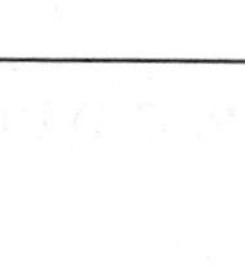

$$-C\overset{\displaystyle O}{\underset{\displaystyle OH}{\big\langle}}$$

The organic acids are derivatives of the hydrocarbons in which a —CH$_3$ group has been replaced by a —COOH group. The

Since there is only one R group, only a hydrogen atom is required in order to generate the formula for the simplest of the monocarboxylic acids, methanoic acid. Also like the aldehydes, the acids are not named according to the scheme of alkyl group–functional group. Once again caution should be exercised in counting all the carbons in the chain, including the one in the functional group, before attempting to name the compound. A common error in naming

Table 16-1 Derivation of carboxylic acids from hydrocarbons

Name of hydrocarbon	Name of corresponding acid	Formula for corresponding acid
Methane	Methanoic acid	HCOOH
Ethane	Ethanoic acid	CH_3COOH
Propane	Propanoic acid	CH_3CH_2COOH
Butane	Butanoic acid	$CH_3CH_2CH_2COOH$

carboxylic acids is naming CH_3COOH as "methanoic acid" instead of the correct name *ethanoic acid*. The reason for this error is seeing

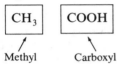

Methyl   Carboxyl

and not double checking the *total* number of carbon atoms in the compound.

2. The second method of naming the aliphatic monocarboxylic acids, which have been known for a long time, makes use of common names that refer to their sources rather than to their chemical structures. Table 16-2 shows the names of the first five members of the series.

Two important monocarboxylic acids are formic and acetic.

Table 16-2 Common names of some carboxylic acids

Systematic name	Common name	Origin
Methanoic acid	Formic acid	L. *formica*, "ant"
Ethanoic acid	Acetic acid	L. *acetum*, "vinegar"
Propanoic acid	Propionic acid	G. *proto*, "first"; *pion*, "fat"
Butanoic acid	Butyric acid	L. *butyrum*, "butter"
Pentanoic acid	Valeric acid	L. *valeo*, "strong"

Formic (methanoic) acid

$$HCOOH \qquad H-\overset{\displaystyle O}{\overset{\displaystyle \|}{C}}-OH$$

Formic is the strongest of the monocarboxylic acids. It is a colorless liquid with a pungent odor and it has a blistering effect on the skin. This simple acid is the active irritant in the defensive secretions of ants, bees, and other insects. Chemically it is an excellent reducing agent and is used in the synthesis of many organic compounds.

Acetic (ethanoic) acid

$$CH_3COOH \qquad H-\overset{\displaystyle H}{\underset{\displaystyle H}{\overset{\displaystyle |}{\underset{\displaystyle |}{C}}}}-\overset{\displaystyle O}{\overset{\displaystyle \|}{C}}-OH$$

Acetic acid gives vinegar its characteristic sharp odor and taste. However, vinegar is a relatively dilute solution (about 4% to 6%) of acetic acid. Pure (99.5%) acetic acid is called *glacial acetic*, since it is sometimes frozen at room temperature into a glasslike solid.

ACIDIC NATURE OF THE CARBOXYLIC ACIDS

Why are these organic compounds called acids? In an aqueous solution they dissociate and form hydrogen ions and a negative ion. Consider the reaction of acetic acid and water:

$$CH_3\overset{\displaystyle O}{\overset{\displaystyle \|}{C}}OH + H_2O \rightleftarrows H_3O^+ + CH_3\overset{\displaystyle O}{\overset{\displaystyle \|}{C}}O^-$$

The hydrogen ion from the acid is transferred to water, producing the hydronium ion and the acetate ion. Since the reaction has increased the hydrogen-ion concentration (really hydronium-ion concentration) of the water, $CH_3\overset{\displaystyle O}{\overset{\displaystyle \|}{C}}OH$ is an acid. By studying the equation for the acidic behavior of acetic acid, we see two facts. First, the acidic hydrogen in these acids is the one in the carboxyl group. Owing to the electronegativity of the two oxygen atoms in the carboxyl group, the electrons in the bond between the oxygen and hydrogen atoms are pulled away from the hydrogen in the direction of the oxygens. This unequal electron distribution between oxygen and hydrogen makes it possible for the polar water molecule to pull the hydrogen as a positive ion away from the carboxyl group. The other hydrogens in the molecule do not undergo the same process because there is essentially an equal sharing of electrons between carbon and hydrogen atoms. The other fact shown by the equation for the ionization of acetic acid is that acetic acid and the other carboxylic acids are weak acids. The double arrow in the equation signifies the partial ionization of these acids.

ORGANIC SALTS

Carboxylic acids undergo the typical reactions of acids that were discussed in Chapter 10. The most important of these is neutralization:

$$carboxylic\ acid + base \longrightarrow salt + HOH$$

When carboxylic acids are neutralized to salts, the hydrogen atom in the COOH group is replaced by a metal. The name of the salt is derived by changing the -ic ending of the acid to -ate preceded by the name of the metal which replaced the hydrogen. Thus, if form*ic* acid is neutralized by *sodium* hydroxide, the salt produced is named *sodium* for*mate*:

$$HCOOH + NaOH \longrightarrow HCOONa + HOH$$

Likewise, neutralization of acetic acid by sodium hydroxide produces sodium acetate, CH_3COONa. Note that the naming of these compounds follows the conventional rule for naming salts.

DICARBOXYLIC ACIDS

Organic acids containing two —COOH groups are called *dicarboxylic acids*. Their structures are analogous to the dialdehydes, which are named as their reduction products. The simplest of this series is oxalic acid, $(COOH)_2$:

$$\overset{\displaystyle O \quad\ \ O}{\underset{}{\overset{\|\quad\ \|}{HO—C—C—OH}}}$$

Like the dialdehydes, this series is generated by interposing methylene (CH_2) groups between the terminal functional (—COOH) groups. Table 16-3 lists the names and formulas of the first four members of the series.

Table 16-3 Dicarboxylic acids

Oxalic acid	HOOC–COOH
Malonic acid	$HOOC–CH_2–COOH$
Succinic acid	$HOOC–(CH_2)_2–COOH$
Glutaric acid	$HOOC–(CH_2)_3–COOH$

Anticoagulants

All carboxylic acids will react with inorganic bases to form salts which are ionic compounds. The sodium, potassium, and ammonium salts of all carboxylic acids are water soluble.

$$\overset{\displaystyle O \quad\ \ O}{\underset{\text{Oxalic acid}}{\overset{\|\quad\ \|}{HO—C—C—OH}}} + 2\ NaOH \longrightarrow$$

$$\overset{\displaystyle O \quad\ \ O}{\underset{\text{Sodium oxalate}}{\overset{\|\quad\ \|}{NaO—C—C—ONa}}} + 2\ H_2O$$

The dicarboxylic acids are singled out for this neutralization study because of the historical role of oxalates as blood anticoagulating agents or water-softening agents in embalming fluids. Remember that the neutralization of an organic acid involves the replacement of the hydrogen atom in the (—COOH) carboxyl group. The anticoagulants referred to previously are:

- ○ Sodium oxalate $Na_2C_2O_4$
- ○ Potassium oxalate $K_2C_2O_4$
- ○ Ammonium oxalate $(NH_4)_2C_2O_4$

These substances function in the following manner. The oxalates react with the ionized calcium in the blood, forming insoluble calcium oxalate. The removal of the calcium ions prevents the initiation of the blood-clotting process. The conversion of these soluble salts of a dicarboxylic acid to an insoluble substance gives rise to the embalming classification of this group of substances as *precipitant anticoagulants*. The mechanisms of this conversion may be illustrated as follows:

$$
Na-O-\overset{\overset{O}{\|}}{C}-\overset{\overset{O}{\|}}{C}-O-Na + Ca^{++} \longrightarrow
$$

$$
\underset{O-Ca-O}{\overset{\overset{O}{\|}}{C}\rule{2cm}{0.4pt}\overset{\overset{O}{\|}}{C}} + 2\,Na^+
$$

Oxalic acid is a poisonous vegetable acid originally obtained from a plant known as the "wood sorrel" and naturally occurring in rhubarb leaves. Lavoisier derived the name for this acid from the Latin word *oxalis*, which designated the sorrel plant. *Oxalis* in turn comes from the Greek word *oxys*, meaning "sour" or "acid." The plant was so named because of its sour, acidlike taste.[1] Calcium oxalate takes the form of cubic crystals which are insoluble in water. Small quantities of this salt are present in the urine.

As indicated previously, oxalates are primarily of historical interest as anticoagulants in embalming fluids. Owing to their toxic nature, the use of these substances has been discontinued. However, the illustration of the mechanism is an important step toward the understanding of the more complex anticoagulant mechanism designated in embalming terminology as a *sequesterant anticoagulant*.

HYDROXY ACIDS

Sequentially, the next acids to be considered should be tricarboxylic. However, in the system of chemical nomenclature, when a hydroxyl (OH) group appears in addition to the carboxyl group (COOH), the OH group takes precedence. Thus, citric acid, $C_3H_4OH(COOH)_3$, is classified as a *hydroxy acid*. Nonetheless, it is still referred to as a *tricarboxylic acid*. In fact, an important metabolic cycle, essential for the oxidation of all nutrients, contains citric acid as an intermediate. One name for this sequence of reactions is the *Krebs cycle*. Another name is the *tri-carboxylic acid (TCA) cycle*. However, our interest lies in the anticoagulant properties of the salts of this acid. The name *citric* comes from *citrus*, a name given to a group of fruit trees including the lemon, lime, orange, and citron. The name *citrus* or *citron* is from the Latin and is believed to stem from either the Greek word *kedros* or cedar or the name of the city of Citron in ancient Judea.[2]

The salts in question are

- ○ Sodium citrate
  $C_3H_4OH(COONa)_3$
- ○ Potassium citrate
  $C_3H_4OH(COOK)_3$

---

[1] Harry Wain, *The Story Behind the Word*, 1958. Courtesy of Charles C Thomas, Publisher, Springfield, Illinois.

[2] *Ibid.*

These substances function as anticoagulants for blood in a different manner than the oxalates. Let us first consider the structure of citric acid: $C_3H_4OH(COOH)_3$.

$$
\begin{array}{c}
\text{H} \\
| \\
\text{H} - \text{C} - \text{COOH} \\
| \\
\text{HO} - \text{C} - \text{COOH} \\
| \\
\text{H} - \text{C} - \text{COOH} \\
| \\
\text{H}
\end{array}
$$

Remember that the neutralization of an organic acid involves the replacement of the hydrogen in the COOH group with a metal. Therefore, the structure of sodium citrate, $C_3H_4OH(COONa)_3$, is

$$
\begin{array}{c}
\text{H} \\
| \\
\text{H} - \text{C} - \text{COONa} \\
| \\
\text{HO} - \text{C} - \text{COONa} \\
| \\
\text{H} - \text{C} - \text{COONa} \\
| \\
\text{H}
\end{array}
$$

These two structures are actually abbreviations, since by definition both oxygen atoms in the carboxyl group are attached to the carbon atom. A more accurate illustration is

$$
\begin{array}{c}
\text{H} \quad \text{O} \\
| \quad\; \parallel \\
\text{H} - \text{C} - \text{C} - \text{O} - \text{Na} \\
| \\
\text{O} \\
\parallel \\
\text{HO} - \text{C} - \text{C} - \text{O} - \text{Na} \\
| \\
\text{O} \\
\parallel \\
\text{H} - \text{C} - \text{C} - \text{O} - \text{Na} \\
| \\
\text{H}
\end{array}
$$

The calcium citrate complex that results from the reaction of sodium citrate with the ionized calcium is

$$
\begin{array}{c}
\text{H} \quad \text{O} \qquad\qquad \text{O} \quad \text{H} \\
| \quad\; \parallel \qquad\qquad\; \parallel \quad\; | \\
\text{H} - \text{C} - \text{C} - \text{O} - \text{Ca} - \text{O} - \text{C} - \text{C} - \text{H} \\
| \qquad\qquad\qquad\qquad\quad | \\
\text{O} \qquad\qquad\qquad\quad \text{O} \\
\parallel \qquad\qquad\qquad\quad\; \parallel \\
\text{HO} - \text{C} - \text{C} - \text{O} - \text{Ca} - \text{O} - \text{C} - \text{C} - \text{OH} \\
| \qquad\qquad\qquad\qquad\quad | \\
\text{O} \qquad\qquad\qquad\quad \text{O} \\
\parallel \qquad\qquad\qquad\quad\; \parallel \\
\text{H} - \text{C} - \text{C} - \text{O} - \text{Ca} - \text{O} - \text{C} - \text{C} - \text{H} \\
| \qquad\qquad\qquad\qquad\quad | \\
\text{H} \qquad\qquad\qquad\qquad \text{H}
\end{array}
$$

Sodium is a monovalent metal, but calcium is divalent. The calcium ions cross-link two molecules of sodium citrate to form this complex. The ionized calcium is tied up and effectively "fenced off"; hence, the term *sequesterant anticoagulant* from the Latin *sequestrum* meaning a depository. Calcium citrate is water soluble but it is a nonionizable complex. In other words, it suppresses the ionization of the calcium.

Citrate anticoagulants are not toxic, but they too are falling into disfavor. Some common bacteria such as *Staphylococcus aureus* produce a series of enzymes called the coagulase factor. The coagulase enzymes demonstrate their properties best in the presence of citrated blood plasma. The end result is a short-cut of the blood-clotting process by converting the soluble precursor fibrinogen into the insoluble fibrin. What this means to the embalmer is that in any case where these bacterially produced exzymes may be present, citrated embalming fluid may actually enhance blood clotting instead of inhibiting it. Thus, blood drainage will be greatly impaired and the entire process will be counterproductive.

CHELATES

Because of the problems inherent in the two previously mentioned anticoagulants, the commercial embalming chemical manufacturers have largely replaced them with other sequesterants called *chelates*. Chelates, from the Greek for *claw-like*, are substances that bind metallic ions. The most commonly used agent of this type in embalming fluid is EDTA (ethylenediaminetetraacetic acid). However, as in the case of the other anti-coagulants, the sodium salt is used rather than the acid itself.

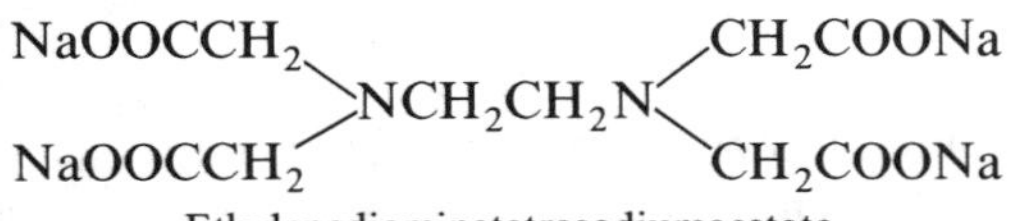

$$NaOOCCH_2 \diagdown \qquad \diagup CH_2COONa$$
$$NCH_2CH_2N$$
$$NaOOCCH_2 \diagup \qquad \diagdown CH_2COONa$$

Ethylenediaminetetrasodiumacetate

The name is the most complex encountered thus far. Breaking it down reveals an inventory of the contents of the compound.

Ethylene	CH_2CH_2
(Note: *no* double bond)	
Di	2
Amine	N
Tetra	4
Sodium acetate	CH_2COONa

The resulting calcium complex may be illustrated as follows:

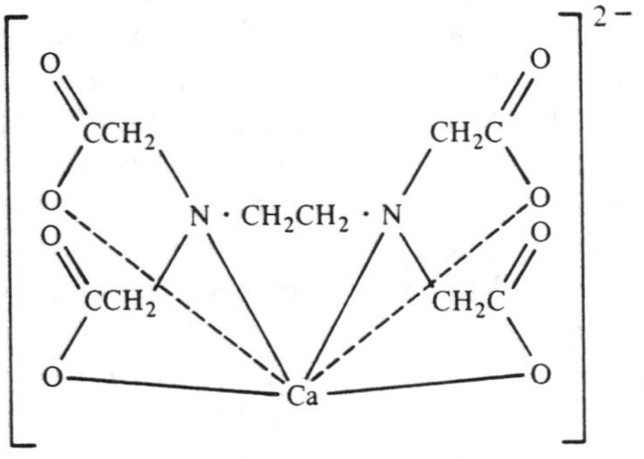

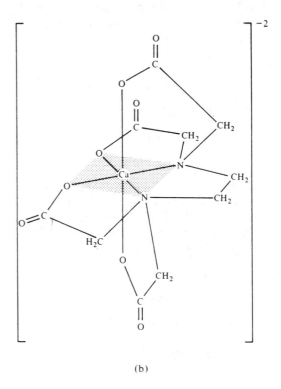

(a)

A more three-dimensional representation is:

(b)

One gram of the tetrasodium salt complexes 201 mg $CaCO_3$. It is an excellent sequestering agent and is not limited by the factors that were detrimental to the previously discussed anticoagulants.

LACTIC ACID

Lactic acid is an important monocarboxylic hydroxy acid so named because it was originally isolated from sour milk. It is produced by the action of *Lactobacillus* bacteria on the milk sugar lactose. All these words are derived from the Latin *lac* or *lactis* meaning milk. These words in turn came from a shortening of the Greek word for milk, *galaktos*.

Lactic acid is formed in the body as an intermediate product in carbohydrate metabolism and is produced by muscle metabolism. Blood lactate levels rise after strenuous exercise and the stiff, sore feelings of muscles as the result of such activity are associated with elevated levels of this compound. It follows naturally, then, that the first theories attempting to explain the onset of rigor mortis centered on the formation of lactic acid. Rigor mortis is a period of muscular rigidity which commonly occurs in dead bodies. It was originally believed that this phenomenon was produced by the action of lactic acid, causing the coagulation of the muscle plasma. This was supposedly brought about by the reaction of lactic acid ($CH_3CHOHCOOH$) with a soluble protein in muscle tissue known as myosinogen. This action converts myosinogen into myosin, which is insoluble. With the conversion of the soluble myosinogen into the insoluble myosin, rigor is complete. This change can be illustrated as follows:

$$\text{myosinogen} + \text{lactic acid} \longrightarrow$$
$$\text{myosin (coagulated protein)}$$

As decomposition proceeds, myosin is readily hydrolyzed by the enzymes present in the tissues as well as those produced by bacterial action. As the myosin is hydrolyzed with the production of amino acids and various intermediate products, rigor passes off. The failure of the embalmer to reestablish the desired firmness during the embalming operation may be due to a lack of these decomposition products to coagulate when treated with formaldehyde.

This theory has largely been supplanted by a more contemporary one. However, in order to fully explain the more current theories, we must understand a great deal more about carbohydrate metabolism. This will be covered in Chapter 21.

ESTERS

Esters are fragrant organic compounds formed by the reaction of an organic acid with an alcohol. The general formula for an ester is
$$R-\overset{\displaystyle O}{\overset{\displaystyle \|}{C}}-O-R' \text{ or } RCOOR'.$$
Consider the following:

$$R-\overset{\displaystyle O}{\overset{\displaystyle \|}{C}}-OH + R'-OH \longrightarrow$$

$$R-\overset{\displaystyle O}{\overset{\displaystyle \|}{C}}-O-R' + HOH$$

Substituting a hydrogen atom for the R and a methyl (CH_3) group for the R' produces

$$H-\overset{\displaystyle O}{\overset{\displaystyle \|}{C}}-OH + H-\overset{\displaystyle H}{\underset{\displaystyle H}{\overset{\displaystyle |}{\underset{\displaystyle |}{C}}}}-OH \longrightarrow$$

$$H-\overset{\displaystyle O}{\overset{\displaystyle \|}{C}}-O-\overset{\displaystyle H}{\underset{\displaystyle H}{\overset{\displaystyle |}{\underset{\displaystyle |}{C}}}}-H + HOH$$

Naming the esters is analogous to naming the salts of carboxylic acids. Consider the previously written esterification reaction between formic acid and methyl alcohol. The name of the product is methyl formate.

$$H-\overset{\displaystyle O}{\overset{\displaystyle \|}{C}}-O-\overset{\displaystyle H}{\underset{\displaystyle H}{\overset{\displaystyle |}{\underset{\displaystyle |}{C}}}}-H$$

Methyl formate

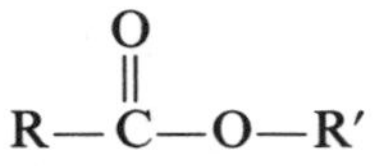

$$\underset{\text{O}}{\overset{\overset{\displaystyle\text{O}}{\|}}{\text{R}-\text{C}-\text{O}-\text{R}'}}$$

The R' alkyl group is named first, then the rest of the compound is named as if it were a neutralized monocarboxylic acid. Note that the R' *must* be a minimum of a methyl (CH_3) group. If, instead, a hydrogen atom is placed in the R' position, the following compound will result:

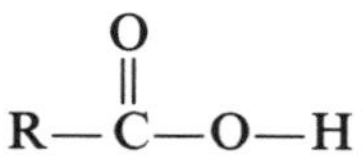

$$\underset{\text{O}}{\overset{\overset{\displaystyle\text{O}}{\|}}{\text{R}-\text{C}-\text{O}-\text{H}}}$$

We have now regenerated the carboxyl (COOH) group. That is why the concept of neutralization is essential to understanding the naming of esters. By way of contrast, however, the R group on the left side of the compound *may* be a minimum of a hydrogen atom. Thus, $HCOOCH_3$ (methyl formate) is the simplest ester. Substituting successive methyl groups for the R and the R' produces the next members of the series. Thus:

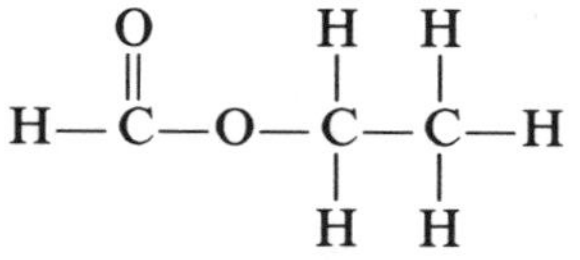

Ethyl formate

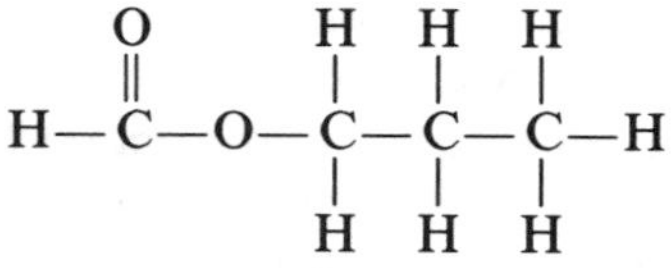

Propyl formate

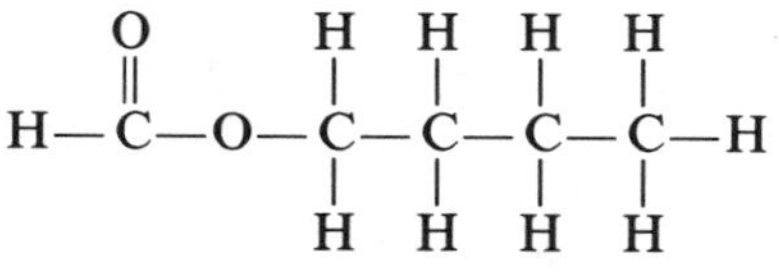

Butyl formate

are all produced by lengthening the carbon chain on the R' side and

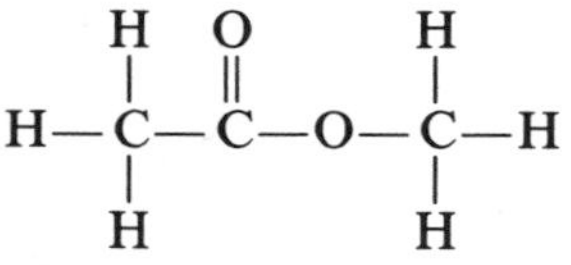

Methyl acetate

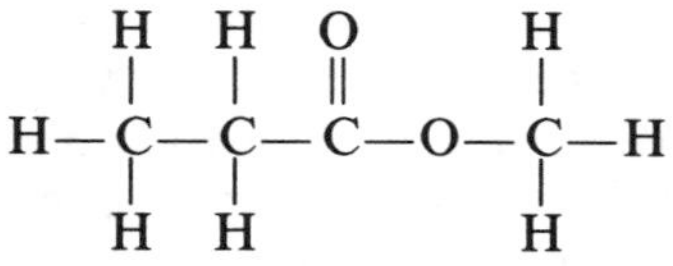

Methyl propionate

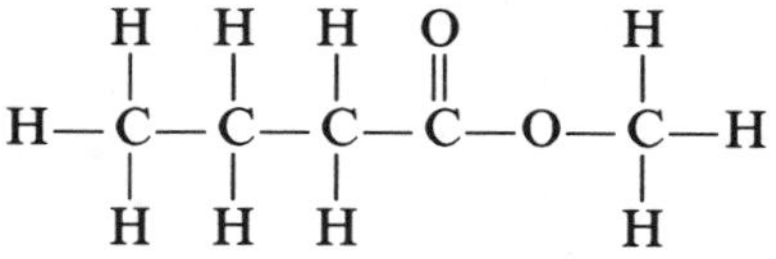

Methyl butyrate

are all produced by lengthening the carbon chain on the R side. Note that the acids have the common names rather than the systematic ones.

Esters are pleasant-smelling substances and are responsible for the fragrances of many flowers, flavors, fruits and perfumes. Table 16-4 lists some common esters.

Esters are used in embalming fluids as reodorants or masking agents. These perfuming substances should not be confused with deodorants, which react chemically with odors and actually neutralize or destroy them instead of merely covering them up. Some reodorants used in embalming were discussed in Chapter 15. Some others will be covered later on, since they represent a combination of two or more of the functional groups. The principal ester used for this purpose is methyl salicylate, commonly known as oil of wintergreen. This substance is produced by reacting methyl alcohol with salicylic acid. Like so many other acids, it is named for its source. The Latin word *salix*

Table 16-4   Structures and fragrances of esters

Ester	Structure	Fragrance
Ethyl formate	$\overset{\displaystyle O}{\overset{\|}{H-C}}-O-C_2H_5$	Rum
Isobutyl formate	$\overset{\displaystyle O}{\overset{\|}{H-C}}-O-CH_2\overset{\displaystyle CH_3}{\overset{\|}{CH}}-CH_3$	Raspberry
Ethyl butyrate	$C_3H_7-\overset{\displaystyle O}{\overset{\|}{C}}-O-C_2H_5$	Pineapple
Pentyl acetate	$CH_3-\overset{\displaystyle O}{\overset{\|}{C}}-O-C_5H_{11}$	Banana
Isopentyl acetate	$CH_3-\overset{\displaystyle O}{\overset{\|}{C}}-O-(CH_2)_2CH\overset{\displaystyle CH_3}{\underset{\displaystyle CH_3}{<}}$	Pear
Pentyl butyrate	$C_3H_7-\overset{\displaystyle O}{\overset{\|}{C}}-O-C_5H_{11}$	Apricot
Isopentyl valerate	$C_4H_9-\overset{\displaystyle O}{\overset{\|}{C}}-O-(CH_2)_2CH\overset{\displaystyle CH_3}{\underset{\displaystyle CH_3}{<}}$	Apple
Octyl acetate	$CH_3-\overset{\displaystyle O}{\overset{\|}{C}}-O-C_8H_{17}$	Orange

means "willow." The fever-reducing properties of willow bark have been known since the fifth century B.C. However, it was not until 1838 that the active ingredient, salicylic acid, was isolated and identified. Structurally salicylic acid contains a carboxyl group attached to phenol.

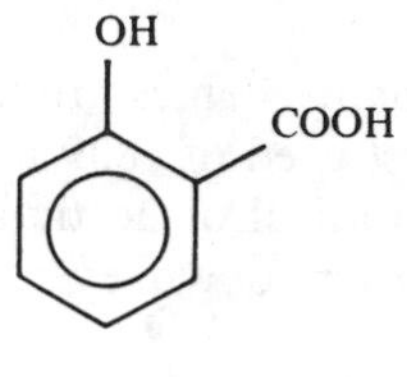

Salicylic acid

The reaction for the formation of methyl salicylate is

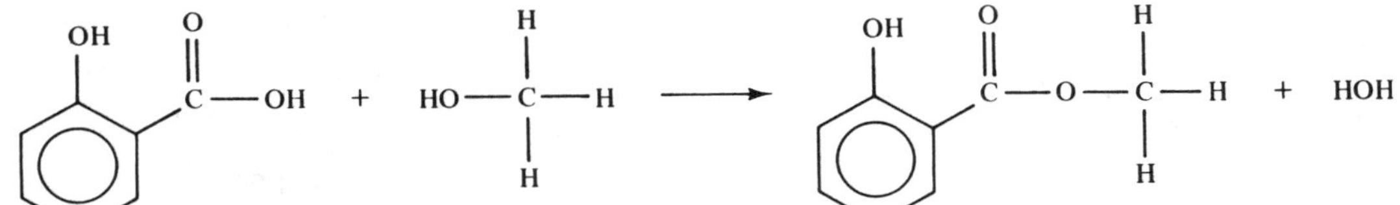

Salicylic acid   Methyl alcohol   Methyl salicylate   Water

Since salicylic acid also contains an alcohol group, it is possible to react it with the carboxyl group of another acid. The reaction of salicylic acid with acetic acid forms one of the most widely used pain killers in the world (which you may be ready for at this point):

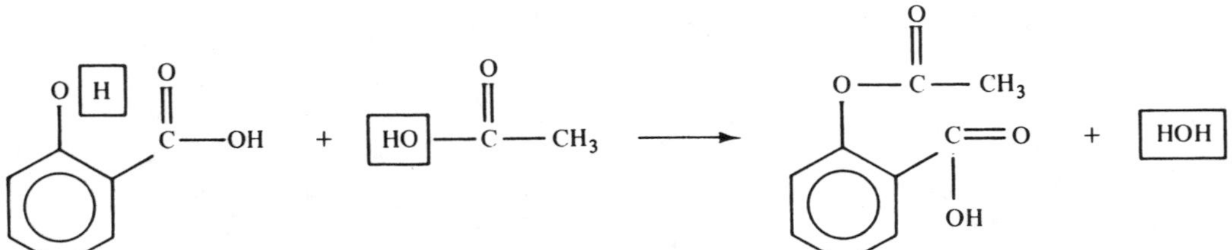

Salicylic acid   Acetic acid   Acetylsalicylic acid   Water
                                            (aspirin)

This process further emphasizes the principle that when the reacting constituents of water (H^+ and OH^-) are brought into close proximity, water will be formed. The acetyl portion of the name comes from $-\overset{\overset{\text{O}}{\|}}{C}-CH_3$, which was first used in 1839 to designate the hypothetical radical of acetic acid. Breaking this acetyl group down even farther yields the acyl group $R-\overset{\overset{\text{O}}{\|}}{C}-$, which remains largely unchanged and serves as a transfer mechanism in many biological reactions.

THIOESTERS

All the previously discussed esters have been oxyesters. In thioesters, the oxygen that is single-bonded to the carbon is replaced by sulfur.

$$\text{RCOOR}' \quad \underset{\text{Oxyester}}{R-\overset{\overset{\text{O}}{\|}}{C}-O-R'}$$

$$\underset{\text{Thioester}}{RCOSR' \quad R-\overset{\overset{\displaystyle O}{\|}}{C}-S-R'}$$

When a thioester is prepared, a thiol is reacted with the acid instead of an alcohol.

$$R-\overset{\overset{\displaystyle O}{\|}}{C}-OH + R-S-H \longrightarrow$$

$$\underset{\text{Acid}}{} \qquad \underset{\text{Thiol}}{}$$

$$\underset{\text{Thioester}}{R-\overset{\overset{\displaystyle O}{\|}}{C}-SR} + \underset{\text{Water}}{HOH}$$

Some thioesters are biologically important. They transfer acyl groups (discussed in the previous section) during the metabolic reactions of carbohydrates, fatty acids, and amino acids. The most important acyl transfer agent in living organisms is *acetyl coenzyme A*. This compound is the ester of acetic acid and coenzyme A, a thiol.

$$H-\overset{\overset{\displaystyle H}{|}}{\underset{\underset{\displaystyle H}{|}}{C}}-\overset{\overset{\displaystyle O}{\|}}{C}-OH + HSCoA \longrightarrow$$

$$\underset{\text{Acetic acid}}{} \qquad \underset{\text{Coenzyme A}}{}$$

$$H-\overset{\overset{\displaystyle H}{|}}{\underset{\underset{\displaystyle H}{|}}{C}}-\overset{\overset{\displaystyle O}{\|}}{C}-SCoA + HOH$$

$$\underset{\text{Acetyl coenzyme A}}{} \qquad \underset{\text{Water}}{}$$

Esterification is the basis for a number of other biologically significant reactions, which will be discussed in Chapter 22.

CHAPTER SUMMARY

The primary application of carboxylic acids to embalming involves their neutralization products. These organic salts, especially those derived from the di- and polycarboxylic acids, function as anticoagulants. Oxalates act as precipitant anticoagulants, whereas citrates and the salts of the higher polycarboxylic acids act as sequesterant anticoagulants. Organic salts are formed by neutralization of organic acids with inorganic alkalis (bases). Esters result from another type of neutralization in which water forms due to reaction of the alcohol functional group and the carboxyl functional group. Esters have pleasant aromas and are used as reodorants in embalming fluids.

QUESTIONS

1. Why is the functional group of the organic acids called the carboxyl group?

2. Give two names for the following monocarboxylic acid: C_4H_9COOH.

3. Why are organic acids generally considered to be weaker than most inorganic acids?

4. What is the difference between a precipitant and a sequesterant anticoagulant?

5. What is a chelate?

6. What is the association between lactic acid and the production of rigor mortis?

7. Why is ester formation considered to be a neutralization reaction

8. What is an organic salt?

9. What is the function of esters in embalming fluids?

10. What is the difference between an oxyester and a thioester?

Organic chemistry has been defined as the study of certain carbon compounds. The other elements involved in the composition of these substances are hydrogen, oxygen, and nitrogen. The last five chapters have illustrated combinations of carbon, hydrogen, and oxygen, but not nitrogen. This chapter introduces nitrogen as a keystone to the structure of protein. This allows us to bridge naturally to biochemistry, the subject of the third section of this text.

AMINES

Amines are organic derivatives of ammonia in which one or more of the three hydrogens of NH_3 have been replaced by alkyl (R) or

$$R—\underset{\underset{H}{|}}{N}—R \qquad R—\underset{\underset{R}{|}}{N}—R$$

Secondary amine   Tertiary amine

Simple amines are named by naming the alkyl group attached to the nitrogen atom followed by the word amine. Thus methyl amine,

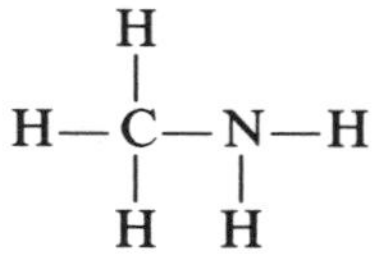

$$H—\underset{\underset{H}{|}}{\overset{\overset{H}{|}}{C}}—\underset{\underset{H}{|}}{N}—H$$

is the simplest of the primary amines. Note that a minimum of one methyl (CH_3) group is necessary; otherwise we still have the derivative substance, ammonia (NH_3).
Continuing with this scheme:

Chapter 17
AMINES AND AMIDES

aromatic groups. As a result, like the alcohols, amines may be designated as primary, secondary, or tertiary according to the position of attachment of the nitrogen.

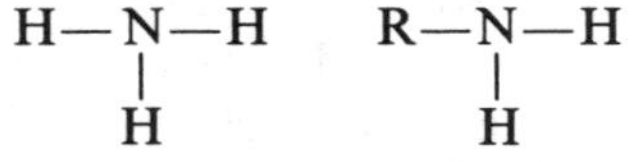

$$H—\underset{\underset{H}{|}}{N}—H \qquad R—\underset{\underset{H}{|}}{N}—H$$

Ammonia   Primary amine

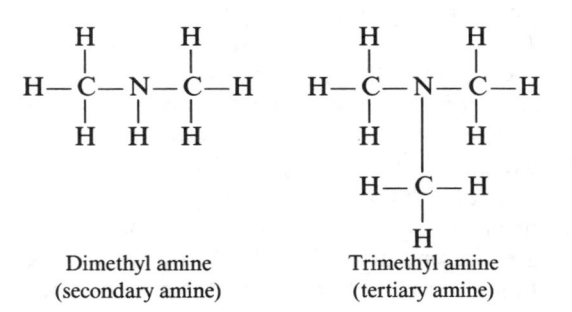

Dimethyl amine
(secondary amine)

Trimethyl amine
(tertiary amine)

Some confusion may occur here, because the terms primary, secondary, and tertiary mean something quite different than when they are applied to the alcohols. Compare a secondary alcohol with a secondary amine.

H   H   H
| | |
H—C—C—C—H
| | |
H   OH H

Isopropyl alcohol
(a secondary alcohol)

H   H   H
| | |
H—C—N—C—C—H
| | | |
H   H   H   H

Methyl ethyl amine
(a secondary amine)

In alcohols this term refers to the number of carbon atoms attached to the *carbon* atom that bears the hydroxyl functional group. In amines the term refers to the number of carbon atoms attached directly to the nitrogen atom.

The functional group for the primary amines is —NH_2 and the general formula is R—NH_2. Amines are characterized by a strong fishlike odor and are produced as decomposition products of proteins and other nitrogenous animal and plant substances. These substances, in embalming terminology, are referred to as *intermediate products of decomposition* and are commonly called *ptomaines*. The word comes from the Greek word *ptoma*, meaning "corpse." It is a very general term used to describe any alkaline product of putrefaction. These substances are present in spoiled food and were once thought to be responsible for the diarrhea and vomiting associated with food poisoning

or food infection. Although the term "ptomaine poisoning" is still commonly used, it is a misnomer. What is overlooked is the fact that food-related diseases are caused by the direct or indirect action of microorganisms contaminating the food rather than the normal decomposition products of the food. Consider the fact that in many areas "aged" beef is considered a delicacy. Ptomaine poisoning does not seem to accompany these gourmet delights, although ptomaines are surely present. Some of the more commonly occurring ptomaines are putrescine and cadaverine. Both of these compounds are diamines, and their colorful names conjure up in our minds more than just a hint of how they smell.

H   H   H   H   H   H
| | | | | |
N—C—C—C—C—N $H_2N(CH_2)_4NH_2$
| | | | | |
H   H   H   H   H   H

Putrescine
(1,4-Diaminobutane)

H   H   H   H   H   H   H
| | | | | | |
N—C—C—C—C—C—N $H_2N(CH_2)_5NH_2$
| | | | | | |
H   H   H   H   H   H   H

Cadaverine
(1,5-Diaminopentane)

REACTIONS OF AMINES

Both ammonia and its derivative substances, the amines, are basic because of the presence of an unshared pair of electrons. Nitrogen has five valence electrons, as shown by its electronic configuration of $1s^2 2s^2 2p^3$. In ammonia, one nitrogen is bonded to three atoms of hydrogen. Each of these atoms has one valence electron. The Lewis structure of ammonia is

$$\begin{array}{c} \times\ \times \\ \text{HO} \times \text{N} \times \text{OH} \\ \times \\ \text{O} \\ \text{H} \end{array}$$

In this compound nitrogen has eight electrons and each hydrogen has two, so by the covalent bonding process they are "happy." Owing to the unshared pair of electrons on the nitrogen, ammonia reacts as a Lewis base. (See Chapter 10.) Nitrogen can share these electrons with electron-deficient atoms and participate in Lewis acid–Lewis base reactions. In an amine, there is also an unshared pair of electrons on the nitrogen. Therefore, amines also are classified as Lewis bases.

Amines rather than alcohols are considered to be the organic equivalent of a base. The previous chapter dealt with some of the neutralization products of carboxylic acids, such as organic salts and esters. Since neutralization is a chemical property of bases as well as acids, we will now consider a number of their products.

Amides

When amines react with carboxylic acids, the products formed are water and an ammonium salt called an amide.

$$\begin{array}{cccc} \text{O} & & \text{H} & \text{H} \\ \| & & | & | \\ \text{H}-\text{C}-\text{OH} & + & \text{H}-\text{C}-\text{N} & \longrightarrow \\ & & | & | \\ & & \text{H} & \text{H} \end{array}$$

Formic acid   Methyl amine

$$\begin{array}{ccc} \text{O} & \text{H} & \text{H} \\ \| & | & | \\ \text{H}-\text{C}-\text{N}-\text{C}-\text{H} & + & \text{H}_2\text{O} \\ & | & \\ & \text{H} & \end{array}$$

Amide   Water

This is no different than other neutralization reactions that we have discussed previously, since neutralization essentially involves

$$\text{acid} + \text{base} \longrightarrow \text{salt} + \text{water}$$

Substituting reactants and products yields

$$\text{carboxylic acid} + \text{amine} \longrightarrow$$
$$\text{amide} + \text{water}$$

As we have seen, the driving force behind this reaction is the formation of water. Remember whenever the reacting constituents of water (H^+ and OH^-) are placed in close proximity, water will be formed.

Amides are named in a similar manner to organic salts. The suffix -amide replaces the -ic name ending of the acids in the same way that the suffix -ate did when organic salts were formed. Thus:

$$\begin{array}{ccc} \text{O} & \text{H} & \text{H} \\ \| & | & | \\ \text{H}-\text{C}-\text{N}-\text{C}-\text{H} \\ & & | \\ & & \text{H} \end{array}$$

is named methyl formamide and

$$\begin{array}{ccccc} \text{H} & \text{O} & \text{H} & \text{H} & \text{H} \\ | & \| & | & | & | \\ \text{H}-\text{C}-\text{C}-\text{N}-\text{C}-\text{C}-\text{H} \\ | & & | & | & \\ \text{H} & & \text{H} & \text{H} \end{array}$$

is named ethyl acetamide. Understanding this reaction is the first step in gaining familiarity with proteins, the primary focus of embalming. Proteins are polymers of amino acids. Amines and carboxylic acids are the constituents of amino acids.

Urea

When urea was synthesized by Wöhler, the vitalistic theory of organic substances ended. Urea is the diamide of carbonic acid (H_2CO_3).

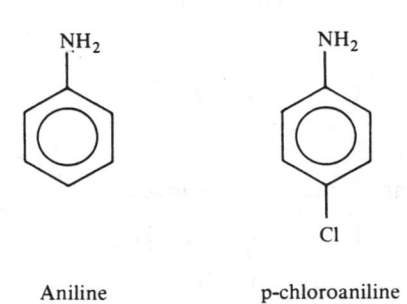

Urea is a waste product of human protein metabolism secreted into the blood by the liver and selectively absorbed and excreted into the urine by the kidneys. The embalming complications related to uremic poisoning were discussed in Chapter 15.

AROMATIC AMINES

The previously named compounds are all open-chain amines. The simplest aromatic amine is called *aniline*. Its derivatives are named accordingly.

Aniline   p-chloroaniline

This substance is a commonly used bactericidal dye obtained from the indigo plant. It is named from the Arabic word *al* (for " the") plus *nila* (meaning "dark blue"), which was the Arabic name for the indigo plant.

HETEROCYCLIC AMINES

If the nitrogen of an amine compound is also part of a carbon ring system, the compound is described as *heterocyclic*, meaning that two different elements are in the ring. Both five-membered and six-membered heterocyclic rings are important in biological systems.

Five-membered rings

Pyrrole   Pyrrole is a five-membered heterocyclic secondary amine.

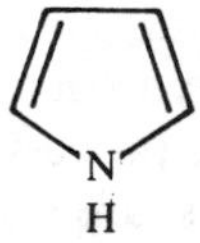

Pyrrole

Pyrrole is the basis for a number of important compounds. A *porphyrin* ring is composed of four pyrrole rings liked by carbon atoms. Porphyrin provides the nucleus for both hemoglobin (see Chapter 19) and chlorophyl (see Chapter 21).

Indole   *Indole* is a heterocyclic amine which contains a pyrrole bonded to a benzene ring. *Skatole* is a derivative of indole which contains a methyl (CH_3) group attached to the pyrrole ring. Both indole and skatole are putrefactive byproducts of proteins that contain the amino acid tryptophan (see Chapter 19) and contribute to the characteristic odor of feces.

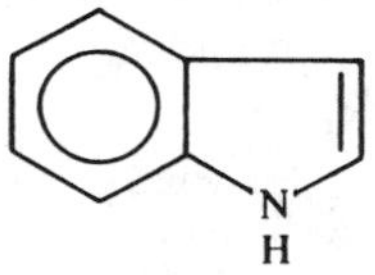

Indole 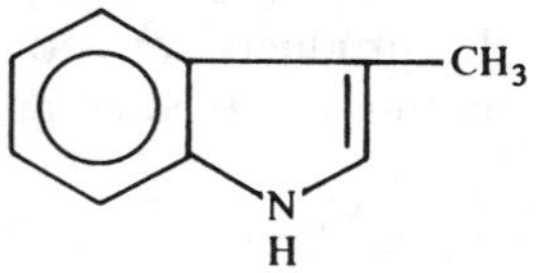   Skatole

Imidazole   This heterocyclic amine contains two nitrogen atoms. Imidazole, subsequently, qualifies as both a secondary and a tertiary amine.

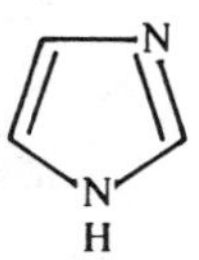

Imidazole

The amino acid *histidine* (see Chapter 19) contains the imidazole ring as the distinguishing feature of its side chain.

Six-membered rings

Pyridine A pyrrole was described as a five-membered heterocyclic amine containing one nitrogen in the ring. If we apply the same nitrogen to a six-membered ring, the resultant structure is a *pyridine*.

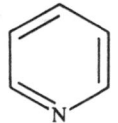

Pyridine

Pyridines are the basis for many biological substances including vitamins, hormones, and antibacterial agents.

Pyrimidine Six-membered heterocyclic amines containing two nitrogens in the ring are called *pyrimidines*.

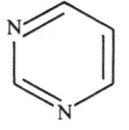

Pyrimidine

Pyrimidines are one of two types of nitrogenous bases incorporated into the compounds that have been determined to be the molecular basis for life, the nucleic acids DNA and RNA. Thymine, cytosine, and uracil are the pyrimidines found in these compounds.

Purine In order to produce the second type of nitrogenous base, it is necessary to combine the diamino pyrimidine with its analogous five-membered ring, the *imidazole*. The result is the following structure, called a *purine*.

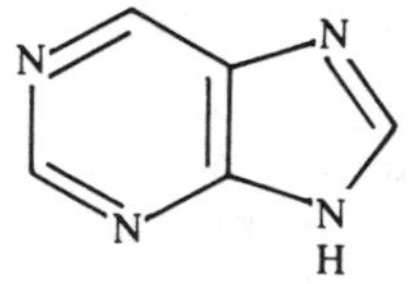

Purine

Adenine and guanine are the two nitrogenous bases which contain the purine nucleus. Caffeine, a stimulant found in coffee, tea, and many soft drinks, is a purine derivative.

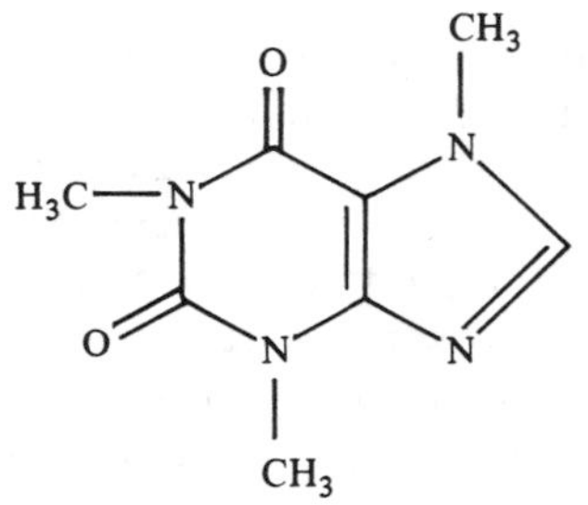

Caffeine

QUATERNARY AMMONIUM COMPOUNDS

We have seen how amines may be classified as primary, secondary, and tertiary. Since nitrogen in amines has an unshared pair of electrons, it can form a fourth, additional covalent bond with a hydrogen ion, an alkyl group, or an aromatic group. These compounds are similar to ammonium salts and are known as *salts of amines*. When all four hydrogen atoms are replaced, the resultant substance is called a *quaternary ammonium ion*. Compounds derived from this ion are called *quaternary ammonium salts*.

$$\left[\begin{array}{c} H \\ | \\ H-N-H \\ | \\ H \end{array}\right]^{+} R^{-} \qquad \left[\begin{array}{c} R \\ | \\ R-N-R \\ | \\ R \end{array}\right]^{+} R^{-}$$

Ammonium salt   Quaternary ammonium
                                          salt

Salts of amines are named by replacing the word amine by ammonium and adding the name of the anion (e.g., sulfate, nitrate, chloride).

$$\left[\begin{array}{c} CH_3 \\ | \\ H_3C-N-CH_3 \\ | \\ CH_3 \end{array}\right]^{+} NO_3^{-}$$

Tetramethyl ammonium nitrate
(a quaternary ammonium salt)

Some quaternary ammonium salts have detergent and disinfectant properties. Benzalkonium chloride (Roccal, Zephirol, Germitol) is a topical antiseptic used in dilute solution (1:1000) to cleanse and disinfect the skin prior to surgery. It has also been employed in nasal sprays to reduce airborne transmission of disease in the hospital environment. It is an excellent surface-active agent which may also be used to disinfect instruments. It is routinely included as a supplementary germicide in arterial embalm-

ing fluids. Its main drawback is that any alkaline substance, particularly soap, renders this compound useless. Reaction between the cation of benzalkonium chloride and the negative ion of a soap molecule produces an insoluble salt. This reaction removes the quaternary ammonium compound from solution.

$$\left[\begin{array}{c} CH_3 \\ | \\ \bigcirc-CH_2-N-R \\ | \\ CH_3 \end{array}\right]^{+} Cl^{-}$$

Benzalkonium chloride
(R represents a long alkyl chain
ranging from C_8H_{17} to $C_{18}H_{37}$)

Benzethonium chloride (phemoral chloride) is another quaternary ammonium compound that is routinely used as a topical antiseptic. It has the same drawbacks as the previously discussed "quat" in that it too is inactivated by the presence of soap. The structure of this compound is slightly more complex than that of its predecessor.

$$\left[\begin{array}{c} CH_3 \qquad CH_3 \qquad\qquad\qquad\qquad CH_3 \\ | \qquad\quad | \qquad\qquad\qquad\qquad\qquad | \\ CH_3-C-CH_2-C-\bigcirc-OCH_2CH_2OCH_2CH_2-N-CH_2-\bigcirc \\ | \qquad\quad | \qquad\qquad\qquad\qquad\qquad | \\ CH_3 \qquad CH_3 \qquad\qquad\qquad\qquad CH_3 \end{array}\right]^{+} {}^{-}Cl \cdot H_2O$$

Benzethonium chloride

A more familiar quaternary ammonium compound is *ceepryn chloride* (Cepacol), commonly marketed in both mouthwash and lozenge form. It possesses antibacterial action against certain pathogenic organisms found in the throat. Its structure is

$$CH_2(CH_2)_{14}CH_3 \cdot H_2O$$

The more technical name for this compound is *cetyl-pyridinium chloride*. This name reflects its origin. It is a monohydrate of the quaternary salt of pyridine and cetylchloride. Cetyl is another way of expressing hexadecyl (16 carbons). Remember that a pyridine is a six-membered heterocyclic amine. The ceepryn configuration incorporates this ring structure with a quaternary structure.

CHAPTER SUMMARY

Amines and amides are organic compounds which contain the element nitrogen. This element is identified with protein, the principal structural and functional biochemical of the body. Nitrogenous compounds comprise not only the building blocks but also the decomposition products of human remains.

Amines are the organic equivalent of a base or alkali. When reacted with organic acids, amines produce amides. After the elimination of water, a

$$\begin{array}{cc} O & H \\ \parallel & \mid \\ -C- & N- \end{array}$$

bond is formed between the reacting acid and base. This linkage will be seen again in Chapter 19 as the bond which is integral to the primary structure of proteins.

Cyclic amines are described in this chapter with special emphasis on their role in biosynthesis as well as decomposition.

The electronic configuration of nitrogen indicates that it may bond to four other atoms. Quaternary ammonium compounds illustrate this property of nitrogen. Since "quats" are incorporated as supplementary germicides in embalming fluids, some common examples are shown and discussed.

QUESTIONS

1. What is the difference between a tertiary amine and a tertiary alcohol?

2. Explain ptomaine poisoning.

3. Illustrate the reaction between propionic acid and butyl amine. Name the resulting amide.

4. Name two products of decomposition which contain the pyrrole ring.

5. What is the difference between a pyridine and a pyrimidine?

6. What are the two heterocyclic amine rings that make up the structure of a purine?

7. If nitrogen has an oxidation number of -3 and the amine group is $-NH_2$, how can a quaternary ammonium compound exist?

8. Explain the function of "quats" in embalming fluids. What is their chief drawback?

Biochemistry, the third major division of chemistry, is the study of those compounds produced and used by living organisms. The next several chapters will discuss proteins, enzymes, carbohydrates, and lipids. We shall consider their chemical structures and how these structures influence biological functions in order to see the role of the compounds in the life of an organism. In the present chapter we shall also consider another group of compounds, the nucleic acids.

ELEMENTAL COMPOSITION

The structures of many of the biochemical compounds may at first seem quite complicated. The chemical composition, however, is quite simple, since most organisms

Table 18-1 Chemical elements found in organisms

Major elements	Monatomic ions		Trace elements	
Hydrogen	Sodium	Na^+	Manganese	Mn^{++}
Carbon	Magnesium	Mg^{++}	Iron	Fe^{++}
Nitrogen	Chloride	Cl^-	Cobalt	Co^{++}
Oxygen	Potassium	K^+	Copper	Cu^{++}
Phosphorus	Calcium	Ca^{++}	Zinc	Zn^{++}
Sulfur				

and their positions on the periodic table, we see that they are the smallest atoms that can attain stable electronic configurations by sharing one, two, three, and four electrons, respectively. All these elements form very stable covalent bonds. In addition, oxygen, nitrogen, and carbon form stable multiple bonds. We have already seen that carbon forms multiple bonds in various organic compounds. In addition, carbon can bond to

Chapter 18
INTRODUCTION

are composed of only 16 chemical elements. (See Table 18-1.) Of these, hydrogen, oxygen, nitrogen, and carbon comprise more than 99% by weight of living matter. What special properties do these elements have that explain their abundance? If we recall their electronic configurations,

H: $1s^1$
O: $1s^2, 2s^2, 2p^4$
N: $1s^2, 2s^2, 2p^3$
C: $1s^2, 2s^2, 2p^2$

oxygen by a double bond either within a biological compound or in the gaseous substance carbon dioxide, a waste product produced by many living organisms. Carbon also bonds very stably to hydrogen and to nitrogen.

In addition to carbon dioxide, another gaseous substance vital to many living organisms is O_2, in which two oxygen atoms join by a double bond. The position of oxygen on the periodic table indicates it is extremely

electronegative. Oxygen easily accepts electrons in energy-yielding biochemical reactions. Many organisms depend on this property of oxygen to satisfy the energy needs of cells.

The action of phosphorus and sulfur in organisms is also related to cellular energy needs. In the presence of water, large amounts of energy are required for these elements to form bonds. Their formation is a means of carrying energy. When these bonds, sometimes called "high-energy bonds," are hydrolyzed, large quantities of energy are released. Molecules such as adenosine triphosphate (ATP) and acetyl coenzyme A, which contains sulfur, act as energy carriers in living organisms.

The various monatomic ions perform a variety of functions in a living organism. Sodium is the major positive ion in extracellular fluids. Likewise, within cells the major positive ion is potassium. They are both involved in the actions of muscles and the nervous system. Osmotic relationships and acid-base balance are influenced by these ions. Within cells, magnesium is second to potassium. It is necessary for the activity of certain enzymes. Chloride is the major negative ion in the human body. Approximately two-thirds of the negative ions in the body are chloride ions. They are mainly in extracellular fluids, where they, like sodium, influence osmotic-pressure relationships and acid-base balance. Calcium ions in the forms of calcium phosphate and calcium hydroxide are important components of bone and teeth. In addition, calcium initiates the blood-clotting process; it also functions in the action of nerves and muscles and is important to the activity of some enzymes and hormones.

The other elements listed in Table 18-1 are trace elements. Humans need ingest only a few milligrams of them per day. Manganese, copper, and zinc act as part of enzyme systems. The proper functioning of nerves and the development of strong bones require manganese. Copper is important for the synthesis of collagen, a connective-tissue protein. A deficiency of copper can affect the structure of hair. Besides being present in some enzymes, zinc is also present in bone. The oxygen-carrying ability of blood is dependent on iron, since in its plus-two oxidation state it forms part of the structure of heme. The vitamin B_{12}, called cobalamin, contains cobalt. A deficiency of this vitamin leads to pernicious anemia.

Copper and iron also play an important role in respiration. Since they can exist in two different oxidation states, copper(I) and copper(II) and iron(II) and iron(III), they participate in a series of oxidation and reduction reactions known as the *electron-transport chain*. These reactions are a part of a series of processes by which cells extract energy from nutrients.

MOLECULAR COMPOSITION

The most abundant molecule found in living organisms is water. Most organisms also contain 30 other small precursor molecules. They are the building blocks for the major biochemical compounds.

Water

As discussed in Chapter 8, water is the most abundant compound both on the earth and in living organisms. It also has certain unique properties that qualify it to be at the basis of life. Two fundamental properties are its polarity and its formation of intermolecular hydrogen bonds. Since it is polar, water easily dissolves other polar substances; therefore, it provides an excellent transport system for nutrients. The extensive hydrogen bonding between molecules of water causes

Table 18-2 Comparison of water to other substances in terms of specific heat, heat of vaporization, and heat of fusion

Substance	Specific heat* (cal/g °C)		Heat of vaporization (cal/g)	Heat of fusion (cal/g)
Benzene	—		94.1	30.0
Chloroform	—		59.0	—
Ethanol	0.58	(25°—50°C)	204.0	24.9
Ethyl ether	—		84.0	—
Gold	0.31	(17°–100°C)	—	15.0
Iron	0.119	(20°–100°C)	—	65.7
Water	1.00	(1°–32°C)	539.6	79.67

*Specific heats are for the temperature ranges listed.

its specific heat, heat of vaporization, and heat of fusion to be unusually high in comparison to those of many other substances. (See Table 18-2.)

The *specific heat* for a compound is the quantity of heat (expressed in calories) that is needed to raise the temperature of one gram of the substance by 1° Celsius. Since approximately 70% of the mass of an adult human is water, a considerable amount of heat can be absorbed or released from a body without much change in body temperature. During life, the temperature of the body must remain relatively constant, close to 37°C, or biochemical processes will not function properly.

Both the heat of vaporization and the heat of fusion of water are also high. The *heat of vaporization* is the amount of heat necessary to change one gram of a substance from the liquid state to the vapor state at its boiling point. Similarly the *heat of fusion* refers to the change of one gram of a liquid to a solid at the melting point. An animal loses small quantities of body fluids in ridding itself of large amounts of heat by surface evaporation. Organisms are protected against freezing by the heat of fusion of water, since large quantities of heat must be removed before freezing occurs.

Amino acids

Twenty *amino acids* are the building blocks of proteins. These may be divided into *essential* and *nonessential* amino acids. The nonessential ones can be synthesized by an adult human from intermediates of carbohydrate breakdown. Humans cannot, however, synthesize the essential amino acids, which therefore must be included in the diet. Plants and many microorganisms are able to synthesize all 20 amino acids, beginning with a source of nitrogen—usually the nitrate ion, NO_3^-.

Aromatic bases

The genetic code which governs growth and reproduction of cells is directed by nucleic acids. Two groups of nucleic acids are ribonucleic acids (RNA) and deoxyribonucleic acids (DNA). Included in their structures are *aromatic bases* called purines and pyrimidines (see Chapter 17). There are two specific purines, adenine and guanine, and three pyrimidines, cytosine, uracil, and thymine. The structures of these heterocyclic amines are drawn in Figure 18-1. The cells of humans synthesize them by rather complex, energy-consuming pathways, using

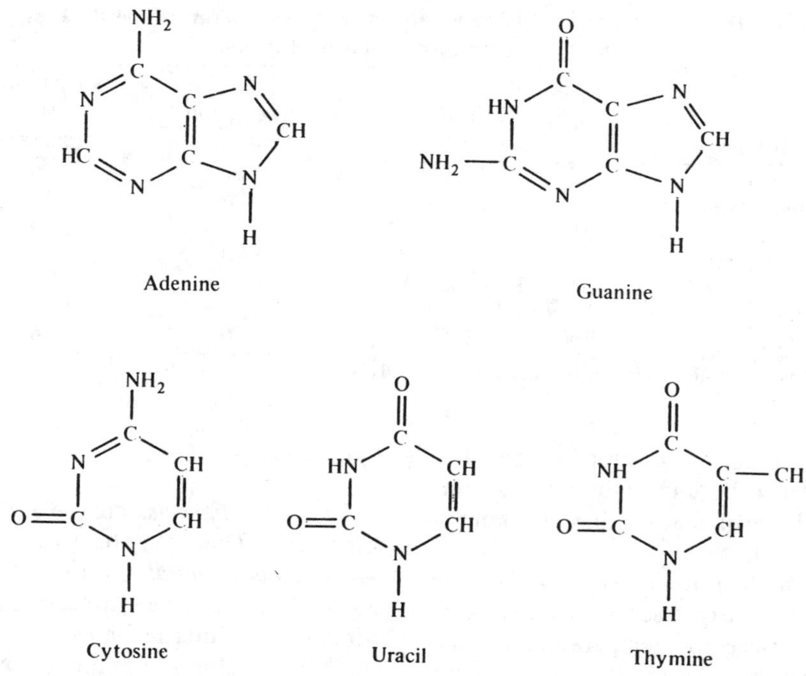

Figure 18-1 Structures of purines and pyrimidines

certain amino acids and compounds derived from the vitamin folic acid.

Sugars

Glucose, a six-carbon sugar, is the building block for the carbohydrate compounds of cellulose, starch, and glycogen. It is also the primary carbohydrate that circulates in the blood. Oxidation of glucose yields energy for cellular needs.

Another sugar, *ribose*, contains five carbons and forms part of the structure of the nucleic acid RNA. In the form of *deoxyribose* (ribose minus one oxygen) it is found in DNA.

Constituents of phospholipids

Membranes that surround both procaryotic cells and eucaryotic cells are composed of phospholipids and proteins. In addition the internal cellular structures of eucaryotic cells are also contained within such membranes. The *phospholipids* are formed from the fatty acid, palmitic acid, the alcohol, glycerol, and the amine, choline. *Palmitic acid* is a saturated, 16-carbon, carboxylic acid. It is synthesized starting with *acetyl coenzyme A*. Acetyl refers to the

$$\underset{CH_3C}{\overset{\overset{\textstyle O}{\|}}{}}$$

group, and the structure of coenzyme A is diagrammed in Chapter 21. The importance of acetyl coenzyme A will become apparent as the reactions that extract energy from carbohydrates are discussed in Chapter 21. Coenzyme A is derived from the vitamin, pantothenic acid.

Glycerol and choline, the other constituents of phospholipids, are products of the digestion of lipids that humans ingest.

MACROMOLECULES

The 30 small precursor molecules join together to form macromolecules. They form 85% to 95% of the dry weight of most organisms. The major types of macromolecules are proteins, carbohydrates, and nucleic acids. The formation of all three is based on reactions between the precursor molecules which involve the elimination of water between reacting sites in the molecules. Just as in the reactions of neutralization and esterification studied in the previous chapters of this book, water forms whenever its constituents (H^+ and OH^-) are close to one another. This simple synthesis, which links together the precursor molecules, is the driving force of the biochemical synthesis reactions. The large macromolecules are broken apart by another reaction, hydrolysis, familiar from inorganic chemistry. These synthesis and degradation reactions also require the presence of enzymes (biological catalysts) which help to properly align the molecules. *Synthesis* is an energy-requiring process and *degradation* is an energy-releasing process. A general name for the former is *endergonic* and for the latter is *exergonic*.

Proteins

Chapter 19 discusses the formation and characteristics of proteins. Polymerization of amino acids produces these macromolecules, which are central to the life of an organism. They have many functions. Not only do they form structures within organisms, but they also exercise dynamic control over cellular reactions. This role is due to their actions as enzymes, biological catalysts, which are discussed in Chapter 20.

Polysaccharides

Polymers of sugar molecules, mostly glucose, act as storage forms of energy in plant, animal, and human organisms. When energy is needed within a cell, polysaccharides are degraded back to the precursor molecules. Under the control of enzymes, these small molecules undergo a series of reactions in the form of energy-producing pathways. The most important ones in man are *glycolysis*, the *Krebs cycle*, and *oxidative phosphorylation*. Each is discussed in Chapter 21.

In plants the polysaccharide cellulose also has a structural role.

Nucleic acids

The two nucleic acids *deoxyribonucleic acid* (*DNA*) and *ribonucleic acid* (*RNA*) are responsible for the transmission of genetic information and the synthesis of protein by a cell. DNA is found in the cell nucleus and RNA in both the nucleus and the cytoplasm. Both are usually joined to proteins, forming *nucleoproteins*. Each individual strand of a nucleic acid is a polymer of units called *nucleotides*. The relationship of a nucleic acid to precursor molecules is diagrammed:

$$\text{NUCLEIC ACID}$$
$$\Updownarrow$$
$$\text{NUCLEOTIDES}$$
$$\Updownarrow$$
$$\text{NUCLEOSIDES} + H_3PO_4$$
$$\Updownarrow$$
$$\text{PURINES and PYRIMIDINES} + \text{PENTOSE}$$

Starting with the aromatic bases and sugars, nucleosides form by a dehydration reaction between an N—H group on the base and a C—OH group on the sugar. This reaction between adenine and ribose is seen in Figure 21-10. In the formation of DNA, deoxyribose is the sugar, while for RNA the sugar is ribose. Structures of these sugars are drawn in Chapter 21. Of the bases, uracil is not found in DNA. Likewise, RNA does not contain thymine.

Nucleosides next join to phosphoric acid by again eliminating water between one —OH on the sugar and an —OH of phos-

phoric acid. Nonionized phosphoric acid has the form:

$$HO-\overset{\overset{\textstyle O}{\|}}{\underset{\underset{\textstyle OH}{|}}{P}}-OH$$

Since there are other —OH groups on the phosphoric acid and on the sugar of each nucleotide, polymerization of nucleotides forms a long strand of a nucleic acid. A simple structure of three nucleotides is

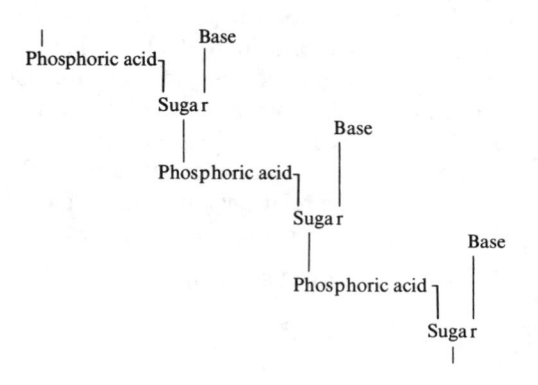

An actual molecule of DNA consists of two chains of nucleotides coiled in a double helical structure. Within each molecule, there is a 1:1 relationship betwen cytosine and guanine nucleotides and a 1:1 relationship between adenine and thymine nucleotides. In 1953, Watson and Crick proposed a model for DNA in which cytosine of one chain is joined by three hydrogen bonds to a guanine of the other chain. Similarly, thymine and adenine in two separate chains join by two hydrogen bonds.

RNA molecules generally are single-stranded. They can form helical structures, owing to intrastrand hydrogen bonding. The bases usually pair adenine-uracil and guanine-cytosine.

METABOLISM

The study of all the enzymatically controlled reactions in a living cell is *metabolism*. This very extensive definition is divided into two parts: catabolism and anabolism. *Catabolism*, "a breaking-down process," produces the precursor molecules used by cells and chemical energy for cellular needs. *Anabolism*, "a building-up process," forms the macromolecules of proteins, carbohydrates, and nucleic acids. Lipids are also produced by these synthetic processes. Since they are not polymers, they are not considered macromolecules. Digestion and absorption of nutrients must occur before the metabolic reactions.

CHAPTER SUMMARY

Water is the most abundant molecule in living organisms. It provides a medium for the building blocks of the major biochemical compounds. They form from 30 precursor molecules, which include 20 amino acids, five aromatic bases, two sugars, and palmitic acid, glycerol, and choline. Within the precursors, the major chemical elements are carbon, hydrogen, oxygen, and nitrogen.

QUESTIONS

1. What four elements form more than 99% by weight of living matter?

2. What is special about the presence of sulfur and phosphorus in living matter?

3. What molecule other than water has certain unique properties that qualify it to be at the basis of life?

4. Would it be possible to produce all the classes of biochemical compounds from less than the 30 precursor molecules discussed in this chapter? What would be the minimum number? Explain your answer.

5. Name two components of cell membranes.

6. What is meant by the term macromolecule? Name the major types.

7. List the component parts of a nucleic acid.

8. Name and describe the two divisions of metabolism.

The most important biochemical compounds are the proteins. Their functions are both structural and dynamic. They along with lipids form biological membranes, in which the proteins are responsible for many of the processes such as transport and communication that the membranes perform. Proteins have other dynamic functions in living organisms. They act as hormones and antibodies, form a portion of the oxygen-carrying molecules hemoglobin and myoglobin, and serve as regulators of all biological reactions, since enzymes (biological catalysts) are proteins. The structural role of proteins is exemplified by the connective-tissue proteins collagen and elastin. The word *protein* comes from the Greek word *proteios*, which means "of the first rank."

amounts of phosphorus, iodine, copper, manganese, magnesium, and zinc. Proteins are very large molecules; their molecular weights range from about 35,000 to 50,000,000. Proteins are polymers of amino acids. Upon hydrolysis they form mixtures of amino acids. Hydrolyzing agents are acids, bases, and enzymes called proteases. To understand the chemistry of proteins first we must study amino acids.

AMINO ACIDS

Twenty amino acids are the building blocks of proteins. These compounds contain two functional groups you should remember from organic chemistry. They are the carboxyl

Chapter 19
PROTEINS

Proteins are the focal point of the work of the embalmer. The embalming operation achieves preservation and disinfection of a body by cross-linking proteins—both the proteins of the human remains and the proteins present in microorganisms.

PROTEIN COMPOSITION

All proteins contain the elements carbon, hydrogen, oxygen, and nitrogen. Many also contain sulfur and some contain small

group,
$$-\overset{\overset{\displaystyle O}{\|}}{C}-OH \text{ or } -COOH,$$
and the amino group, $-NH_2$. All amino acids contain another carbon, another hydrogen, and a side chain called an *R group*. The general formula for any amino acid is

$$H_2N-\overset{\overset{\displaystyle R}{|}}{\underset{\underset{\displaystyle H}{|}}{C}}-COOH$$

The amino group is always attached to the carbon next to the carboxyl group. In organic

chemistry terminology this carbon is the *alpha carbon*. Hence, amino acids of this form are called *alpha amino acids*.

A specific amino acid is identified by its R group. The simplest is *glycine*, in which the R group is a hydrogen atom.

$$H_2N-\overset{\overset{\displaystyle H}{|}}{\underset{\underset{\displaystyle H}{|}}{C}}-COOH$$

Structures for additional amino acids are written by changing the R group. When the side chain is a methyl group, the amino acid is alanine. Incorporation of other hydrocarbon side chains results in the structures of valine, leucine, isoleucine, and proline. (See Table 19-1.)

The side chain may include the hydroxyl group. Examples are serine and threonine.

Some amino acids are aromatic, since they contain a benzene ring. These are phenylalanine, tyrosine, and tryptophan.

Two amino acids, cysteine and methionine, contain a sulfur atom in their R groups.

Since all amino acids have both the carboxyl group and amino group, they may act as both acids and bases. More is said about this in a later section. Three amino acids have additional ability to act as bases, since they contain nitrogen atoms in the side chains. They are lysine, arginine, and histidine. Two amino acids, aspartic acid and glutamic acid, have a carboxyl group in their side chains. They are acidic amino acids. Amide forms of them also exist. They are called asparagine and glutamine.

The structures of the amino acids range from very simple (glycine) to rather complex (tryptophan or arginine). Fortunately the major properties of the amino acids are inherent in the properties of the carboxyl and amino groups. Two of these properties are amphoterism and peptide bond formation.

AMPHOTERISM

Since amino acids contain the carboxyl group and the amino group, they act as both acids and bases. Recall from organic chemistry that when the carboxyl group is in a compound, it is a weak acid (proton donor), owing to the following ionization:

$$-\overset{\overset{\displaystyle O}{\|}}{C}-OH + H_2O \longrightarrow$$

$$-\overset{\overset{\displaystyle O}{\|}}{C}-O^- + H_3O^+$$

Similarly the presence of the amino group in a compound gives it basic (proton acceptor) properties.

$$-NH_2 + H^+ \longrightarrow -NH_3^+$$

Since both of these groups are found in each amino acid, an acid-base reaction may occur within each molecule.

$$H_2N-\overset{\overset{\displaystyle R}{|}}{\underset{\underset{\displaystyle H}{|}}{C}}-COOH \longrightarrow$$

$$^+H_3N-\overset{\overset{\displaystyle R}{|}}{\underset{\underset{\displaystyle H}{|}}{C}}-COO^-$$

The product of this reaction is a dipolar ion. Another name for a dipolar ion is the German *Zwitterion*. In neutral solution ($pH = 7$) the predominant form of amino acids has the carboxyl and amino groups ionized. In very acid solution ($pH = 1$) the major form of amino acids is a positively charged ion.

$$^+H_3N-\overset{\overset{\displaystyle R}{|}}{\underset{\underset{\displaystyle H}{|}}{C}}-COOH$$

Table 19-1   Structures of amino acids classified by side chains

SIMPLEST

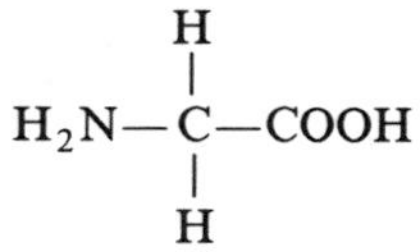

$$H_2N - \overset{\overset{\displaystyle H}{|}}{\underset{\underset{\displaystyle H}{|}}{C}} - COOH$$

Glycine

ALIPHATIC SIDE CHAINS

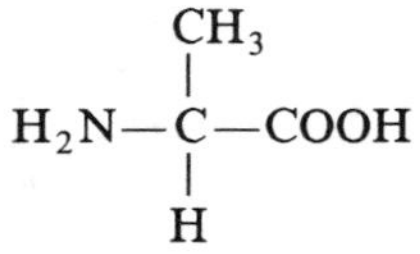

$$H_2N - \overset{\overset{\displaystyle CH_3}{|}}{\underset{\underset{\displaystyle H}{|}}{C}} - COOH$$

Alanine

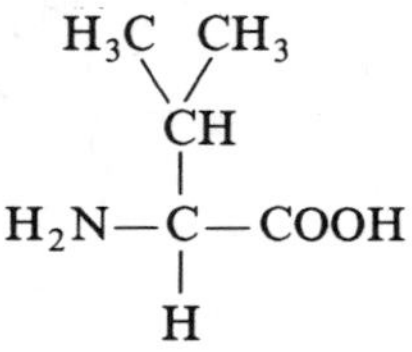

$$H_2N - \overset{\overset{\displaystyle CH}{|}}{\underset{\underset{\displaystyle H}{|}}{C}} - COOH \qquad \overset{H_3C \ \ CH_3}{}$$

Valine

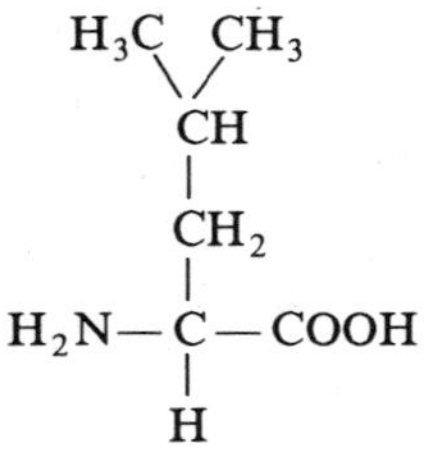

$$H_2N - \overset{\overset{\displaystyle CH_2}{|}}{\underset{\underset{\displaystyle H}{|}}{C}} - COOH \qquad \overset{\displaystyle H_3C \ \ CH_3}{\overset{\displaystyle CH}{|}}$$

Leucine

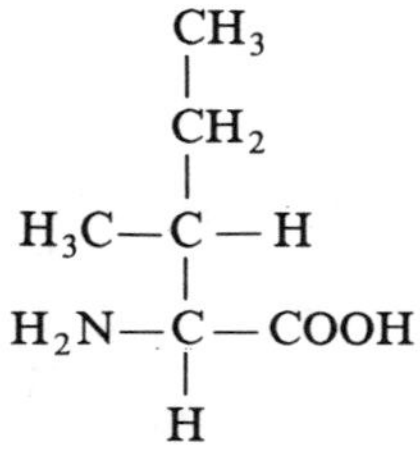

$$H_2N - \overset{\overset{\displaystyle H_3C - C - H}{|}}{\underset{\underset{\displaystyle H}{|}}{C}} - COOH$$

Isoleucine

$$HN - \overset{\overset{\displaystyle CH_2}{|}}{\underset{\underset{\displaystyle H}{|}}{C}} - COOH$$

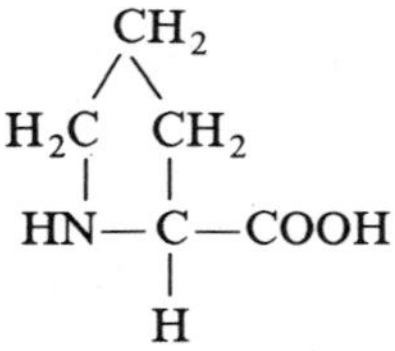

Proline

ALIPHATIC HYDROXYL SIDE CHAINS

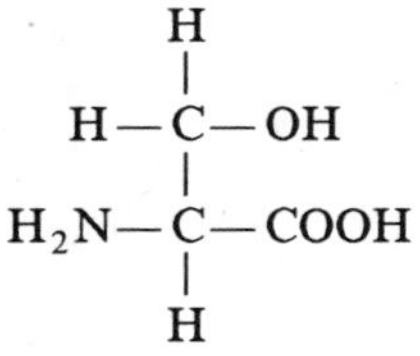

$$H_2N - \overset{\overset{\displaystyle H - C - OH}{|}}{\underset{\underset{\displaystyle H}{|}}{C}} - COOH$$

Serine

$$H_2N - \overset{\overset{\displaystyle H - C - OH}{|}}{\underset{\underset{\displaystyle H}{|}}{C}} - COOH \qquad \overset{\displaystyle CH_3}{}$$

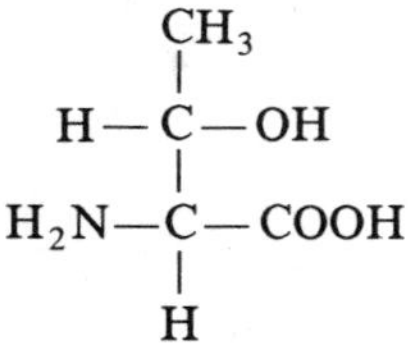

Threonine

Table 19-1 (*Continued*)

BASIC SIDE CHAINS

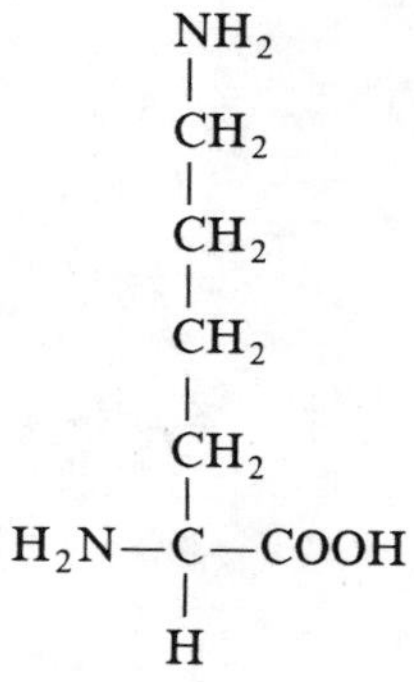

$$
\begin{array}{c}
NH_2 \\
| \\
CH_2 \\
| \\
CH_2 \\
| \\
CH_2 \\
| \\
CH_2 \\
| \\
H_2N-C-COOH \\
| \\
H
\end{array}
$$

Lysine

$$
\begin{array}{c}
NH_2 \\
| \\
C=NH \\
| \\
N-H \\
| \\
CH_2 \\
| \\
CH_2 \\
| \\
CH_2 \\
| \\
H_2N-C-COOH \\
| \\
H
\end{array}
$$

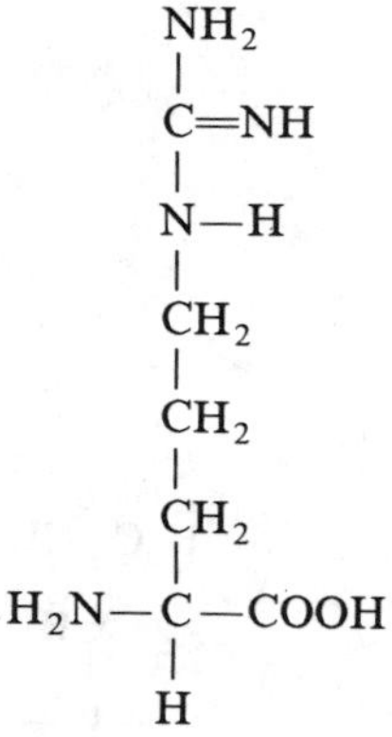

Arginine

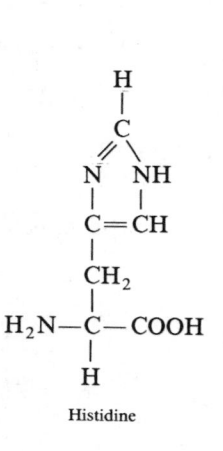

Histidine

ACIDIC SIDE CHAINS

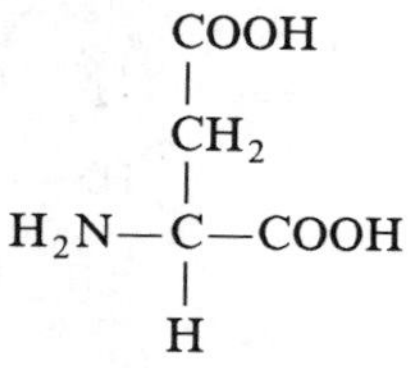

$$
\begin{array}{c}
COOH \\
| \\
CH_2 \\
| \\
H_2N-C-COOH \\
| \\
H
\end{array}
$$

Aspartic acid

$$
\begin{array}{c}
COOH \\
| \\
CH_2 \\
| \\
CH_2 \\
| \\
H_2N-C-COOH \\
| \\
H
\end{array}
$$

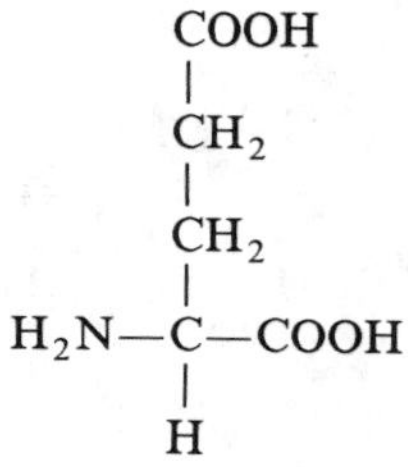

Glutamic acid

AMIDE SIDE CHAINS

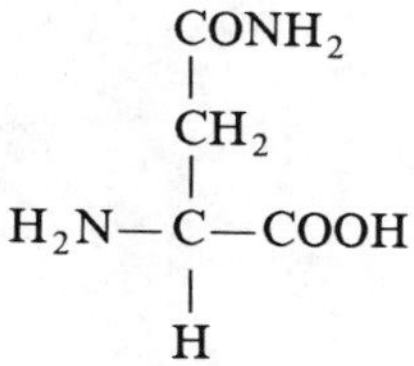

$$
\begin{array}{c}
CONH_2 \\
| \\
CH_2 \\
| \\
H_2N-C-COOH \\
| \\
H
\end{array}
$$

Asparagine

$$
\begin{array}{c}
CONH_2 \\
| \\
CH_2 \\
| \\
CH_2 \\
| \\
H_2N-C-COOH \\
| \\
H
\end{array}
$$

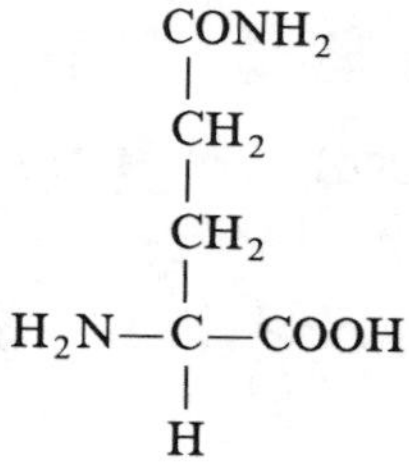

Glutamine

Table 19-1   (*Continued*)

AROMATIC SIDE CHAINS

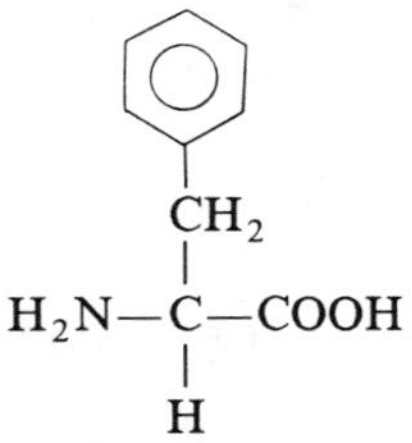

$$
\begin{array}{c}
\text{(phenyl ring)} \\
| \\
CH_2 \\
| \\
H_2N - C - COOH \\
| \\
H
\end{array}
$$

Phenylalanine

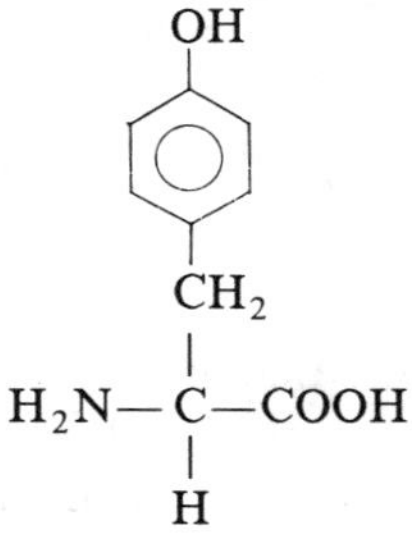

$$
\begin{array}{c}
OH \\
| \\
\text{(phenyl ring)} \\
| \\
CH_2 \\
| \\
H_2N - C - COOH \\
| \\
H
\end{array}
$$

Tyrosine

$$
\begin{array}{c}
H \\
| \\
N \\
\text{(indole ring)} \\
| \\
CH_2 \\
| \\
H_2N - C - COOH \\
| \\
H
\end{array}
$$

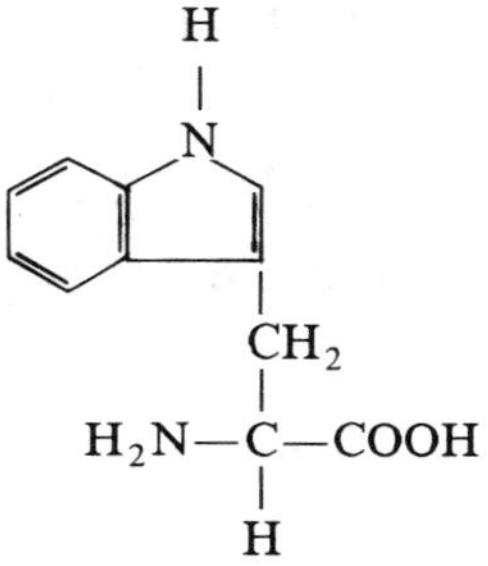

Tryptophan

SULFUR SIDE CHAINS

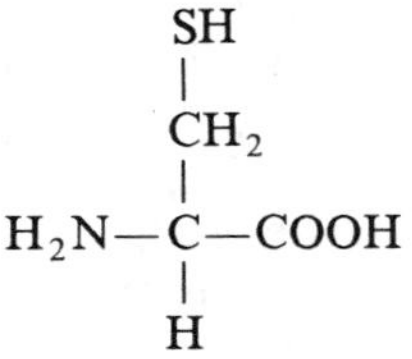

$$
\begin{array}{c}
SH \\
| \\
CH_2 \\
| \\
H_2N - C - COOH \\
| \\
H
\end{array}
$$

Cysteine

$$
\begin{array}{c}
CH_3 \\
| \\
S \\
| \\
CH_2 \\
| \\
CH_2 \\
| \\
H_2N - C - COOH \\
| \\
H
\end{array}
$$

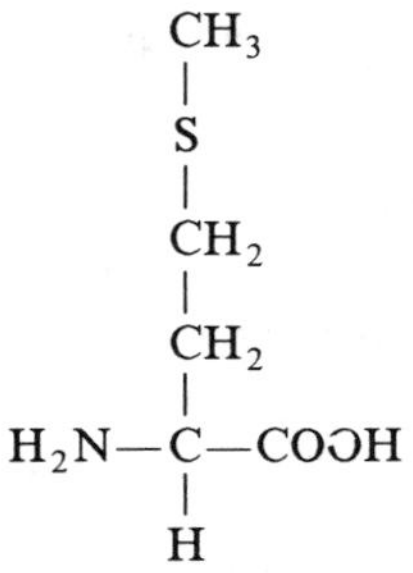

Methionine

In very basic solution ($pH = 12$) the predominant form is a negatively charged ion.

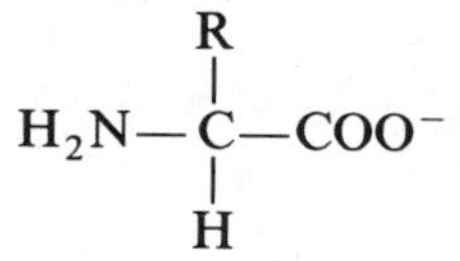

$$H_2N-\underset{\underset{H}{|}}{\overset{\overset{R}{|}}{C}}-COO^-$$

Any compound that can act as both an acid and a base is called *amphoteric*. Amphoterism is a property of all amino acids. Equations that show this property can be written with the zwitterion form of glycine.

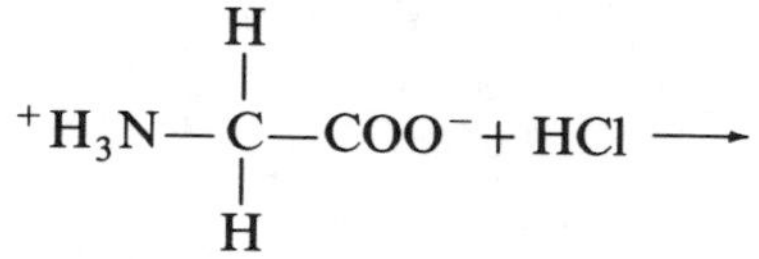

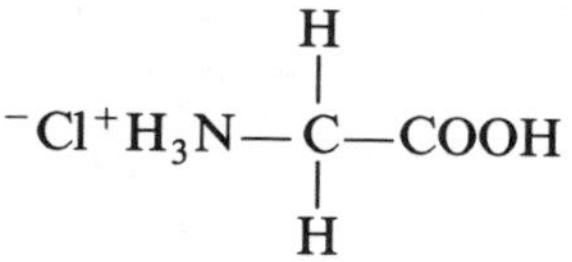

$$^+H_3N-\underset{\underset{H}{|}}{\overset{\overset{H}{|}}{C}}-COO^- + HCl \longrightarrow$$

$$^-Cl\,^+H_3N-\underset{\underset{H}{|}}{\overset{\overset{H}{|}}{C}}-COOH$$

Here, glycine acts as a base when reacted with hydrochloric acid. The product is a salt. Similarly,

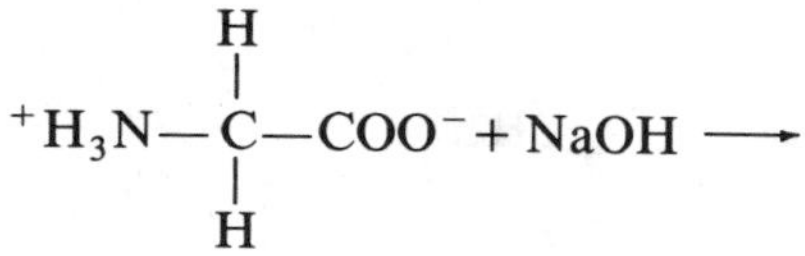

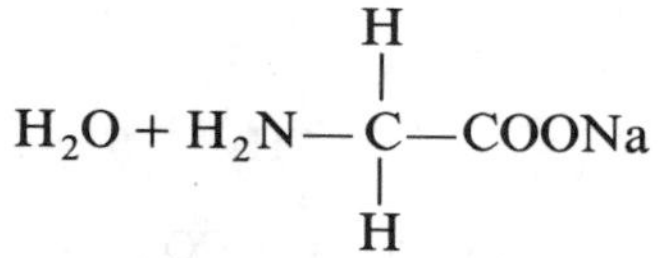

$$^+H_3N-\underset{\underset{H}{|}}{\overset{\overset{H}{|}}{C}}-COO^- + NaOH \longrightarrow$$

$$H_2O + H_2N-\underset{\underset{H}{|}}{\overset{\overset{H}{|}}{C}}-COONa$$

In this case glycine acts as an acid and neutralizes the base sodium hydroxide. The reaction forms typical neutralization products of water and a salt.

Owing to their amphoteric nature, amino acids are buffers in solution. To *buffer* means "to protect." Buffers are compounds that protect a solution against changes in pH. By neutralizing either acids or bases that enter a solution, amino acids keep the pH of a solution relatively constant within limits of added acid or base. Since proteins are polymers of amino acids, they also are buffers.

PEPTIDE LINKAGE

By definition, a protein is a chain of alpha amino acids joined together by the peptide linkage. What is the peptide linkage? If we draw the structures for any two amino acids with the carboxyl group of one next to the amino group of another, their chemical linkage can be demonstrated. Consider the joining of glycine and alanine:

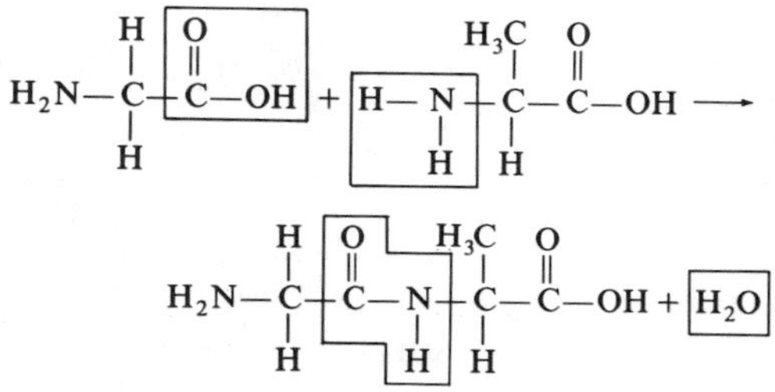

Two products, the joined amino acids and water, are formed. The common phenomenon of the formation of water whenever its constituents (OH^- and H^+) are brought together is the driving force of this reaction.

The group $-\overset{\overset{O}{\|}}{C}-\overset{\overset{H}{|}}{N}$ that joins the two amino acids is the *peptide linkage*. It contains the carbonyl group $-\overset{\overset{O}{\|}}{C}-$ and the imino group $-\overset{\overset{H}{|}}{N}-$. The product of joining together two amino acids is a *dipeptide*. Two more amino acids can be joined to it at its ends. By this

joining of the carboxyl group of one amino acid to the amino group of another, large chains of amino acids, proteins, form. It is important to see that no matter how large the protein, on one end will always be a free carboxyl group and on the other a free amino group.

Like amino acids, proteins are amphoteric and act as buffers. In addition to the terminal acidic and basic groups, the buffering action of proteins is enhanced by acidic and basic groups present in the R groups of amino acids such as aspartic acid and lysine. Proteins buffer the blood by donating protons if it becomes too basic and accepting protons if it becomes too acidic. An example of a protein that buffers the blood is albumin.

CROSS-LINKING OF PROTEINS

During the embalming process, proteins are cross-linked to one another. This cross-linking results in the firmness of embalmed tissue. The most commonly used cross-linking agent is formaldehyde. Other aldehydes, such as glutaraldehyde, also will join proteins together.

The basis of cross-linking is the chemical reactivity of aldehydes with different forms of nitrogen. Three forms of nitrogen found in proteins are imide groups, amino groups, and the peptide linkage. (See Figure 19-1.)

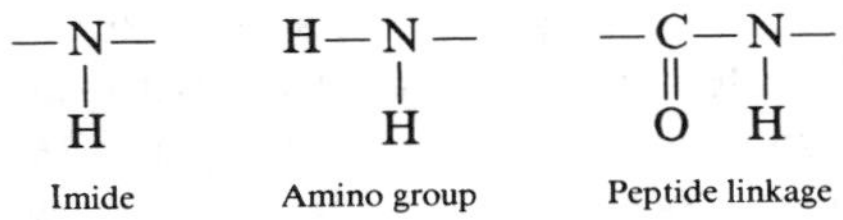

Figure 19-1 Forms of nitrogen found in proteins

Imide group

The amino acids proline, hydroxyproline, tryptophan, arginine, and histidine contain this group. Hydroxyproline, derived from proline, is found in collagen. The reaction of the two imide groups with formaldehyde is

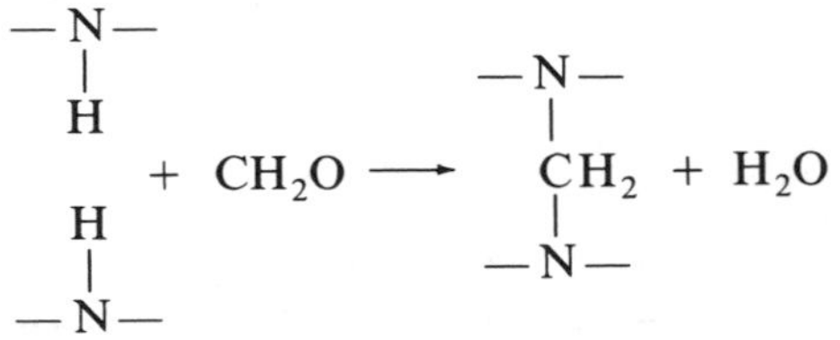

$$-\underset{\underset{\displaystyle -N-}{\overset{\displaystyle H}{\underset{|}{\overset{|}{N}}}}{\overset{\displaystyle H}{\underset{|}{\overset{|}{N}}}}- \quad + \; CH_2O \longrightarrow \quad -\underset{-N-}{\overset{-N-}{\underset{|}{\overset{|}{CH_2}}}}- + H_2O$$

By this reaction two protein chains are linked together. In the process a methylene group is inserted between the nitrogens of the imide groups and one molecule of water is formed.

Amino group

Every protein has a terminal amino group. Some amino acids such as lysine, arginine, and glutamine also contain an amino group in their R groups. The reaction is

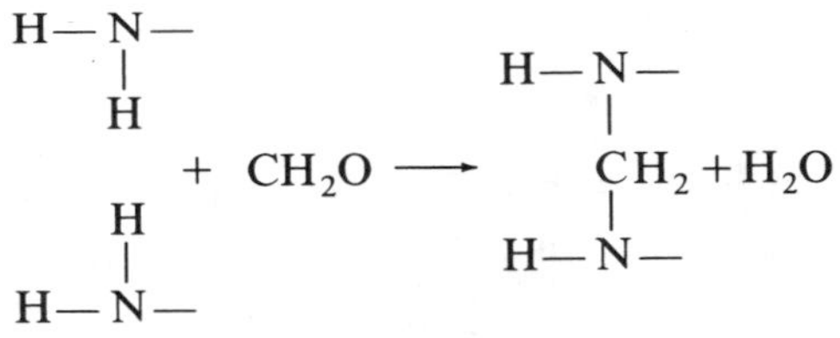

$$H-\underset{\underset{\displaystyle H-N-}{\overset{\displaystyle H}{\underset{|}{\overset{|}{N}}}}{\overset{\displaystyle H}{\underset{|}{\overset{|}{N}}}}- \quad + \; CH_2O \longrightarrow \quad H-\underset{H-N-}{\overset{H-N-}{\underset{|}{\overset{|}{CH_2}}}}+ H_2O$$

Two protein chains are linked together by this reaction, and, as in the previous example, one molecule of water forms.

Peptide linkage

This is the most important cross-linking site in a protein. Between every two amino acids in the chain is a peptide linkage. Reaction with formaldehyde at these linkages joins many protein chains together. The reaction

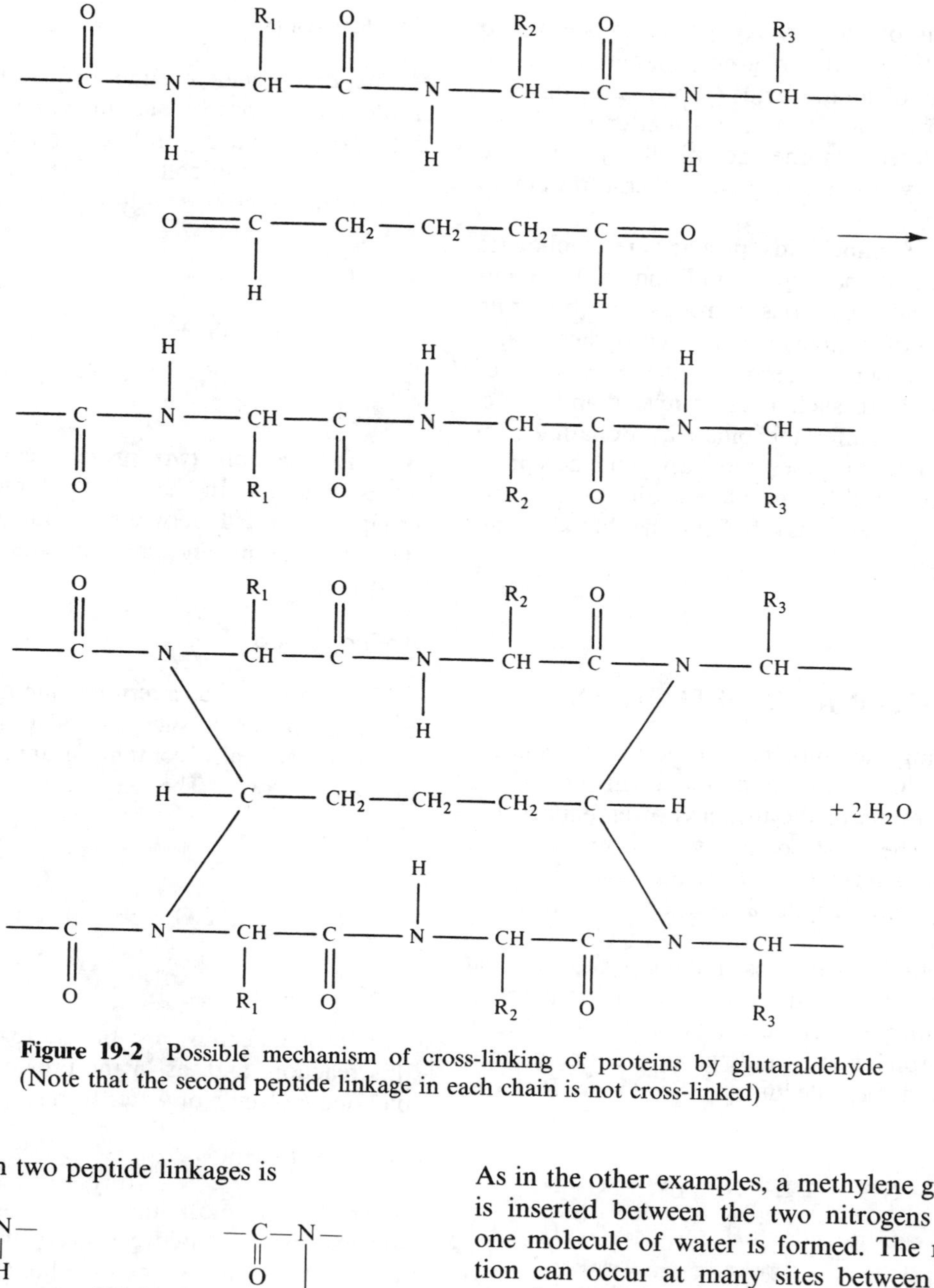

Figure 19-2 Possible mechanism of cross-linking of proteins by glutaraldehyde (Note that the second peptide linkage in each chain is not cross-linked)

between two peptide linkages is

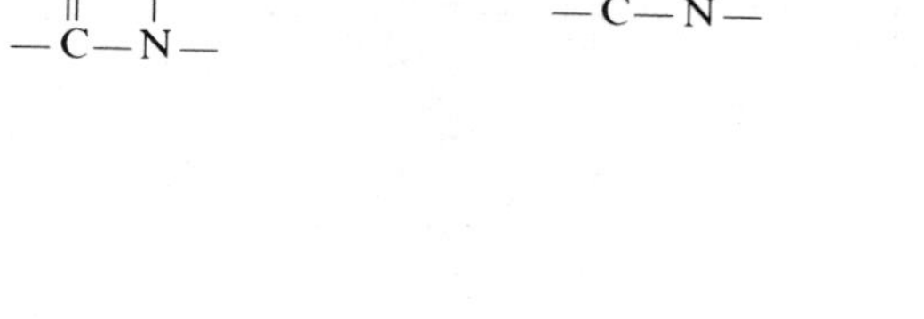

$$
\begin{array}{c}
-\underset{\underset{O}{\parallel}}{C}-\underset{\underset{H}{|}}{N}- \\
\\
+ \quad CH_2O \quad \longrightarrow \\
\\
-\underset{\underset{O}{\parallel}}{C}-\underset{\underset{H}{|}}{N}-
\end{array}
\qquad
\begin{array}{c}
-\underset{\underset{O}{\parallel}}{C}-\underset{}{N}- \\
\\
\underset{\underset{O}{|}}{CH_2} + H_2O \\
\\
-\underset{\underset{O}{\parallel}}{C}-\underset{}{N}-
\end{array}
$$

As in the other examples, a methylene group is inserted between the two nitrogens and one molecule of water is formed. The reaction can occur at many sites between two protein chains, forming a very tightly linked product. The formation of water in these reactions has two implications. First, since water is removed by drainage, embalming

with formaldehyde is dehydrating to the embalmed tissue. Second, the cross-linking reactions may be reversed by excess amounts of water. In the embalming of an edematous limb it has been observed that, several hours after tissue hardness is achieved, the tissue is found again to be soft. A possible explanation is that the high water concentration has reversed the cross-linking reaction.

Another cross-linking agent is the dialdehyde glutaraldehyde. A possible mechanism for its cross-liking action is seen in Figure 19-2. This type of cross-link does not join every peptide linkage as is possible with formaldehyde. The size of the five-carbon glutaraldehyde sterically prevents a reaction at every peptide site. Tissue embalmed with glutaraldehyde is not as hard as that embalmed with formaldehyde. A possible explanation for this is the lesser number of cross-links that result from this glutaraldehyde mechanism.

PROTEIN STRUCTURE

Some proteins are one polypeptide chain. Others consist of two or more chains. Myoglobin, the oxygen-carrying protein of muscle, is a single polypeptide. Hemoglobin contains four chains. The important hormone insulin has two chains per insulin molecule. To understand protein structure, we discuss it at different levels referred to as primary, secondary, tertiary, and quaternary. Only proteins with more than one chain have a quaternary structure.

Primary structure

This is the sequence of amino acids in a protein. The tripeptide Gly-Gly-Ala has a different primary structure than the tripeptide Gly-Ala-Gly. Standard abbreviations for the amino acid residues are used in these descriptions. Although both of these peptides

contain two glycines and one alanine, they are different molecules, since the orders of the amino acids are not the same. The primary structure also tells if there are disulfide bridges in the protein. These are covalent bonds between sulfur atoms in two different cysteine amino acids. For example, if a section of a protein has the structure

the —SH groups on the cysteines can be oxidized to form a covalent bond

called a *disulfide bridge*.

The first protein whose primary structure was determined was insulin. (See Figure 19-3.) This was accomplished in 1953 by the British biochemist Frederick Sanger. Bovine insulin contains 51 amino acids in two polypeptide chains linked by disulfide bridges. Determination of the primary structure of a protein is a very formidable task utilizing many analytical techniques. First a sample of the protein is hydrolyzed; then chromatography techniques are used to determine the amino acid content. Once it is known what amino acids are present, the laborious but exciting task of sequence determination is performed. Using enzymes and reagents specific for peptide linkages between certain amino acids, samples of the nonhydrolyzed protein are cleaved at different linkage sites. The results of these cleavage experiments generally show overlapping sections of polypeptides, from which the primary structure is deduced.

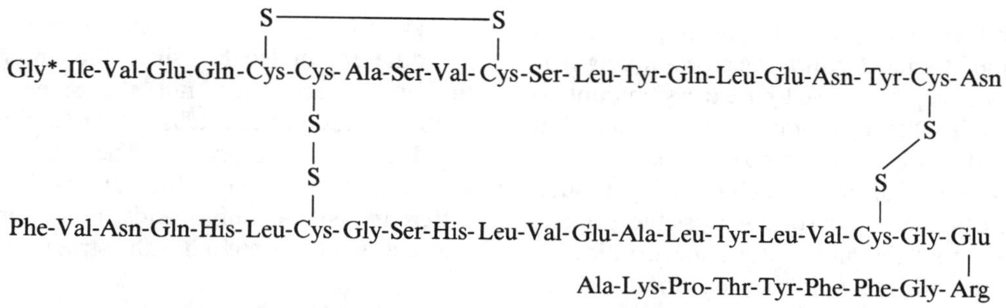

```
          S—————————————S
          |               |
Gly*-Ile-Val-Glu-Gln-Cys-Cys- Ala-Ser-Val- Cys-Ser- Leu-Tyr-Gln-Leu-Glu-Asn- Tyr-Cys- Asn
                         |                                                           |
                         S                                                           S
                         |                                                          /
                         S                                                        S
                         |                                                        |
Phe-Val-Asn-Gln-His- Leu-Cys- Gly-Ser-His- Leu-Val- Glu-Ala-Leu-Tyr-Leu-Val- Cys-Gly- Glu
                                                                                      |
                                            Ala-Lys-Pro-Thr-Tyr-Phe- Phe-Gly- Arg
```

*Abbreviations are standard ones for amino acids.

Figure 19-3   Primary structure of beef insulin

The primary structures of several hundred proteins have been determined since Sanger's experiment. The biological activity of a protein is related to its primary structure. A change of one amino acid in the sequence can alter biological function. The disease sickle-cell anemia is caused by an abnormal form of hemoglobin called hemoglobin S. In a normal hemoglobin molecule there are 534 amino acids arranged in four polypeptide chains. Two chains, each called alpha, have identical primary structures, and the other two, called beta, also have the same primary structure. If a glutamic acid at position six in one of the beta chains is replaced by valine, the disease-causing hemoglobin S is formed.

Secondary structure

Our picture at this point of a protein is as a chain of alpha amino acids. The chains take certain shapes, owing to electrostatic interactions between atoms within one chain or between chains. Three common shapes of proteins are the alpha helix, the beta pleated sheet, and the triple-stranded helix of collagen. Fundamental to these shapes is hydrogen bonding. In our discussion of water we introduced this concept. A hydrogen atom in one polar water molecule is attracted to an oxygen atom in another polar water mole-

cule. This electrostatic interaction between slightly positive hydrogen and slightly negative oxygen in different water molecules is a hydrogen bond. Similar interactions occur in proteins. A hydrogen atom attached to a nitrogen in one peptide linkage (N—H) is attracted to an oxygen atom in another peptide linkage (C=O). This attraction or hydrogen bond holds the protein in a definite shape. Therefore, the secondary structure of a protein is its shape due to hydrogen bonding between imino hydrogen

$$(-\overset{\mid}{N}-H)$$

of one peptide linkage and carbonyl oxygen

$$(-\overset{O}{\overset{\|}{C}}-)$$

of another peptide.

Alpha helix   In some polypeptide chains, hydrogen bonding occurs between the

$$\overset{O}{\overset{\|}{-C-}}$$

group of each amino acid and the

$$\overset{H}{\overset{\mid}{-N-}}$$

group of the amino acid that is four amino acids ahead in the same chain. A linear representation of this intrapeptide bonding is

$$-N-C-C-N-C-C-N-C-C-N-C-C-N-C-C-$$

In addition to the bond between amino acids one and five, there is also one between amino acids two and six, three and seven, and so forth. The shape of the protein with this kind of bonding is the *alpha helix*. (See Figure 19-4.) In this very stable structure there are 3.6 amino acids per turn of the helix. The turns of the helix can be likened to the grooves of a screw. Right-handed screws (clockwise turns) and left-handed screws (counterclockwise turns) are possible. The helices in proteins are righthanded.

The structure of the alpha helix was proposed in 1951 by Linus Pauling and Robert Corey. Examples of proteins with this secondary structure are wool, myoglobin, and hemoglobin. Two or more alpha helices may coil around each other to form a cable. Keratin in hair and fibrin in blood clots have alpha-helical cables.

Beta pleated sheets The work of Pauling and Corey also resulted in knowledge of another type of protein secondary structure, the *beta pleated sheet* (called beta because the alpha helix was studied first). In this secondary structure the polypeptide chains are stretched in a linear manner rather than being coiled. Hydrogen bonding occurs between the carbonyl groups and imino groups in adjacent polypeptide chains. (See Figure 19-5.) The strands may run in the same direction, in which case a *parallel* beta sheet

is formed, or in opposite directions, which is an *antiparallel* beta sheet. The direction depends on whether the N-terminal amino acids (those with free amino groups) are at the same end or opposite ends. Fibroin, the protein found in silk, has an antiparallel beta pleated sheet secondary structure. Silk fibers' strength and resistance to stretch are results of this structure.

Triple-stranded helix of collagen Collagen is a fibrous protein found in skin, bone, teeth, tendons, blood vessels, and cartilage. It is an unusual protein in that every third amino acid in its primary structure is glycine. The glycine content of most proteins is much lower. Collagen also contains a larger amount of the amino acid proline than most proteins. Recall that proline contains a five-membered ring including its nitrogen atom.

Collagen has a triple-stranded superhelical secondary structure. Each individual strand is also in the shape of a helix. There are no hydrogen bonds in these helices as in alpha helices; rather they take their shape to minimize repulsions between the rings in the prolines. (See Figure 19-6.)

Three of these helices wind around each other to form the superhelical cable, called *tropocollagen*. (See Figure 19-7.) Hydrogen bonding, mainly between

$$-N-H$$

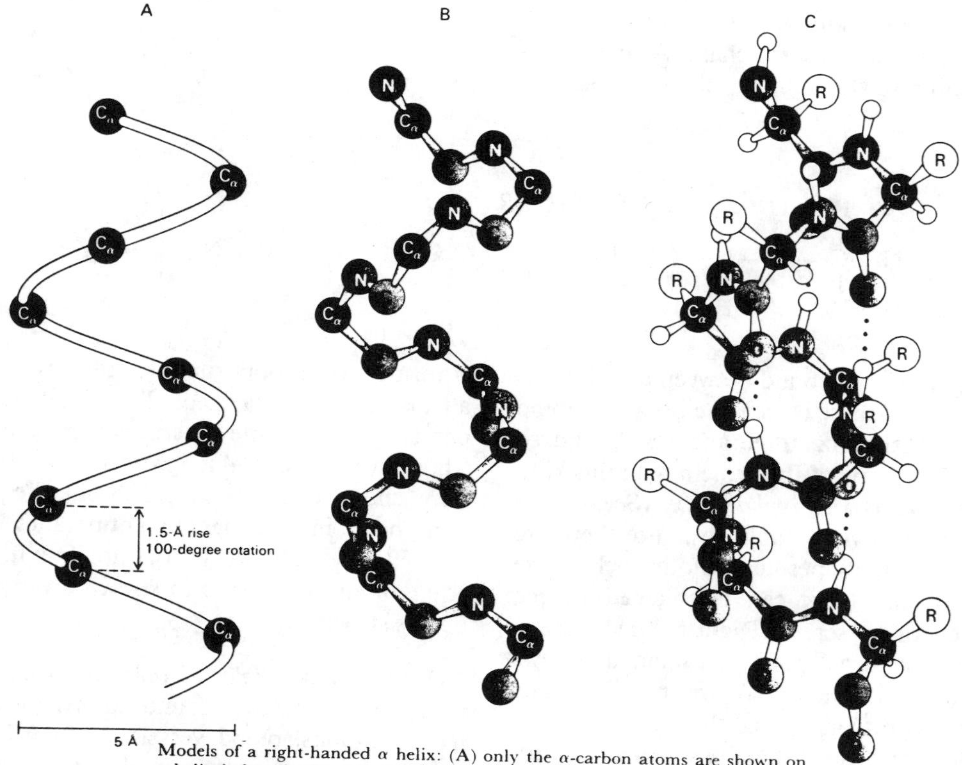

A

B

C

1.5-Å rise
100-degree rotation

5 Å

Models of a right-handed α helix: (A) only the α-carbon atoms are shown on a helical thread; (B) only the backbone nitrogen (N), α-carbon (C$_\alpha$), and carbonyl carbon (C) atoms are shown; (C) entire helix. Hydrogen bonds (denoted in part C by · · ·) between NH and CO groups stabilize the helix.

Figure 19-4 Alpha helix (from *Biochemistry*, second edition, by Lubert Stryer. W. H. Freeman and Company, 1981.)

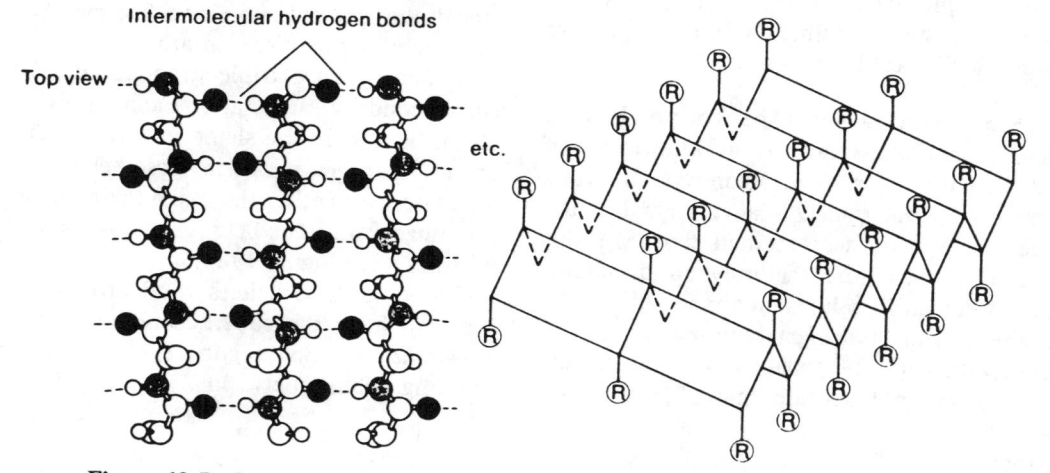

Intermolecular hydrogen bonds

Top view

etc.

Figure 19-5 Beta pleated sheet (from *Fundamentals of Organic Chemistry*, by C. David Gutsche and David J. Pasto. Prentice-Hall, 1975, p. 1044.)

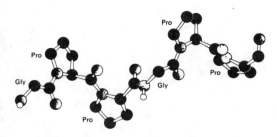

Conformation of a single strand of the collagen triple helix. The sequence shown here is -Gly-Pro-Pro-Gly-Pro-Pro.

Figure 19-6 Conformation of a single strand of the collagen triple helix (from *Biochemistry*, second edition, by Lubert Stryer. W. H. Freeman and Company, 1981.)

groups on glycines in one strand and

$$\overset{\displaystyle O}{\underset{\displaystyle \|}{-C-}}$$

groups in another strand, stabilizes the superhelix. This structure accounts for the large content of glycine in collagen. Glycine is the only amino acid small enough to fit in the superhelical structure and hydrogen-bond the strands.

An important characteristic of collagen is its high tensile strength. Besides having its strands linked together by hydrogen bonds, the collagen superhelix is stabilized by covalent bonds between side chains in the collagen amino acids. Also, covalent bonds cross-link one tropocollagen to another by intermolecular bonding. The amount of cross-linking in collagen can be increased by treating it with cross-linking agents such as formaldehyde. In this way the tanning industry converts animal skin to leather.

Tertiary structure

We have centered our discussion of the primary and secondary structures of proteins on interactions between the carboxyl group and amino group of the amino acids. Their interaction provides the basis of the primary structure by forming the peptide bond.

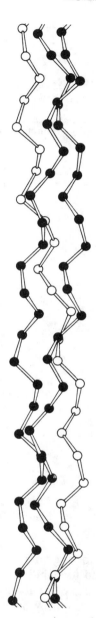

Model of the triple-stranded collagen helix. Only the α-carbon atoms are shown.

Figure 19-7 Model of the triple-stranded collagen helix (from *Biochemistry*, second edition, by Lubert Stryer. W. H. Freeman and Company, 1981.)

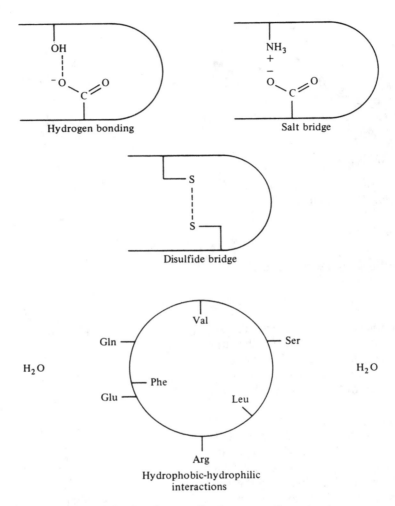

Figure 19-8   Bonds contributing to tertiary structure

Atoms participating in peptide bonds also hydrogen-bond to stabilize the protein's secondary structure. What about the many other atoms in the protein? What influence do the atoms in the R groups have on protein structure? Interactions between these groups are responsible for folding of the protein molecules, often into very compact shapes. This folding is referred to as the *tertiary structure*. Several types of bonds that influence the tertiary structure of a protein are hydrogen bonds, ionic bonds called salt bridges, disulfide bridges, and hydrophobic-hydrophilic interactions. (See Figure 19-8.)

Amino acids containing hydroxyl groups can hydrogen-bond to ionized carboxyl groups of acidic amino acids. If the amino acid serine is several amino acids away from the amino acid aspartic acid in a peptide chain, the chain may fold so that the serine's

—OH and aspartate's COO⁻ may interact. Similarly an acid-base interaction between basic amino acids and acidic amino acids forms *salt bridges* that contribute to folding. The —NH$_2$ group of lysine's side chain and the —COOH group of glutamic acid interact in this way. Folding is further stabilized by the forming of disulfide bridges between cysteine residues. This mechanism was discussed as a part of primary structure.

Also very significant in determining the shape of a protein are hydrophobic-hydrophilic interactions. *Hydrophobic* literally means "water fearing" and *hydrophilic* means "water loving." Those amino acids with nonpolar hydrocarbon side chains such as valine, leucine, and phenylalanine are hydrophobic. Hydrophilic amino acids have polar regions in their side chains. A few examples are serine, arginine, glutamic acid, and glutamine. Proteins in an aqueous environment will assume a shape that minimizes the contact between the hydrophobic side chains and water and maximizes the contact of the hydrophilic groups with water. A protein may form a sphere, a cigar-shaped structure, or a very random arrangement by keeping its nonpolar parts on the inside of the structure and the more polar parts on the outside. Water is squeezed out of the inner part of the structure away from the hydrophobic amino acids.

Quaternary structure

The complete structure of a protein with one polypeptide chain is described by its primary, secondary, and tertiary structures. Those proteins with more than one polypeptide chain have another level of structure called *quaternary*. The polypeptide chains in these proteins are called *subunits*. A protein's quaternary structure tells how the subunits are arranged. It has already been stated that hemoglobin consists of four polypeptide chains. These four chains arrange themselves tetrahedrally in one hemoglobin molecule. The quaternary structure of hemoglobin, therefore, is four subunits in a tetrahedral shape. Since hemoglobin performs the necessary function of carrying oxygen and carbon dioxide, its structure is described in detail in the next section.

HEMOGLOBIN

One molecule of hemoglobin contains a protein part, *globin*, and a nonprotein part, *heme*. Our knowledge of the three-dimensional structure of hemoglobin is due to the X-ray crystallography work of the British chemist, Max Perutz.

Every molecule of hemoglobin contains four polypeptide chains and four hemes. Two of the subunits, designated as alpha chains, each contain 141 amino acids. The other two, which are beta chains, each contain 146 amino acids. Each chain is in the form of an alpha helix and has a folded tertiary structure. There are no disulfide bridges within the structure. Noncovalent interactions occur among the chains, which have a tetrahedral quaternary structure. Nestled within the folds of each subunit is a molecule of heme.

The structure of heme is shown in Figure 19-9. It is composed of an atom of iron joined to an organic part called a *protoporphyrin ring*. The iron is bound to four nitrogens in this ring. The iron can also form two bonds on either side of the plane of heme. One of these bonds is to the amino acid histidine of the polypeptide chain. The other bond is to oxygen. In order to bind the oxygen the iron must be in the +2 oxidation state. Iron in the +3 oxidation state does not bind oxygen.

Since each molecule of hemoglobin contains four hemes, a little bookkeeping shows

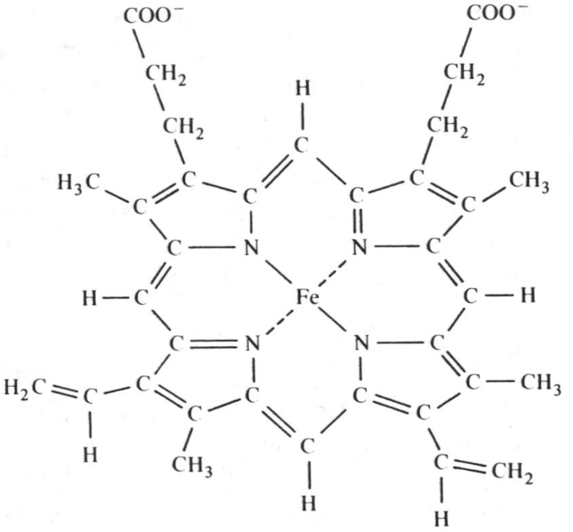

Figure 19-9   Structure of heme

one molecule of hemoglobin contains four iron atoms, four protoporphyrin rings, and carries four oxygens through binding to iron.

Hemoglobin carries oxygen in blood. A similar function is performed by *myoglobin* in muscle. A molecule of myoglobin contains one polypeptide chain and one heme. The protein portion contains 153 amino acids. The sequence is quite different from that of the alpha or beta chains of hemoglobin. However, the three-dimensional structure of myoglobin is very similar to one subunit of hemoglobin.

BREAKDOWN OF HEMOGLOBIN

Red blood cells have a lifespan of about 120 days. Their degradation occurs in the spleen. The protein portion of hemoglobin is metabolized to amino acids. Heme is degraded in a stepwise procedure to several compounds of interest to the embalmer. (See Figure 19-10.) In the first step heme is converted to *biliverdin*, a green compound. A molecule of carbon monoxide is also formed.

This production of toxic carbon monoxide is at a low enough level not to be detrimental to the organism. The second step is the reduction of biliverdin to *bilirubin*, a yellow compound. Both reactions require certain enzymes and coenzymes present in a living organism. The bilirubin is then carried by serum albumin to the liver, from which it is secreted as bile.

Why are these compounds important to the embalmer? Nondegraded hemoglobin is the cause of post-mortem stain. Approximately six hours after death, owing to hemolysis of red blood cells, hemoglobin may seep from the capillaries to the tissues. The pigment discolors the tissues, a condition known as post-mortem stain. These stains cannot be removed by normal arterial injection and venous drainage. If the stain is on the face, hands, or neck, masking cosmetics are usually used.

The breakdown products of hemoglobin, bilirubin and biliverdin, cause another cosmetic problem for the embalmer. This situation occurs in the embalming of a jaundiced human remains. What is jaundice? Normal human blood serum contains 0.1–1.5 mg bilirubin per 100 ml. Higher concentrations of serum bilirubin cause it to escape into the tissues. The resulting yellowing of the tissues is known as jaundice. Reaction of formaldehyde with the excess bilirubin reconverts it to biliverdin. As a result, the embalmed body has a greenish discoloration.

DENATURATION

A protein is *denatured* when its structure is changed in a way that modifies its properties. The extreme result of denaturation of a protein is loss of biological activity. In an aqueous solution denaturation is generally observed by precipitation of the protein. Denaturing agents interfere with the secondary

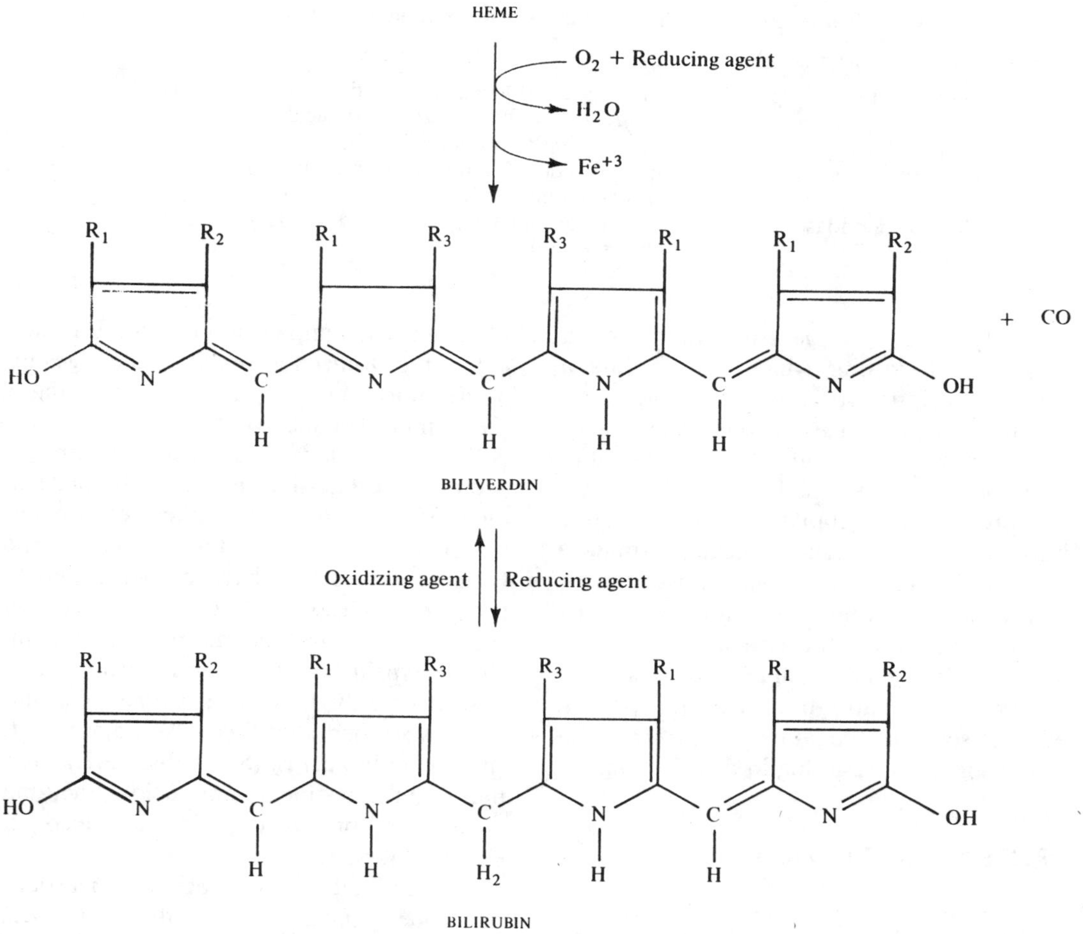

Figure 19-10 Degradation of heme to biliverdin and to bilirubin (Note: R_1 = methyl; R_2 = vinyl; R_3 = propionate.)

and tertiary structures of a protein. The protein may unfold and expose groups that are hydrophobic, causing precipitation. Addition of urea, concentrated acids or bases, salts of heavy metals, alcohol, or alkaloidal reagents and exposure to heat, light, X-rays, or ultraviolet radiation are common ways to denature a protein.

Denaturation by urea, which attracts hydrogen bonds, is usually reversible. De-

naturation by many other agents, however, is irreversible. When egg albumin is heated, hydrogen bonds are irreversibly broken, causing precipitation of egg white. Addition of a strong acid or base to a protein changes the pH. In this way salt bridges are broken, owing to changes in side-chain charges.

Denaturation may have both bad and good effects. Loss of biological activity by enzymes which have been denatured may

Table 19-2 Specificity of enzymes involved in protein digestion

Enzyme	Specificity
Pepsin (rather nonspecific)	Amine side of leucine, aspartic acid, phenylalanine, tyrosine, tryptophan, and aspartic acid
Trypsin (highly specific)	Carboxyl side of lysine and arginine
Chymotrypsin	Carboxyl side of tyrosine, tryptophan, phenylalanine, and methionine
Carboxypeptidase A	Carboxyl terminal peptide bond. Prefers aromatic or bulky side chains

seriously affect an organism. On the other hand, blood clotting, which is the result of protein precipitation, is a normal biological function. The use of alkaloidal reagents such as tannic and picric acid for the treatment of burns is another beneficial example of protein precipitation. Applying these agents to a burn precipitates tissue proteins, forming a natural bandage over the burn. Loss of moisture from the burned area and invasion by microorganisms are prevented.

The disinfectant action of alcohol is based on protein denaturation. Seventy percent ethanol solutions denature the protein content of bacteria, resulting in disinfection.

PROTEIN BREAKDOWN

We shall discuss two kinds of breakdown of proteins. One is the normal digestion of protein that occurs in our bodies after we ingest food. The other is putrefaction, the decomposition of protein, that occurs after death. These processes have both similarities and dissimilarities.

Digestion of protein

Protein breakdown into smaller molecules begins in the stomach. The reactions are all catalyzed by enzymes. Here in an acid environment the enzyme pepsin catalyzes the hydrolysis of peptide linkages adjacent to amino acids such as phenylalanine, tyrosine,

glutamic acid, and aspartic acid. The acid pH of the stomach also aids in the digestion by denaturation of the protein. Uncoiling of the compact shapes of some proteins provides better surface contact between the protein and digestive enzymes. The partially digested proteins, which are now smaller polypeptides, move to the small intestine, where enzymes that have been secreted by the pancreas essentially complete digestion. Important enzymes acting here are trypsin, chymotrypsin, elastase, and carboxypeptidase A and B. Like pepsin, these enzymes hydrolyze peptide linkages adjacent to specific amino acids. (See Table 19-2.) From the small intestine amino acids, the final products of protein digestion, are absorbed into the bloodstream.

In the blood the amino acids form a source of protein material called the *amino acid pool*. They may be removed from the pool to build new proteins for the body's use or may undergo oxidation. The final oxidation products of protein breakdown are carbon dioxide, water, urea, and energy. The energy liberated during the oxidative process is about 4 Kcal of heat per gram of protein. Urea is formed in the liver from carbon dioxide, water, and ammonia by a series of enzyme-dependent energy-requiring reactions. Urea has the following structure:

$$H_2N-\overset{\overset{\textstyle O}{\|}}{C}-NH_2$$

After its formation, urea is carried by the bloodstream from the liver to the kidneys, from which it is excreted in the urine.

Putrefaction

The anaerobic decomposition of proteins brought about by the action of enzymes is putrefaction. It begins after cellular death. The rate at which it occurs depends upon several factors, including temperature, humidity, moisture content of the body, and cause of death. It is favored by moisture and the presence of bacteria and increases with temperature. The rate of proteolysis also varies in different parts of the body. Generally, tissues that contain high concentrations of proteolytic enzymes are the first to be affected. Some examples are the lining of the gastrointestinal tract and the epithelium of the pancreas.

Putrefaction involves three major chemical reactions: hydrolysis, deamination, and decarboxylation.

Hydrolysis This chemical reaction initiates the putrefactive process. *Hydrolysis* is a chemical property of water. In this process, biological compounds are broken apart and the constituents of water are incorporated into their structures. Enzymes are necessary for the process to occur. As in digestion, amino acids are the final hydrolysis products of putrefaction. Intermediate products are proteoses, peptones, and polypeptides. Since these substances provide a good food source for bacteria, the number of microorganisms increases dramatically during putrefaction.

$$\text{Proteins} \xrightarrow{\text{enzymes}} \text{amino acids}$$

Deamination This reaction is the removal of the amino group from an amino acid. Each amino acid undergoes a specific reac-

tion, but in general ammonia and an organic acid are the products.

$$\text{Amino acid} \xrightarrow{\text{deamination}}$$
$$\text{ammonia} + \text{carboxylic acid}$$

The formation of ammonia as a product of putrefaction is significant to the embalming process. Formaldehyde reacts with ammonia, producing hexamethylene tetraamine or urotropin.

$$4\,NH_3 + 6\,CH_2O \longrightarrow$$
$$(CH_2)_6N_4 + 6\,H_2O$$

If extensive putrefaction has occurred before embalming, there will be a higher-than-normal formaldehyde demand due to this production of ammonia.

Decarboxylation By this reaction the carboxyl group of an amino acid is removed. The products are carbon dioxide, water, and an amine. The identity of the amine depends on the amino acid.

$$\text{Amino acid} \xrightarrow{\text{decarboxylation}}$$
$$\text{carbon dioxide} + \text{water} + \text{amine}$$

The amines may be further broken down into ammonia and various hydrocarbons.

Actually during putrefaction both deamination and decarboxylation occur simultaneously. Overall the decomposition of proteins produces hydrocarbons, organic acids, amines, ammonia, and carbon dioxide. In addition those amino acids containing sulfur liberate gaseous hydrogen sulfide.

CHAPTER SUMMARY

Preservation and disinfection of a human remains are accomplished by cross-linking of proteins. During life these compounds perform various structural and dynamic functions. Proteins are polymers of 20 amino acids. Each amino acid contains a carboxyl group, an amino group, and a characteristic group known as an "R group." Reaction between the carboxyl group of one amino acid and the amino group of another forms a molecule of water and joins the amino acids by the peptide linkage. Proteins are cross-linked by reaction of formaldehyde (HCHO) or of glutaraldehyde (a dialdehyde) at amide groups, at amine groups, and at peptide linkages.

The structure of proteins is studied at four levels: primary, secondary, tertiary, and quaternary. The primary structure is the amino acid sequence. The shape of a protein due to hydrogen bonding is the secondary structure. Three shapes are the alpha helix, the beta pleated sheet, and the triple-stranded helix of collagen. Folding of these shapes due to interactions between atoms in the R groups is the tertiary structure. Those proteins, such as hemoglobin, that are composed of more than one polypeptide chain have a quaternary structure, which is the arrangement of these chains, called subunits. A molecule of hemoglobin has four protein chains arranged tetrahedrally. Nestled within each chain is a molecule of heme, a nonprotein iron-containing compound which binds molecular oxygen.

Proteins may lose their biological activity by exposure to certain chemicals or forms of radiation. This is called denaturation.

Two processes that result in the breakdown of proteins are digestion and putrefaction. Both require enzymes. The final products of protein digestion are amino acids. Their oxidation yields carbon dioxide, water, urea, and energy. Putrefaction is the anaerobic decomposition of proteins that occurs after cellular death. Hydrolysis, deamination, and decarboxylation occur during putrefaction. The final decomposition products are hydrocarbons, organic acids, amines, ammonia, carbon dioxide, and hydrogen sulfide.

QUESTIONS

1. List all the amino acids having side chains that contain:
   (a) Hydrocarbons.
   (b) Hydroxyl groups.
   (c) Benzene rings.
   (d) Sulfur atoms.
   (e) Acid (carboxyl) groups.
   (f) Basic groups.
   (g) Amide groups.
   (h) Amino groups.

2. On the basis of question 1, divide the 20 amino acids into two groups: (a) polar and (b) nonpolar.

3. Define amphoterism. Explain how amphoterism enables amino acids and proteins to function as buffers in the blood.

4. What is the role of the peptide linkage in the cross-linking of proteins?

5. How does glutaraldehyde cross-link proteins in a different way than formaldehyde?

6. Distinguish among primary, secondary, tertiary, and quaternary structures of proteins.

7. What is the relationship of hemoglobin to post-mortem stain? to jaundice?

8. What is meant by denaturation of protein? List one good effect and one bad effect of denaturation.

9. List two similarities and two differences between digestion of protein and putrefaction of protein.

10. Predict the specific structural products of the deamination and decarboxylation of glycine and of alanine.

This chapter will discuss the most highly specialized type of proteins, the enzymes. Since they are proteins, everything discussed in the previous chapter applies to them. However, since they are so important—actually vital—to the functioning of an organism, they have additional unique properties.

ENZYME FUNCTION

Each cell in the human body has in excess of one thousand different enzymes. What do they do? They function as catalysts. Remember from Chapter 6 that a catalyst is a compound that speeds up a chemical reaction without itself being permanently changed. It does this by lowering the energy of acti-

actants must acquire this energy and form the transition state if they are to produce the products of the reaction.

In nonbiochemical reactions occurring in a laboratory situation reactants are sometimes heated to help them reach the transition state. The situation in the human body is different. Here, there must be a mechanism to help millions of chemical reactions to occur without an internal flame providing each with sufficient energies to reach its transition state. This is the function of enzymes. Interactions between enzymes and reactants produce a new reaction pathway with a lower energy of activation. (See Figure 20-2.) By the help of enzymes the transition state is acquired under conditions that are compatible with the environment of a cell.

Chapter 20
ENZYMES

vation of a reaction. Consider the reaction $A + B \longrightarrow C + D$. The reactants A and B have a certain energy, as do the products C and D. In order for the reaction to occur, the reaction must acquire an energy higher than either that of the reactants or the products. This higher energy state is the *transition state*. (See Figure 20-1.) The difference in energy between the reactants and the transition state is called the *energy of activation*. The re-

NOMENCLATURE

The compound or type of compound upon which an enzyme works is its *substrate*. Many enzymes are named by adding *-ase* to the root of the name of the substrate. An example is the enzyme *sucrase*. This enzyme catalyzes the hydrolysis of the sugar sucrose forming two simpler sugars, glucose and fructose. Similarly, *urease* catalyzes the

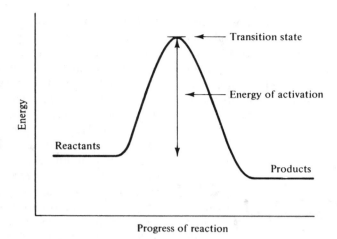

Figure 20-1 Energy pathway of a chemical reaction

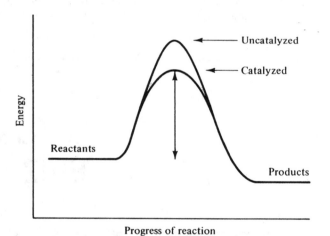

Figure 20-2 Comparison of energy pathway of a catalyzed and uncatalyzed reaction (note that the energy of activation is lowered by the catalyst)

breakdown of its substrate urea. There are also general classes of enzymes called *proteases* and *lipases*; protein breakdown is the work of the proteases and lipids are the substrates for lipases.

Most enzymes are characterized by the *-ase* ending. Some, however, were discovered and named before any set of rules of nomenclature had been determined. Frequently these enzymes were named according to their source. A good example are *zymases*, enzymes found in yeast. The Greek word *zyme* means "a leaven." These enzymes, as all good wine makers know, catalyze the fermentation of glucose to ethyl alcohol and carbon dioxide. The source of the word *enzyme* can also be traced to the Greek word *zyme*, since the first substances from which enzymes were isolated were yeasts.

CHEMICAL PROPERTIES OF ENZYMES

Enzymes, we have noted, are proteins. As proteins, they have a primary, secondary, and tertiary structure. If composed of subunits, they may also have a quaternary structure. Like other proteins, enzymes have a three-dimensional shape determined by interactions among the constituent amino acids. The shape of the enzyme must be complementary to that of its substrate so they may interact. The portion of the enzyme that binds to the substrate is called the *active site* or *catalytic center*. The active site, a relatively small part of the entire enzyme molecule, is a three-dimensional entity with a shape that must be matched by that of the substrate. Experimental studies on enzyme structures show the active sites to be clefts or crevices within the entire molecule's shape.

Specificity of action

The fact that enzyme and substrate must fit together is the basis of this property. Enzymes are very specific concerning the type of reactions they catalyze and what substrates they bind. There are varying degrees of specificity among enzymes. Sucrase and urease show absolute specificity for their substrates. Sucrase catalyzes only the hydrolysis of sucrose. It will not work with other sugars. Likewise, urea and urease are a one-to-one substrate-enzyme pair. A lesser degree of specificity is shown by some proteases, which split any peptide linkage. The activity of other proteases is dependent on the amino acid side chains attached to the peptide bonds. Chymotrypsin splits only those

THROMBIN

Figure 20-3 Specificity of thrombin

peptide bonds next to aromatic amino acids. This enzyme is said to be *linkage specific*. An extremely linkage-specific protease is the clotting factor thrombin. It hydrolyzes only peptide linkages that have arginine on the carboxyl side of the peptide linkage and glycine on the amino side. (See Figure 20-3.)

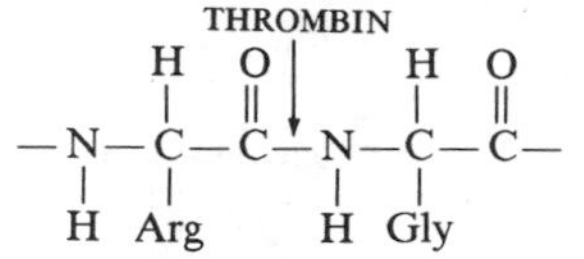

Specificity of action is a major difference between the catalytic properties of enzymes and classical inorganic catalysts. These catalysts such as platinum and nickel can act as catalysts for many reactions. The specificity of biological catalysts accounts for the large number of different enzymes in every living cell.

The stereospecificity existing between an enzyme and its substrate was described in 1890 by Emil Fischer's *lock and key theory*. According to this theory, the binding of the active site of an enzyme and its substrate is analogous to the complementary shapes that a lock and key must have. Recent studies have shown that many active sites are less rigid. They assume the shape of the substrate only after binding occurs. Interactions between enzyme and substrate before binding induce a fit between them. This is a more dynamic picture of the complementarity between enzyme and substrate.

pH sensitivity

Since enzymes are proteins, their activity is influenced by the hydrogen-ion concentration of their environment. The secondary and tertiary structures of an enzyme may be altered by changes in pH. Such alterations

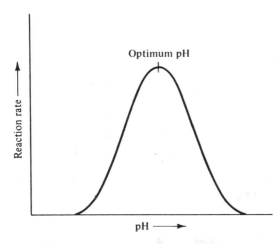

Figure 20-4   Effect of pH on enzymes

affect the proper fitting together of an enzyme and substrate. Enzymes have an optimum pH at which they function most effectively. A typical curve relating reaction rate to pH is seen in Figure 20-4. The optimum pH for most enzymes is close to physiological pH of 7.2–7.4. However, those that function in the stomach, such as pepsin, have a very acid optimum pH. Likewise, trypsin, which digests protein in the small intestine, most effectively catalyzes at an alkaline pH of 8.2.

Temperature sensitivity

Heat denatures proteins. Therefore high temperatures will destroy the activity of enzymes. Low temperatures also affect the activity of enzymes; reaction rates decrease as the temperature decreases. Most enzymes have an active temperature range of 10° to 50°C. As is to be expected, the optimal temperature for enzymes in the human body is 37°C.

REGULATION OF ENZYME ACTIVITY

The activity of most enzymes is regulated. Some mechanisms of regulation are (1) proenzymes, (2) cofactors, (3) allosteric enzymes, and (4) chemical inhibitors.

Proenzymes

This form of regulation is characteristic of digestive enzymes and of some enzymes involved in the clotting of blood. The digestive enzymes pepsin and trypsin are initially formed as the inactive compounds pepsinogen and trypsinogen. When they are needed to digest ingested proteins, they are converted into their active forms. Pepsinogen is secreted by the gastric mucosa. The acid pH of the stomach activates it. Similarly trypsinogen is formed in the pancreas and is converted to trypsin by the enzyme enterokinase found in intestinal juice. These conversions occur only after protein has been ingested. The formation of these enzymes as inactive forms is a protective mechanism. The same is true in the blood-clotting process, since our bodies are not constantly in need of enzymes that promote the clotting of blood. Several reactions are involved in the blood-clotting process. Formation of a clot depends on the conversion of prothrombin to thrombin.

Prothrombin $\longrightarrow$ thrombin
(inactive)   (active)

The enzyme thrombin catalyzes the conversion of fibrinogen to fibrin. Fibrinogen is a soluble blood protein. Cleavage of part of its structure by thrombin forms fibrin, insoluble fibers that constitute the clot.

Dissolving of blood clots is controlled by another enzyme, plasmin. It is first formed in the inactive form, proplasmin.

Inactive precursors of enzymes are called *proenzymes* or *zymogens*. Many can be recognized by their characteristic *-ogen* ending.

Cofactors

Some enzymes must be bound to a nonprotein substance in order to function. These nonprotein parts are *cofactors*. Two types of cofactors are metal ions and organic molecules called *coenzymes*.

The enzyme hexokinase, which catalyzes the first step in our bodies' degradation of glucose, requires Mg^{+2}. Other common metal cofactors are zinc, manganese, copper, and iron. They must be included in our diets for proper enzyme functioning.

Several of the enzymes that occur in the Krebs cycle require coenzymes. The *Krebs cycle* is a series of reactions forming the common metabolic pathway that our bodies use for extracting energy from ingested carbohydrates, lipids, and proteins. The coenzymes of this pathway are either vitamins or compounds derived from vitamins.

Allosteric enzymes

Many of the compounds that our bodies synthesize are formed by a stepwise series of reactions. Each reaction is catalyzed by enzymes. When enough of the desired product has been synthesized, there must be a way to stop the pathway. One way to do this is by a process known as *feedback inhibition*. Let's consider a pathway by which D is being synthesized from A with intermediate formation of B and C.

$$A \xrightarrow{E_1} B \xrightarrow{E_2} C \xrightarrow{E_3} D$$

When sufficient D has formed for the needs of the cell, its presence inhibits the activity of E_1, the first enzyme in this pathway. In this way the series of reactions stops until the cell again needs compound D, the end product. The activity of E_1 is sensitive to the concentration of D. When D's concentration is low, the enzyme works; when D's concentration is high, the enzyme is deactivated. The inhibition of the enzyme occurs by compound D's binding to it at a site other than that of the active site. This site is called an *allosteric site*. Binding of the inhibitor to it changes the shape of the enzyme so that it no longer fits the substrate. An enzyme whose activity can be controlled in this way is called a *regulatory enzyme* or an *allosteric enzyme*.

An example of a regulatory enzyme is phosphofructokinase (PFK). It regulates the breakdown of glucose. The final end product of this breakdown is adenosine triphosphate (ATP). When ATP concentration is sufficient for cellular needs, PFK is inhibited. When ATP concentration is low, PFK is activated.

Inhibitors

Enzyme activity can be inhibited by foreign molecules introduced into a living organism. The effects of enzyme inhibition may be good or bad. The mechanisms of some drugs and many poisons are based on their ability to inhibit enzyme activity. Two types of inhibition are competitive and noncompetitive.

In *competitive inhibition* the inhibitor competes with the normal substrate for the active site of the enzyme. The inhibitor and substrate must have similar shapes or structures. We have seen that an enzyme and its substrate must fit together at the active site. When they interact, they form an enzyme-substrate complex, which later in the reaction breaks apart to form the products and free enzyme. Binding of the inhibitor to the enzyme's active site prevents formation of this enzyme-substrate complex. Instead, an enzyme-inhibitor complex forms which does not lead to the products of the reaction. Competitive inhibition is a reversible process. Normal enzyme functioning is restored in the absence of the inhibitor.

An example of competitive inhibition is the action of the sulfa drugs on bacteria. In order to grow, bacteria need folic acid, which they synthesize from paraaminobenzoic acid (PABA). The sulfa drugs, one example being sulfanilamide, are very similar in structure to PABA.

PABA   Sulfanilamide

If a person is suffering from a disease caused by bacteria, he may be administered sulfanilamide. It competes with PABA for the active site of the bacterial enzyme which synthesizes folic acid. If sufficient quantities of the drug are present, essentially all of the enzyme will be bound to the inhibitor. The bacteria, unable to multiply, can then be destroyed by the body's normal defense mechanisms.

Another example of competitive inhibition is the treatment for ingestion of either ethylene glycol or methyl alcohol. Both of these substances are enzymatically degraded to poisonous substances. Oxidation of ethylene glycol eventually produces oxalic acid and, as we have already seen, oxidation of methyl alcohol produces formaldehyde. Both

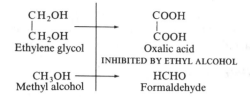

Figure 20-5 Inhibition of oxidation of ethylene glycol and methyl alcohol by ethyl alcohol

oxidations are catalyzed by alcohol dehydrogenase. The same enzyme also catalyzes the oxidative breakdown of ethyl alcohol. Inhibition of this enzyme's activity on both ethylene glycol and methyl alcohol can be achieved by administering to a person near-intoxicating amounts of ethyl alcohol. The enzyme will act on the ethyl alcohol, allowing the ethylene glycol or the methyl alcohol to be excreted without being decomposed to its toxic products. (See Figure 20-5.)

Another type of inhibition of enzyme activity is caused by *noncompetitive inhibitors*, substances which bind to the enzyme at some point other than the substrate binding site. The poison cyanide functions in this way. It binds to metal ions that are essential to the activity of enzymes called cytochrome oxidases. A final step in the series of reactions by which cells extract energy from nutrients involves the reduction of molecular oxygen. The electrons are carried by iron and copper ions which are part of the cytochrome oxidases. The cyanide ion binds to the metal ions, preventing the transfer of electrons, which in turn stops the process of cellular respiration. A fatal dose of cyanide in humans can be as low as 50 mg.

THE ROLE OF ENZYMES IN DECOMPOSITION

The enzymes catalyzing the decomposition of human remains are generally *proteolytic* (dissolve protein) and *hydrolytic* (mediate hydrolysis reactions) in nature. There are two distinct sources of these putrefactive catalysts, saprophytic bacteria and lysosomes. *Saprophytic bacteria* use dead organic matter as a source of nutrition. These organisms are normal residents of the human digestive tract. After death has occurred, they translocate and proliferate, using any available necrotic tissue as a food source. In addition to bacterially mediated decomposition, animal cells possess their own "self-destruct" mechanism. In life, organelles (little organs) called *lysosomes* provide the digestive function of human cells. After death, the pH change from alkaline to acid causes rupture of the membrane surrounding the lysosome. Unenclosed by their compartment, these enzymes digest the surrounding cellular substances. The process is called *autolysis*—literally, self cell digestion. Thus, even if we could totally sterilize a human remains, we would eliminate only one source of decompositive enzymes, the bacteria. The other source, the autolytic enzymes, would still have to be inactivated, because they are an integral part of the cellular structure.

CHAPTER SUMMARY

Enzymes are proteins that function as biological catalysts. They lower the energy of activation of chemical reactions, so these reactions may occur at conditions compatible with cellular environments.

The compound or type of compound on which an enzyme works is its substrate. Many enzymes are named by adding the ending *-ase* to the root of the substrate. An enzyme and its substrate bind at a specific site on the enzyme molecule. This site is usually a small portion of the entire enzyme molecule and is called an active site or catalytic center. A unique property of enzymes is specificity of action. For many enzymes and their substrates, there is an exclusive one-to-one pairing of enzyme and substrate. Others have lesser degrees of specificity, but, nevertheless, the structure of the substrate must fit that of the enzyme. Proper fit and hence enzyme activity are influenced by pH and temperature, since enzymes are proteins.

To maintain efficient harmony among cellular reactions, enzyme activity must be controlled. Mechanisms for regulation are proenzymes, cofactors, allosteric enzymes, and chemical inhibitors.

Two sources of enzymes that catalyze the decomposition of human remains are saprophytic bacteria of the digestive tract and lysosomes of the cells. Autolysis, self cell digestion, is caused by enzymes liberated from the lysosomes when the pH change from alkaline to acid occurs after death.

QUESTIONS

1. Show by a diagram the meaning of the energy of activation of a reaction and the transition state. What effect do enzymes have on the energy of activation?

2. Give examples of two enzymes with absolute specificity and two with linkage specificity.

3. What does *allosteric* mean? Give an example of an allosteric enzyme.

4. Explain the difference between competitive and noncompetitive inhibition. Give an example of each.

5. What is meant by the optimal pH of an enzyme? Why does pH influence enzyme activity?

6. What are two sources of enzymes that catalyze the decomposition of human remains?

7. What does *autolysis* mean?

8. Explain the significance of the endings *-ogen* and *-ase* on names of chemical compounds.

This chapter will discuss carbohydrates, a major type of biochemical compound. Ingestion of carbohydrates is generally considered a means for a living organism to acquire energy. Carbohydrates also act as storage molecules of chemical energy and as structural parts of cell walls and membranes.

Within a cell, the carbohydrates are fewer in number and in type than proteins.

DEFINITION AND CLASSIFICATION

The word *carbohydrate* is a synthesis of the two words "carbon hydrate." The molecular formulas of many of these compounds may be written to look like carbon hydrates. For instance, the molecular formula of glucose is

the ketone group in the structures of carbohydrates. Those that are aldehydes are called *aldoses*. Ketonic carbohydrates are referred to as *ketoses*. Third, the definition also says that carbohydrates contain the alcohol functional group. (See Figure 21-1.)

Carbohydrates are classified into three groups: monosaccharides, disaccharides, and polysaccharides. *Saccharide* is from the Latin word *saccharon*, which means "sugar." The monosaccharides are simple sugars that cannot be hydrolyzed to a smaller carbohydrate molecule. *Disaccharides* can be hydrolyzed into two monosaccharide units. *Polysaccharides* are carbohydrates that upon hydrolysis form many monosaccharide units. In the laboratory hydrolyzing agents are usually acid and heat. In our bodies specific enzymes

Chapter 21
CARBOHYDRATES

$C_6H_{12}O_6$. If this is rearranged to $(C \cdot H_2O)_6$ it looks like a hydrate containing carbon. However, carbohydrates are *not* hydrates. Rather, they are organic compounds containing carbon, hydrogen, and oxygen that are aldehyde or ketone derivatives of polyhydroxy alcohols. This definition has three important parts. First, it tells what elements are present in carbohydrates. Second, it tells you to expect to find either the aldehyde group or

catalyze the hydrolysis of the various carbohydrates.

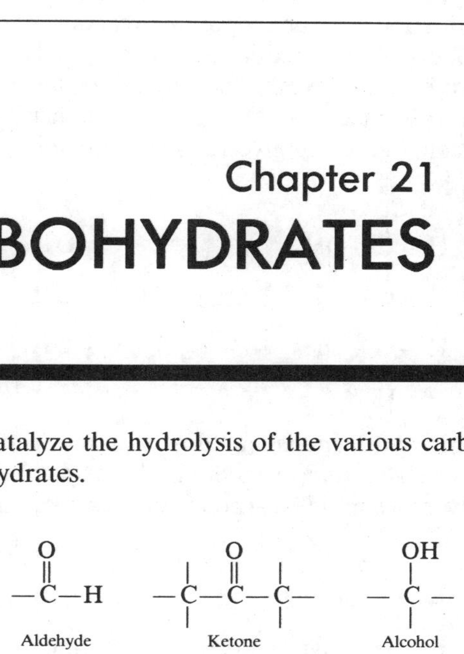

Figure 21-1 Functional groups found in carbohydrates

MONOSACCHARIDES

These simple sugars are further classified on the basis of the number of carbon atoms in their structure.

Number of carbons	Type of monosaccharide
3	Triose
4	Tetrose
5	Pentose
6	Hexose
7	Heptose

The ending -ose is characteristic of carbohydrates. Specific attention will be given to the trioses, pentoses, and hexoses.

Trioses

These compounds are aldehyde and ketone derivatives of the trihydroxy alcohol glycerol. In Chapter 14 you learned that oxidation was an important reaction of alcohols. Upon oxidation primary alcohols produce aldehydes, and secondary alcohols produce ketones. Oxidation of either end alcohol group of glycerol yields an aldehyde.

This compound is an aldose with the specific name glyceraldehyde. Similarly, oxidation of glycerol's middle carbon produces a ketone.

The product, which is a ketose, is named dihydroxyacetone. These two trioses are important intermediates when our bodies metabolize carbohydrates.

Pentoses

Pentoses contain five carbons. Two pentoses of interest are ribose and 2-deoxyribose. They are both aldoses.

Ribose   2-Deoxyribose

The difference between them is that 2-deoxyribose contains one less oxygen than ribose. The oxygen at carbon number 2 of ribose is removed to form 2-deoxyribose. Numbering of the carbons starts with the aldehyde carbon.

The significance of these compounds is that they form the sugar portion of nucleic acids. Hydrolysis of RNA (ribonucleic acid) yields ribose. Likewise 2-deoxyribose is a hydrolysis product of DNA (deoxyribonucleic acid).

Hexoses

Hexoses are simple sugars that contain six carbons. Of all the monosaccharides they are the most important nutritionally. Their molecular formula is $C_6H_{12}O_6$. Twenty-four isomeric forms can be drawn from this formula. The most significant hexoses are glucose, fructose, and galactose. Glucose and fructose occur freely in nature. Galactose is found only in combined forms. Both glucose and galactose are aldoses, while fructose is a ketose. These classifications can be verified by looking at their structures.

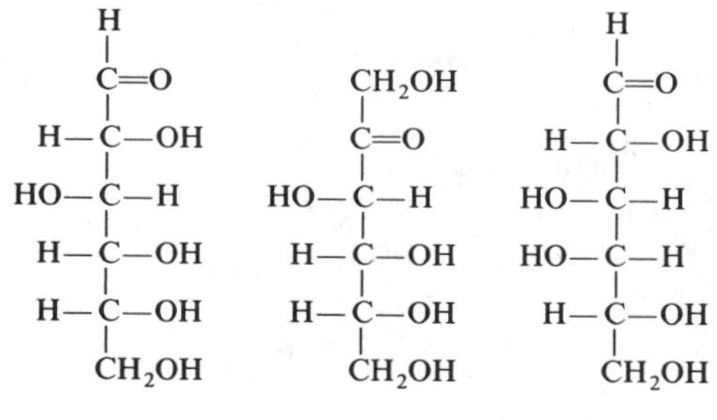

| Glucose | Fructose | Galactose |

These structures represent open-chain forms of the sugars. In solution they also exist as cyclic compounds. Their formation results from a reaction between the aldehyde or ketone functional group and an alcohol functional group within one sugar molecule. The reaction between an aldehyde and alcohol produces a *hemiacetal*.

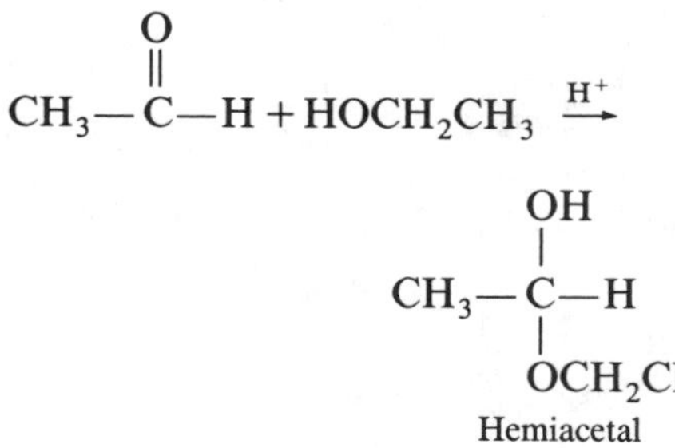

Hemiacetal

Likewise, ketones react with alcohols forming *hemiketals*.

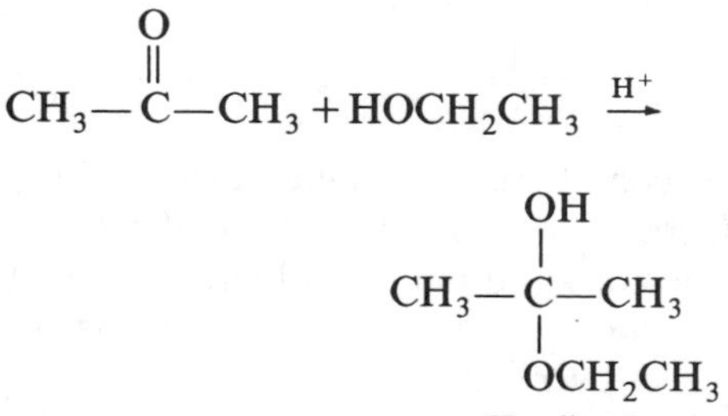

Hemiketal

To see how the sugars form cyclic compounds, first we will look at glucose. The process involves three steps: (1) Number the carbons on glucose beginning with the aldehyde carbon. (2) Fold the chain so that carbon 1 and carbon 5 are close to one another. The cyclization reaction occurs between groups attached to these carbons. (3) React the aldehyde group of carbon 1 with the alcohol group of carbon 5 to close the ring. (See Figure 21-2.)

The production of the cyclic hemiacetal is reversible. The hemiacetal group is a potential free aldehyde group. When it forms, the OH on carbon 1 may be either below the plane of the ring as in the representation in Figure 21-2 or above the plane. The two isomers are distinguished as α-glucose (OH below the plane) and β-glucose (OH above the plane). In a solution, glucose exists in three different forms: open chain, α-isomer, and β-isomer. (See Figure 21-3.) An equilibrium exists between the three forms with approximate amounts of 0.02% open chain, 36% α-glucose, and 64% β-glucose.

The same kind of cyclization reaction occurs for galactose. An open chain and two ring forms are present in solution. (See Figure 21-4.) The only difference between glucose and galactose is the direction of the OH on carbon 4.

Fructose, a ketose, forms ring compounds by a reaction between its carbonyl group on carbon 2 and the hydroxyl group on carbon 5. The resulting product is a five-membered ring. Both alpha and beta forms exist, depending on the orientation of OH groups at position 2. Stepwise ring closure of fructose is shown in Figure 21-5.

Glucose   This is the normal sugar of the blood. Its metabolism provides energy for the cells. Our bodies normally maintain a constant blood glucose level of 70–90 mg per

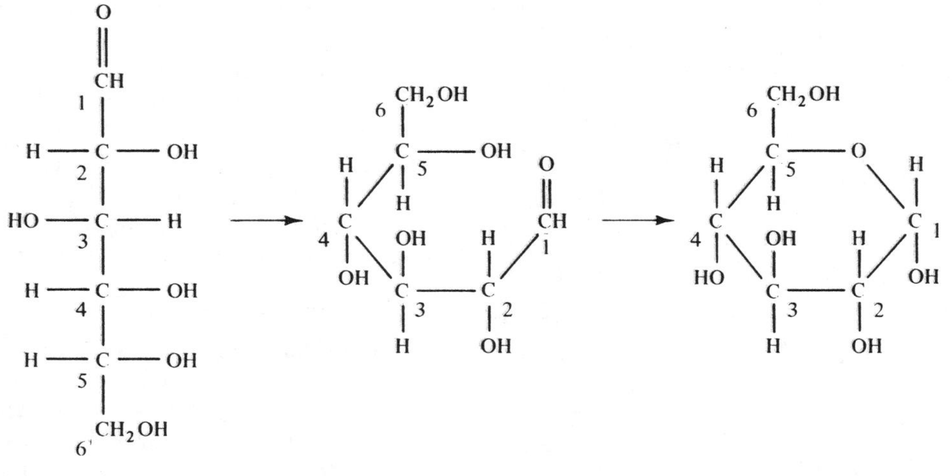

Figure 21-2 Cyclization of glucose

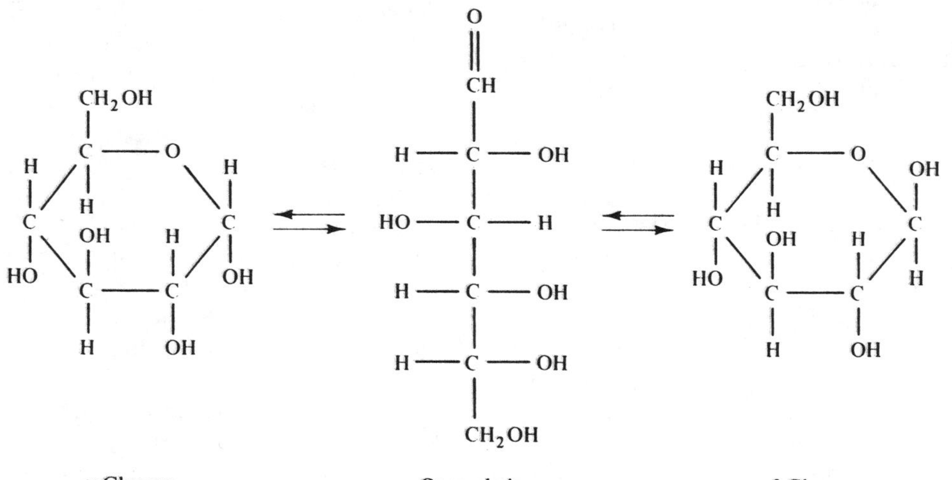

α-Glucose　　　　　　　Open chain　　　　　　　β-Glucose

Figure 21-3 Forms of glucose in solution

100 ml of blood. If the level increases above this range, glucose is converted into glycogen, a glucose polymer, which is stored in liver and muscle. The hormone insulin, produced by the pancreas, controls this process. Insufficient production of insulin results in the condition of diabetes mellitus. A high glucose blood level is *hyperglycemia*. The opposite condition, low blood sugar, is *hypoglycemia*. It is corrected by conversion of stored liver glycogen to free glucose. The hormones epinephrine and glucagon are es-

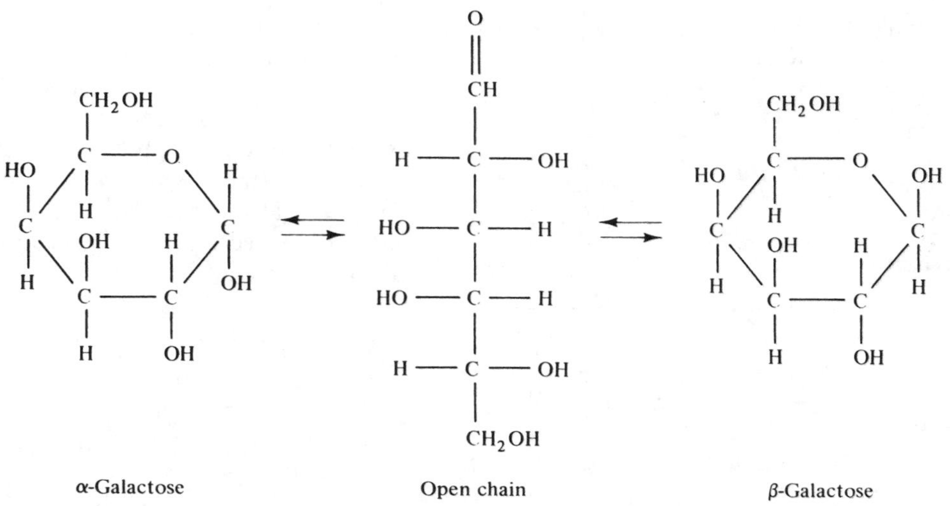

Figure 21-4 Forms of galactose in solution

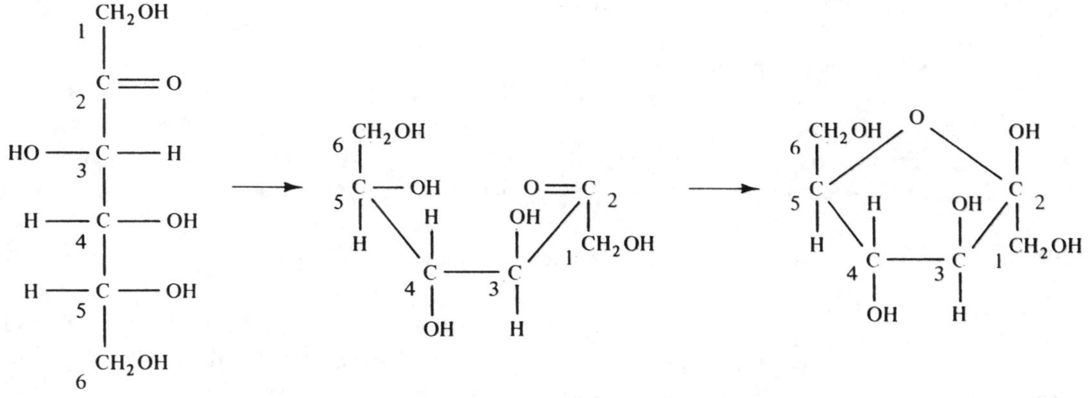

Figure 21-5 Cyclization of fructose

sential for the conversion. Epinephrine is produced by the adrenal glands and glucagon by the pancreas.

Two other names for glucose are *dextrose* and *grape sugar*. Solutions labeled dextrose are given intravenously to hospital patients for nourishment. As the name grape sugar suggests, grapes are a good source of glucose.

It is also found in honey and in the saps of plants.

Galactose This aldose does not occur freely in nature. It is found in brain and nervous tissue as a component of compounds called *cerebrosides* (see Chapter 22). Nutritionally it is formed from the hydrolysis of

Table 21-1   Sweetness of sugars in comparison to sucrose

Sugar	Relative sweetness
Lactose	0.16
Galactose	0.22
Maltose	0.32
Glucose	0.74
Sucrose	1.00
Invert sugar	1.30
Fructose	1.73

the disaccharide lactose. This sugar is in milk. Galactose also polymerizes to form *agar-agar*, which is found in seaweed and is used to solidify broth in microbiology.

Fructose   As we saw earlier, fructose is a ketose. Other names for it are *levulose* and *fruit sugar*. It is found in honey in a one-to-one ratio with glucose, in many fruits, and in human semen.

Fructose is the sweetest of the sugars. The relative sweetness of various sugars compared to sucrose (table sugar) is listed in Table 21-1. Sucrose is arbitrarily given a value of one in these comparisons.

DISACCHARIDES

Disaccharides (two sugars) are carbohydrates that can be hydrolyzed to two monosaccharide units. The general formula for all disaccharides is $C_{12}H_{22}O_{11}$. They are formed when two monosaccharides combine by splitting out a molecule of water.

$$2 \; C_6H_{12}O_6 \longrightarrow C_{12}H_{22}O_{11} + H_2O$$

The three major disaccharides are lactose, maltose, and sucrose.

Lactose

Lactose, also called *milk sugar*, is synthesized in mammary glands from glucose in the blood. Human milk contains about 6% to 8%

lactose. When milk sours, lactose is converted into lactic acid by the microorganism *Lactobacillus*. Lactic acid is responsible for the taste and smell of sour milk and forms curds by denaturing the protein in milk.

Lactose is formed by a dehydration reaction between galactose and glucose. Reaction occurs between carbon 1 of galactose and carbon 4 of glucose:

Lactose

Two products, lactose and water, are formed.

Hydrolysis of lactose yields its constituent monosaccharides, galactose and glucose. The necessary enzyme is lactase.

$$\text{Lactose} \xrightarrow{\text{lactase}} \text{galactose} + \text{glucose}$$

Children of African, Middle Eastern, and Oriental descent frequently have the condition known as *lactase deficiency*. Their lack of lactase prevents hydrolysis of lactose to the simpler monosaccharides. Lactose is not able to be absorbed. It stays in the walls of the small intestine, where its presence causes retention of water. If a person with lactase deficiency eats lactose, he suffers from diarrhea and often abdominal cramps. Children with lactase deficiency are generally fed milk substitutes rather than natural milk. As people grow older, their production of lactase may decrease, so frequently adults also have lactase deficiency.

Maltose

Maltose, a disaccharide, is found in germinating grains. It is also produced by enzymes called *amylases* that break down starch. Sources of these enzymes are yeast, saliva, and malt. Another name for maltose is *malt sugar*.

This disaccharide is formed by the union of two glucose units. Similar to lactose, a molecule of water is formed when the two monosaccharides link between carbon 1 of one glucose and carbon 4 of the next.

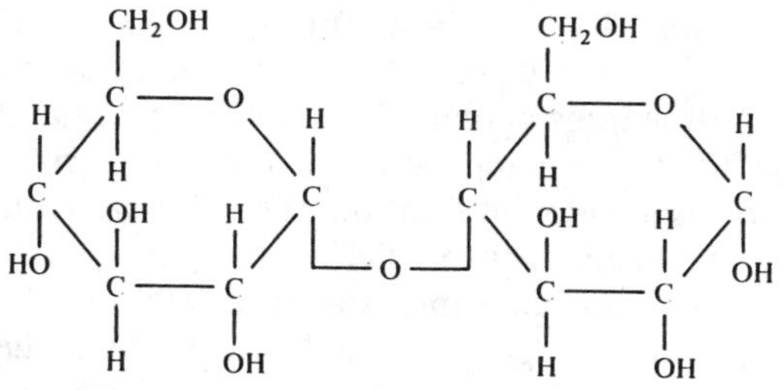

Maltose

Hydrolysis of maltose produces two molecules of glucose. This reaction is catalyzed by maltase.

$$\text{Maltose} \xrightarrow{\text{maltase}} 2 \text{ glucose}$$

Sucrose

Probably the most frequently used disaccharide is sucrose, common table sugar. It is also referred to as *cane sugar*. Two of its natural sources are sugar cane and sugar beets.

One molecule of sucrose is composed of the two monosaccharides, fructose and glucose. The linkage is between carbon 2 of fructose and carbon 1 of glucose. As in the formation of the other disaccharides, a molecule of water is produced when the monosaccharides bond.

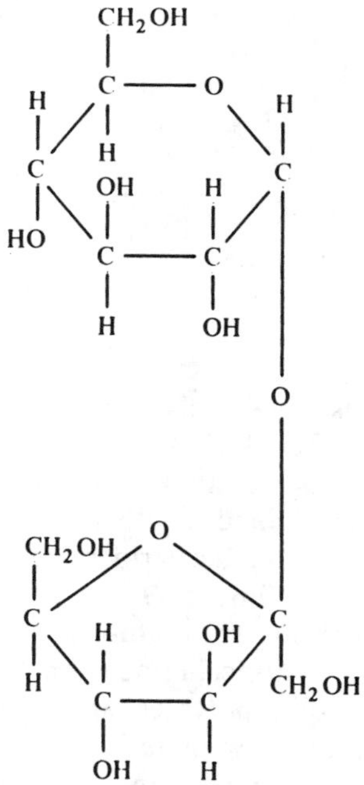

Sucrose

Hydrolysis of sucrose occurs by the action of sucrase.

$$\text{Sucrose} + \text{H}_2\text{O} \xrightarrow{\text{sucrase}} \text{glucose} + \text{fructose}$$

A one-to-one mixture of fructose and glucose is produced. This mixture, called *invert sugar*, also occurs naturally in honey. Cooking of some fruits or berries with sucrose produces invert sugar. Since these foods contain acids, sucrose is hydrolyzed by the heating process. Invert sugar is sweeter than sucrose.

POLYSACCHARIDES

Compounds in the third major group of the carbohydrates are polysaccharides. Upon hydrolysis these compounds yield many mono-

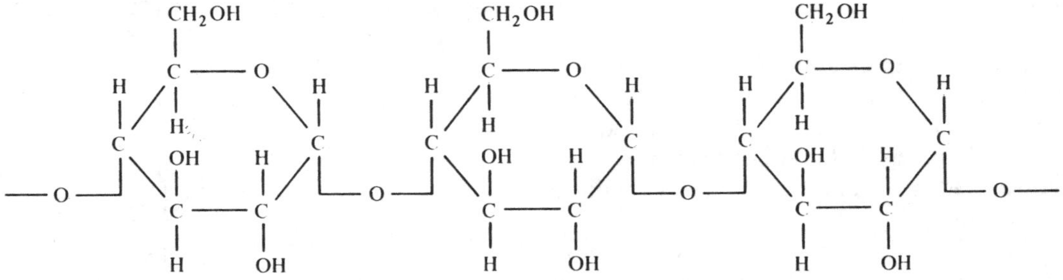

Figure 21-6 Structure of amylose

saccharides. The polysaccharide molecular formula is $(C_6H_{10}O_5)_X$, where X, a large number, indicates that many monosaccharide units are joined together.

Common polysaccharides are starch, glycogen, and cellulose. Their properties are quite different from those of monosaccharides and disaccharides. An obvious difference is that polysaccharides have much higher molecular weights. Polysaccharides are tasteless in contrast to the sweet taste of the other carbohydrates. There is also a difference in water solubility. The monosaccharides and disaccharides are water soluble. Polysaccharides either are insoluble in water or form colloidal solutions.

Starch

Plants make glucose by the process of photosynthesis. They store this energy source in the form of *starch*, a polymer of glucose. There are two forms of starch. One, called *amylose*, is a straight chain of glucose molecules linked from the first to the fourth carbons. (See Figure 21-6.) Molecular weights of amylose range from 10,000 to 50,000 depending on the source. The other form of starch, *amylopectin*, has a molecular weight of 300,000 to 1 million. It is a branched chain of glucoses joined from carbon 1 to

carbon 4 and carbon 1 to carbon 6. (See Figure 21-7.) In both forms of starch the glucose molecules are in the alpha form. Most starchs contain 20%–25% amylose and 75%–80% amylopectin. The amylose portion forms a colloidal solution in hot water, while amylopectin is insoluble.

Humans consume starch chiefly in the form of rice, potatoes, and cereal grain. The large starch molecules are broken down enzymatically to smaller and smaller units. One product of this breakdown is the disaccharide maltose. Complete hydrolysis of starch produces many glucoses. Partial hydrolysis is done with acid and heat in a laboratory situation to produce compounds called *dextrins*. They are composed of several glucoses with alpha 1–4 linkages and an alpha 1–6 linkage. When wet, dextrins are sticky, making them good pastes and mucilages.

Glycogen

Another large, branched polymer of glucose is *glycogen*. Also called *animal starch*, it is the storage form of carbohydrates in humans and in higher animals. Like amylopectin it contains α-glucoses linked from carbon 1 to carbon 4, with branching occurring from carbon 1 to carbon 6. It has a higher molecular weight than amylopectin and more fre-

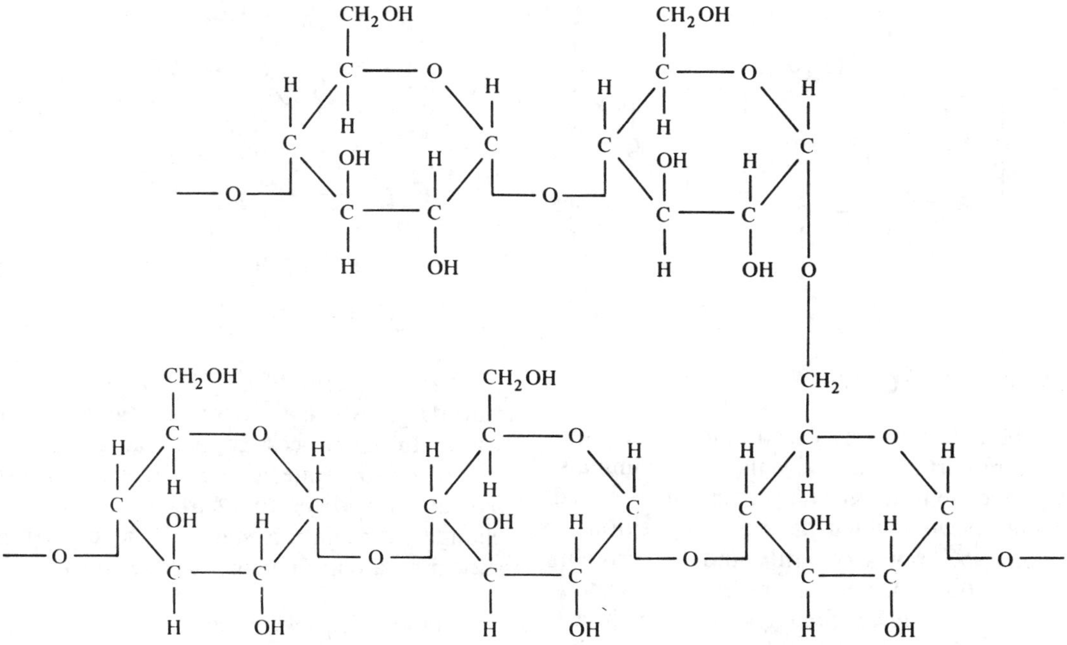

Figure 21-7 Structure of amylopectin

quent branching. In amylopectin, branches occur at about every 30 glucose units, while in glycogen there is a branch for every 10 glucoses.

Excess glucose ingested by animals is polymerized to glycogen and stored mainly in muscle and liver. One function of the liver is to maintain a relatively constant concentration of glucose in the blood. By enzymatic breakdown of glycogen, glucose is released from the liver if the blood glucose level decreases. Similarly, muscle glycogen is broken down by enzymes to satisfy muscle energy needs.

Cellulose

The most abundant organic compound in the biosphere is cellulose. It is the major component of cell walls and woody struc-tures of plants. Cellulose is similar to amylose, since both are unbranched polymers of glucose units. They differ in that cellulose contains beta carbon 1 to carbon 4 linkages. (See Figure 21-8.)

Cellulose is insoluble in water. Humans and most animals cannot digest it, since they lack the necessary enzyme to break the beta linkages. Grazing animals, such as cows, sheep, and horses, and also termites are able to digest cellulose. They have microbes in their digestive tracts which produce the enzymes for cellulose digestion.

An important source of cellulose is cotton. Treatment with sodium hydroxide increases its strength. This process, named *mercerization*, converts the cotton to a form suitable for clothing. By other chemical reactions, familiar products such as rayon and cellophane are also made from cellulose.

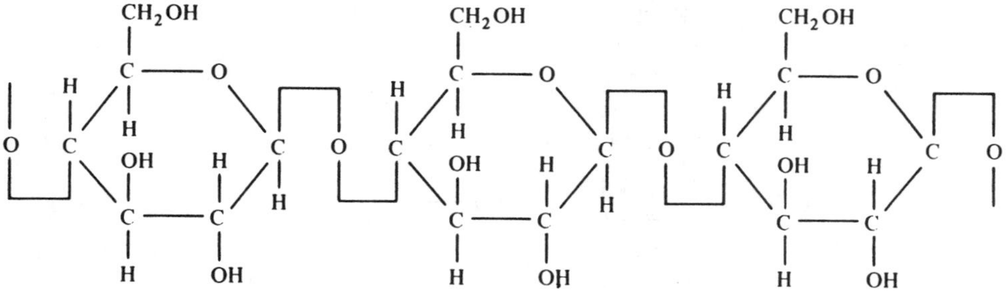

Figure 21-8 Structure of cellulose

PROTEOGLYCANS

Carbohydrates are also found as an important part of connective tissue in mammals. Connective tissue contains compounds called *proteoglycans*, which have a composition of about 95% polysaccharide and 5% protein. The polysaccharide chains of the proteoglycans are *glycosaminoglycans*, which are composed of disaccharide repeating units. Examples are hyaluronate, chondroitin-6-sulfate, and heparin. (See Figure 21-9.) The negative portions bind to water and positive ions. Both hyaluronate and chondroitin-6-sulfate are found in the ground substance or intercellular cement of connective tissue. Heparin, which has anticoagulant properties, is found in the walls of large arteries and in the liver and in the lungs.

REACTIONS OF CARBOHYDRATES

As we have seen, carbohydrates contain hydroxyl groups and either an aldehyde or ketone group. When drawn in the ring form, the aldehyde or ketone groups are potential. The reactions of carbohydrates are largely determined by the properties of these groups.

Reducing agents

Some carbohydrates can be oxidized to carboxylic acids. In such reactions the carbohydrates are reducing agents. A typical oxidizing agent for carbohydrates is $Cu(OH)_2$, which undergoes reduction to Cu_2O. In this process copper changes from a $+2$ oxidation state to $+1$, while the carbohydrate is oxidized to a carboxylic acid. The change in oxidation state of the copper is shown by a color change of blue to red.

$$\text{Sugar} + 2\ Cu(OH)_2 \xrightarrow{\text{heat}}$$
$$\text{blue solution}$$

$$\text{carboxylic acid} + Cu_2O\downarrow + 2\ H_2O$$
$$\text{red-orange}$$

This reaction is the basis for *Benedict's test* and *Fehling's test* for carbohydrates. Those which react positively are called *reducing sugars*. All monosaccharides and all disaccharides except sucrose are reducing sugars. Polysaccharides give a negative result. They are *nonreducing sugars*.

These tests are used in clinical laboratories to test for glucose in urine. Urine from a person with normal carbohydrate metabolism gives a negative result.

Hydrolysis

As we have seen, hydrolysis is the breakdown of a compound into simpler units by addition of the components of water. To review:

1. Monosaccharides do not undergo hydrolysis.

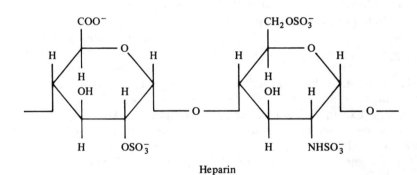

Figure 21-9   Structures of proteoglycans

2. Disaccharides upon hydrolysis form monosaccharides.

Lactose + H_2O ⟶ galactose + glucose
Maltose + H_2O ⟶ glucose + glucose
Sucrose + H_2O ⟶ fructose + glucose

3. Polysaccharides are first hydrolyzed to disaccharides and then, upon complete hydrolysis, to monosaccharides.

$$\underset{\text{Polysaccharide}}{\text{Starch}} + H_2O \longrightarrow \underset{\text{Disaccharide}}{\text{Maltose}}$$

$$\underset{\text{Disaccharide}}{\text{Maltose}} + H_2O \longrightarrow \underset{\text{Monosaccharide}}{\text{2 Glucose}}$$

Oxidation

Complete oxidation of monosaccharides produces carbon dioxide, water, and energy. For every gram of sugar that is oxidized about 4 Kcal of heat are liberated.

$$C_6H_{12}O_6 + 6\ O_2 \longrightarrow$$
$$6\ CO_2 + 6\ H_2O + heat$$

In our bodies carbohydrates (mainly in the form of glucose) follow certain metabolic pathways to produce heat and other forms of energy, with carbon dioxide and water as waste products. These pathways are enzymatically controlled and involve a series of reactions, in contrast to the one equation previously written for complete oxidation.

Fermentation

The process by which zymase, an enzyme in yeast, produces ethyl alcohol from hexoses is *fermentation*. Galactose is not fermented by zymases. Carbon dioxide is also a product of the reaction.

$$C_6H_{12}O_6 \xrightarrow{\ zymase\ } 2\ C_2H_5OH + 2\ CO_2$$

Disaccharides must first be enzymatically converted to monosaccharides before fermentation occurs. Except for lactose, yeast also contains the necessary enzymes for hydrolysis reactions of disaccharides.

Starch in grains may be used as a source of ethyl alcohol. The starch is first converted by amylase and maltase to glucose, which undergoes the fermentation reaction.

Starch $\xrightarrow{\ amylase\ }$ maltose $\xrightarrow{\ maltase\ }$ glucose

Glucose $\xrightarrow{\ zymase\ }$ ethyl alcohol + carbon dioxide

If the source of the starch is corn, the overall process produces bourbon. Scotch whiskey is formed if the starting material is barley.

Photosynthesis

Green plants are able to synthesize carbohydrates from carbon dioxide and water. The process called *photosynthesis* needs sunlight, the green pigment chlorophyll, and certain enzymes. The overall equation for formation of hexoses is

$$6\ CO_2 + 6\ H_2O \xrightarrow[light]{chlorophyll} C_6H_{12}O_6 + 6\ O_2$$

Actually photosynthesis is a very complex process which is divided into stages: the light reactions and the dark reactions. The *light reactions* occur in the chloroplasts of plants. Chlorophyll absorbs sunlight and converts it into chemical energy in the form of energy-storage molecules. Two of the products of the light reactions are oxygen and adenosine triphosphate. Subsequently, the *dark reactions* use the energy-storage molecules to convert carbon dioxide into carbohydrates. Light is not necessary for these reactions.

The processes of photosynthesis, ingestion of plants by animals and man, and oxidation of the carbohydrate material represent a cycle. By absorption of sunlight, the low-energy compounds, carbon dioxide and water, form higher-energy carbohydrate compounds. Animals and humans extract energy from them through oxidation, reforming carbon dioxide and water, which are again available for intake by plants.

SYNTHESIS OF ATP

How do our bodies extract energy from carbohydrates? The process can be divided into four stages. In the first stage ingested or stored carbohydrates are hydrolyzed to simple sugars such as glucose. In the second

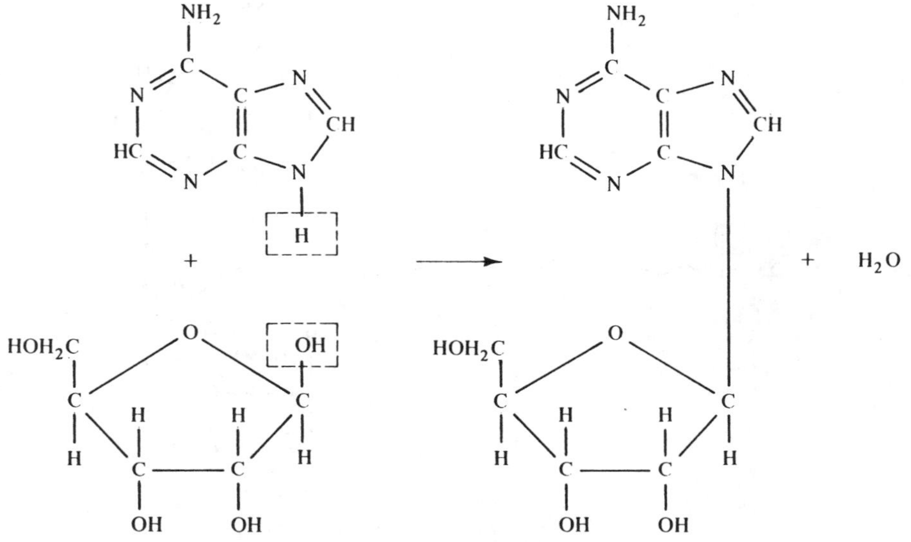

Figure 21-10   Formation of adenosine

stage glucose is converted into the acetyl unit $(CH_3—\overset{\overset{\displaystyle O}{\|}}{C}—)$ of the compound *acetyl coenzyme A*. Stage three is the Krebs cycle, and the fourth stage is a series of reactions called *oxidative phosphorylation*. During the second, third, and fourth stages *adenosine triphosphate*, ATP, is synthesized. This compound represents the major energy-carrier molecule in our bodies. Its hydrolysis to *adenosine diphosphate*, ADP, liberates the energy used by most of the energy-consuming processes in our bodies.

Structure of ATP

We will first look at the structure of ATP and then at the three ATP-generating stages of carbohydrate metabolism. Adenosine triphosphate is composed of one molecule of adenosine and three phosphate groups joined together as a triphosphate unit. Adenosine is formed by a dehydration reaction between ribose and adenine. We have seen that ribose is a five-carbon sugar. Adenine is a heterocyclic compound whose basic properties are due to its nitrogen content. The reaction for the formation of adenosine is shown in Figure 21-10.

As we have seen in many other chemical reactions, the driving force of this reaction is the formation of a molecule of water. Consequently a carbon atom from the sugar is joined to a nitrogen in the five-membered ring of the base. By another dehydration reaction, the $HOCH_2$ group of the sugar and the OH group of a phosphate form adenosine monophosphate. Stepwise addition of two more phosphates yields ADP and ATP. Figure 21-11 shows the structures of these compounds. The phosphates are shown ionized as they would be at physiological pH.

NH$_2$

Adenosine monophosphate (AMP)

Adenosine diphosphate (ADP)

Adenosine triphosphate (ATP)

Figure 21-11 Structures of AMP, ADP, and ATP

Hydrolysis of ATP produces ADP, inorganic phosphate (P$_i$), and energy.

$$ATP + H_2O \rightleftharpoons ADP + P_i + energy$$

The reverse reaction occurs during a synthesis of ATP by living organisms. The cells in our bodies are constantly extracting energy from ATP and then resynthesizing it from ADP, inorganic phosphate, and energy obtained from fuel molecules. Fundamental to life is the ATP–ADP cycle.

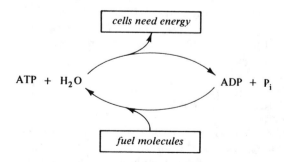

In most cells an ATP molecule is hydrolyzed within a minute of its formation.

Glycolysis

We begin our study of the formation of ATP by assuming that, after digestion of food and absorption of nutrients into the bloodstream, glucose has reached the cytoplasm of cells. Here, by a series of reactions called *glycolysis*, one molecule of glucose is converted into two molecules of pyruvate (Figure 21-12) and the cell gains two molecules of ATP. The process involves several steps (Figure 21-13) that can be expressed by the following net reaction:

$$\text{glucose} + 2\,P_i + 2\,ADP + 2\,NAD^+ \longrightarrow$$
$$2\text{ pyruvate} + 2\,ATP + 2\,NADH$$
$$+ 2\,H^+ + 2\,H_2O \qquad (1)$$

In this equation NAD^+ stands for *nicotinamide adenine dinucleotide*. It is derived from the vitamin niacin and acts as a coenzyme. We learned in Chapter 20 that some enzymes need helper molecules, coenzymes, for proper functioning. The purpose of NAD^+ is to undergo a reduction in the form of

$$NAD^+ + XH_2 \longrightarrow NADH + H^+ + X$$

by which it receives a hydrogen as a hydride ion from an intermediate XH_2 in the pathway. The fate of the formed NADH will be discussed later.

It is important to remember at this point that the conversion of glucose to pyruvate occurs in the cytoplasm with a net production of two ATP's. Depending on cellular conditions the pyruvate may follow two different pathways. If the supply of oxygen is low, pyruvate is reduced to lactate. This condition occurs in muscles during strenuous exercise and in cells after somatic death. The reaction is

$$\text{pyruvate} + NADH + H^+ \longrightarrow$$
$$\text{lactate} + NAD^+$$

$$
\begin{array}{c}
COO^- \\
| \\
C{=}O \\
| \\
CH_3
\end{array}
$$

Figure 21-12   Structure of pyruvate

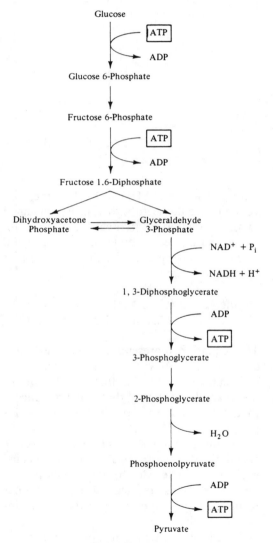

Figure 21-13   Reactions of glycolysis

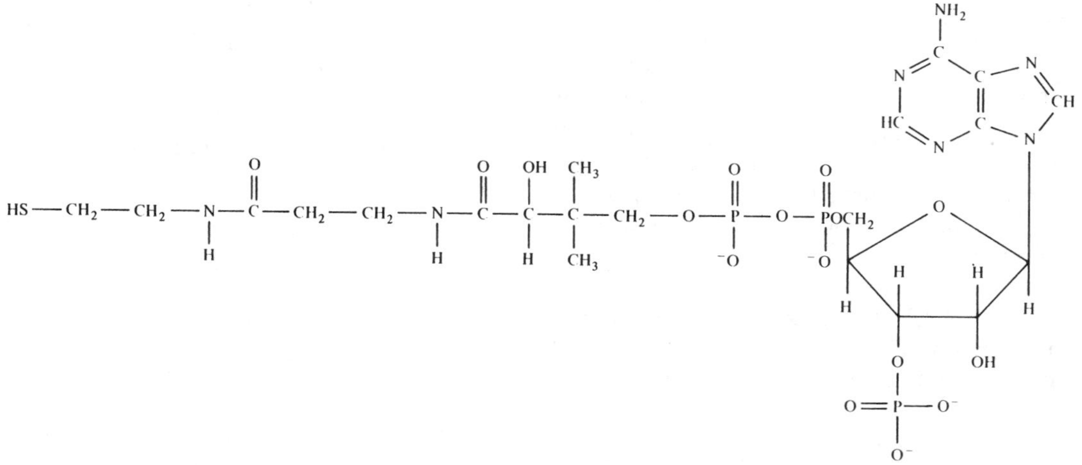

Figure 21-14 Structure of coenzyme A

Notice that the NADH formed in the conversion of glucose to pyruvate is consumed in the reduction of pyruvate. NAD$^+$ is reformed so that equation (1) can occur again.

The overall equation for the conversion of glucose to lactate is

$$\text{glucose} + 2\ P_i + 2\ ADP \longrightarrow$$
$$2\ \text{lactate} + 2\ ATP + 2\ H_2O$$

This equation represents an anaerobic process. Molecular oxygen is not necessary for it to occur. One way to define glycolysis is as the anaerobic pathway that converts glucose to lactate with the net production of 2 ATP's per glucose.

During strenuous muscle activity lactate accumulates in muscle cells, eventually causing fatigue. After death, when cells are no longer receiving oxygen, the lactate that forms during anaerobic glycolysis causes increased acidity.

When sufficient oxygen is present in a cell, lactate does not form. Instead pyruvate is oxidized to acetate in the form of acetyl coenzyme A.

$$\text{pyruvate} + NAD^+ + \text{CoA} \longrightarrow$$
$$\text{acetyl CoA} + CO_2 + \text{NADH}$$

Coenzyme A is a large organic molecule (Figure 21-14) which acts as a cofactor in many enzyme-catalyzed reactions. Acetyl CoA is formed by linking an acetyl group to coenzyme A at its terminal sulfhydryl group. The structure of acetyl CoA is abbreviated as

$$\overset{\displaystyle O}{\underset{\displaystyle \parallel}{H_3C-C}}-S-CoA$$

The reaction for the formation of acetyl CoA from pyruvate occurs in the mitochondria of cells. Acetyl CoA next enters the Krebs cycle.

Krebs cycle

The *Krebs cycle*, also known as the *citric acid cycle* and the *tri-carboxylic acid cycle*, is the common pathway for carbohydrate, lipid, and protein metabolism. In the last section we saw how glucose is ultimately converted

Table 21-2   Krebs-cycle intermediates formed from amino acids

Intermediate	Amino acid
Acetyl CoA	Isoleucine
	Leucine
	Tryptophan
α-Ketoglutarate	Glutamic acid
	Glutamine
	Histidine
	Proline
	Arginine
Succinyl CoA	Isoleucine
	Methionine
	Threonine
	Valine
Fumarate	Tyrosine
	Phenylalanine
	Aspartic acid
Oxaloacetate	Asparagine
	Aspartic acid

to acetyl CoA. Catabolism of fatty acids from lipids and of certain amino acids also produces acetyl CoA. Some amino acids are broken down to other Krebs-cycle intermediates and enter it in the form of these compounds. (See Table 21-2.)

Our discussion concerns the entry of acetyl CoA into the Krebs cycle and the energy derived from it. An overall diagram of the cycle is shown in Figure 21-15. The names of its intermediates are given with their number of carbon atoms. Products of the various steps are shown leading away from the cycle. These products include carbon dioxide, ATP, and hydrogen carriers that will participate in the fourth stage of the energy-extracting process.

The cycle begins with the two-carbon acetyl unit of acetyl CoA joining a four-carbon compound, *oxaloacetate*. The result is a six-carbon tricarboxylic acid, *citric acid*, which is called *citrate* in its ionized form. The other two names for the Krebs cycle are based on formation of this acid. Isomerization of citrate to *isocitrate* is followed by its

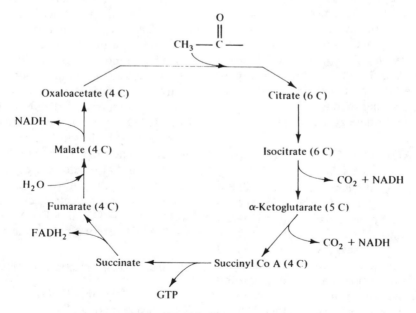

Figure 21-15   The Krebs cycle

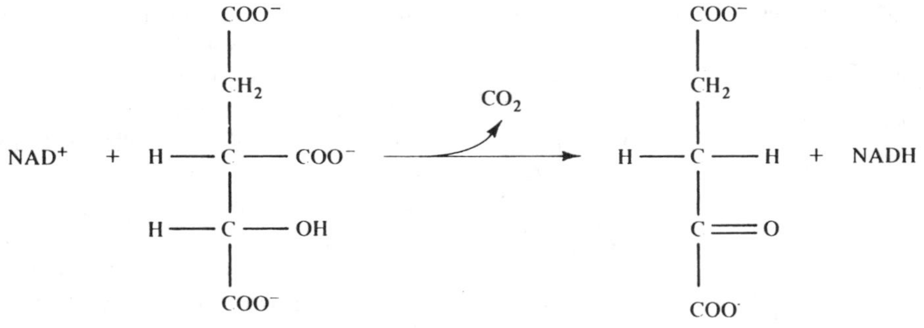

$$NAD^+ \;+\; \begin{array}{c} COO^- \\ | \\ CH_2 \\ | \\ H\!-\!C\!-\!COO^- \\ | \\ H\!-\!C\!-\!OH \\ | \\ COO^- \end{array} \quad \xrightarrow{\;\;CO_2\;\;} \quad \begin{array}{c} COO^- \\ | \\ CH_2 \\ | \\ H\!-\!C\!-\!H \\ | \\ C\!=\!O \\ | \\ COO^- \end{array} \;+\; NADH$$

Figure 21-16 Conversion of isocitrate to α-ketoglutarate

oxidative decarboxylation. This is the first of four oxidation-reduction reactions in the cycle. Its products are carbon dioxide and a five-carbon compound, *alpha-ketoglutarate*. The coenzyme NAD^+ must be simultaneously converted to NADH (Figure 21-16). Next, alpha-ketoglutarate undergoes oxidative decarboxylation, forming carbon dioxide and succinyl CoA. Again transfer of hydrogen must occur producing another NADH.

Succinyl CoA is an energy-rich compound. It transfers its energy to *guanosine diphosphate* (GDP) by a phosphorylation reaction that yields *succinate* and *guanosine triphosphate* (GTP). GDP and GTP are similar to ADP and ATP except that they contain the base guanine rather than adenine. GTP easily transfers a phosphate group to ADP

$$GTP + ADP \;\rightleftharpoons\; GDP + ATP \qquad (2)$$

so at this step of the Krebs cycle, one ATP is formed. The enzyme for equation (2) is *nucleoside diphosphokinase*, affectionately known as "nudiki" (nu-dee-kai)!

The rest of the cycle involves reactions of four-carbon compounds by which succinate is converted to oxaloacetate. Two oxidations occur with the formation of two more molecules of hydrogen carriers, another NADH and a new carrier called *flavin adenine di-*

nucleotide (FAD). The vitamin riboflavin is a precursor of this coenzyme.

At this point of the cycle, oxaloacetate has been regenerated for another turn.

What are the important facts to be remembered about the Krebs cycle? First, the reactions occur within the mitochondria of a cell. Second, the starting compound is acetyl CoA. Two carbons enter the cycle as its acetyl unit and two carbons leave the cycle in the form of two molecules of carbon dioxide. The two that enter are not removed in the same turn that they have entered. Third, and most important, one ATP is synthesized per turn of the cycle and four molecules of hydrogen carriers, three NADH's and one $FADH_2$, are formed. When NADH is formed from NAD^+, it adds the hydrogen as a hydride ion, a hydrogen atom with an extra electron. The formation of $FADH_2$ from FAD involves the addition of two hydrogen atoms. As hydrogen carriers, NADH and $FADH_2$ are also electron carriers. In comparison to NAD^+ and FAD, both NADH and $FADH_2$ carry a pair of electrons.

Electron-transport chain

The NADH and $FADH_2$ formed in the Krebs cycle next undergo a series of oxidation–reduction reactions which constitute an

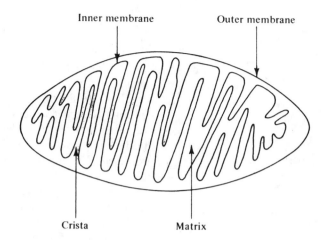

Inner membrane   Outer membrane

Crista   Matrix

Figure 21-17   Structure of mitochondria

electron-transport chain. As electrons are passed along the chain, energy is released. The energy phosphorylates ADP, forming ATP. Most of the ATP formed during the oxidation of glucose is produced by the electron-transport chain. The ultimate acceptor of the electrons is molecular oxygen. Overall equations for the oxidation of NADH and $FADH_2$ are

$$NADH + H^+ + \tfrac{1}{2} O_2 \longrightarrow NAD^+ + H_2O$$
$$FADH_2 + \tfrac{1}{2} O_2 \longrightarrow FAD + H_2O$$

Actually many steps occur as the electrons are passed form either NADH or $FADH_2$ to O_2. These reactions occur in the inner membrane of mitochondria. Often referred to as the "powerhouses of the cell," they are oval-shaped structures with a double membrane (Figure 21-17). The inner membrane is extensively folded into ridges called *cristae*. This inner membrane bounds a space called the *matrix*. The enzymes for the electron-transport reactions are located on the inner membrane. Most of the reactions of the Krebs cycle occur in the matrix.

As electrons are transferred from NADH to O_2, they are carried by four types of compounds: (1) flavoproteins, (2) iron–sulfur proteins, (3) coenzyme Q, and (4) cytochromes. The process of electron transport may seem overwhelming, but we can simplify it by remembering that each step is an oxidation-reduction reaction. As one compound loses electrons, the next in the chain gains them. The first step is NADH's transferring two electrons to a flavoprotein. These compounds are enzymes (protein), which have as their coenzymes flavin mononucleotide.

$$NADH + \underset{ox}{flavoprotein} \longrightarrow$$
$$NAD^+ + \underset{red}{flavoprotein}$$

When NADH loses the pair of electrons, they are gained by the flavoprotein, changing it to its reduced form. The electrons are next gained by an iron–sulfur protein, which changes from its oxidized form to its reduced form.

$$\underset{red}{Flavoprotein} + \underset{ox}{Fe\text{—}S\ protein} \longrightarrow$$
$$\underset{ox}{flavoprotein} + \underset{red}{Fe\text{—}S\ protein}$$

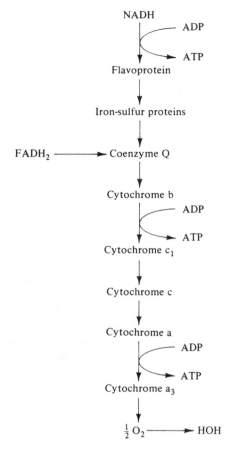

Figure 21-18 Reactions of the electron-transport chain

There are five cytochromes in the chain. The last, cytochrome a_3, also contains copper. This cytochrome transfers the electrons to molecular oxygen for the final reaction of the chain.

How are all these oxidation-reduction reactions related to the synthesis of ATP? As the electrons are transferred from one compound to the next in the chain, energy is released. Starting with oxidation of a pair of electrons from NADH to NAD^+, there are three places in the chain where enough energy is released to add a phosphate unit to ADP. Each NADH that undergoes oxidation yields three ATP molecules. Since $FADH_2$ enters the chain at a later point (coenzyme Q), the transfer of its pair of electrons produces two molecules of ATP. The process by which ATP forms as electrons are transferred from NADH or $FADH_2$ to molecular oxygen by the carrier molecules of the electron transport is *oxidative phosphorylation*. Of the three ATP-producing stages of carbohydrates, the majority of the ATP is produced by oxidative phosphorylation.

Bookkeeping: How many net ATP's from one glucose?

ATP is synthesized from one glucose by a series of three processes: glycolysis, the Krebs cycle, and the electron-transport chain. Let us do some simple bookkeeping to see how many ATP's a cell gains from the oxidation of one molecule of glucose. To clearly see this, we should remember that one molecule of glucose (six carbons) is oxidized to two molecules of pyruvate during glycolysis. These two pyruvates then form two molecules of acetyl CoA that enter the Krebs cycle and produce the hydrogen carriers for the electron-transport chain. A simple diagram (Figure 21-19) may help us see the relationships among the three processes. For each process it is important to remember

Oxidations and reductions continue as outlined in Figure 21-18. Coenzyme Q is the only electron carrier in the chain not bound to a protein. $FADH_2$, the other compound besides NADH coming from the Krebs cycle, enters the electron-transport chain by transferring its electrons to coenzyme Q. The predominant electron carriers from coenzyme Q to molecular oxygen are cytochromes. A cytochrome is a protein of the electron-transport chain that contains a heme group. Crucial to transfer of electrons is the oxidation-reduction of the iron in these hemes.

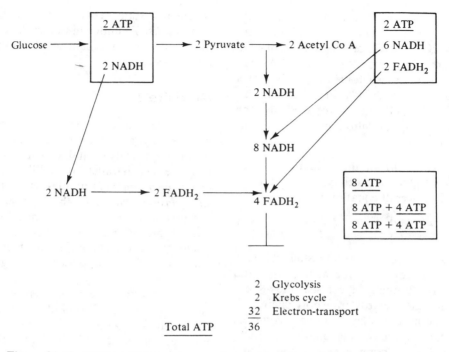

Figure 21-19   ATP yield from the complete oxidation of one molecule of glucose

where in the cell it occurs, what its products are, and how many ATP's are formed.

Glycolysis   The reactions of glycolysis occur in the cytoplasm, where one glucose yields two ATP's, two pyruvates, and two NADH's. What happens to the pyruvates and NADH's is based on the permeability of mitochondria to these substances. The two pyruvates enter the mitochondria, where in the matrix they are converted to two acetyl CoA's with the formation of two NADH's. These NADH's enter the electron-transport chain at the level of the flavoproteins.

Mitochondria are not permeable to NADH. Therefore, the two formed during glycolysis cannot immediately participate in the electron-transport chain. Instead, the electrons from NADH in the cytoplasm are

carried across the mitochondrial membrane by glycerol-3-phosphate. Here they are transferred to FAD, forming $FADH_2$. Since $FADH_2$ enters the electron-transport chain at the level of coenzyme Q, an NADH formed in the cytoplasm is equivalent to an $FADH_2$ with respect to electron-transport reactions.

Krebs cycle   Inside the mitochondria, two acetyl CoA's enter the Krebs cycle. This means that from one glucose the reactions of the Krebs cycle occur twice, producing a total of two ATP's, six NADH's, and two $FADH_2$'s.

Electron-transport chain   A total of eight NADH's per glucose enter the chain. As their electrons are passed from one compound to the next, a total of 24 ATP's are formed. At the site of coenzyme Q, four $FADH_2$'s enter the chain. Two of these are from the Krebs cycle and two are from the cytoplasmic formation of NADH. As the electrons from these four $FADH_2$'s travel the chain, eight ATP's are formed. All together 32 ATP's are produced by the oxidative phosphorylation of the electron-transport chain.

Total ATP's   From the oxidation of one molecule of glucose, a cell gains a total of 36 ATP's. The overall equation is

$$\text{glucose} + 36\ ADP + 36\ P_i + 36\ H^+ + 6\ O_2 \rightarrow$$
$$6\ CO_2 + 36\ ATP + 42\ H_2O$$

This equation represents the sum of many stepwise reactions, starting with glucose and proceeding through glycolysis, the Krebs cycle, and the electron-transport chain. Although the process may seem very complex, the products of the overall equation are those expected for the complete oxidation of any organic compound.

Complete oxidation of glucose is represented by the equation

$$\text{glucose} + 6\ O_2 \rightarrow 6\ CO_2 + 6\ H_2O + \text{energy}$$

Comparison of the energy content of 36 ATP's with the energy liberated by complete oxidation of glucose shows biological oxidation to be about 38% efficient. Cells convert about 38% of the potential energy of glucose into a form, ATP, that they can use for their energy needs. An efficiency of 38% is high compared to common human inventions for converting one form of energy to another.

MUSCLE CONTRACTION: RIGOR MORTIS

Contraction and relaxation of muscle cells are ATP-requiring processes. The depletion of ATP after death causes muscle to be in a contracted state. This is the condition of *rigor mortis*. To understand how it occurs, we must study the mechanism of muscle contraction.

Muscle cells

Skeletal muscle consists of cells surrounded by a membrane, the *sarcolemma*, that is electrically excitable. Three parts of a cell are (1) parallel, threadlike structures called *myofibrils*; (2) tubules which form the *sarcoplasmic reticulum*; they are parallel to the myofibrils and contain ionized calcium; and (3) a fluid called the *sarcoplasm* that is analogous to the cytoplasm of other cells. It contains ATP, phosphocreatine, glycogen, and enzymes.

The myofibrils contain repeating units called *sarcomeres*. Two kinds of protein filaments, thick and thin, are seen in an electron micrograph of myofibrils. The thick filaments are composed mainly of *myosin*, a protein of high molecular weight which has a double-headed globular region and a linear tail. The heads form cross bridges by which the myosin's thick filaments interact with the myofibril's thin filaments. The latter run parallel to the thick filaments and are composed mainly of the protein *actin* and smaller amounts of two other proteins, *tropomyosin* and *troponin*. An actin molecule has the appearance of two strands of beads coiled around each other. The surface of actin contains a filament of tropomyosin. The third protein, troponin, occurs at regular intervals along the filament. Troponin has three subunits. One is bound to tropomyosin and one to actin, holding the tropomyosin so that interaction between the thin filament, actin, and thick filament, myosin, does not occur in a nonexcited muscle. Interaction between the thick and thin filaments is stimulated by calcium ions which bind to the third subunit

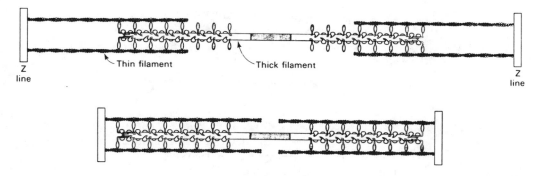

Schematic diagram showing the interaction of thick and thin filaments in skeletal muscle contraction. [After a diagram kindly provided by Dr. James Spudich.]

Figure 21-20   Interaction of thick and thin filaments in muscle contraction (from *Biochemistry*, second edition, by Lubert Stryer. Dr. James Spudick, artist. W. H. Freeman and Company. Copyright © 1981.)

of troponin, changing its configuration so that the tropomyosin no longer blocks the interaction between myosin and actin.

Muscle contraction

The theory of muscle contraction was proposed in the 1950s by two groups of experimenters working individually. This *sliding filament theory* says that during muscle contraction the lengths of the sarcomeres change by the thin filaments' sliding past the thick ones. Shortening of the sarcomeres contracts the muscle. The energy for this movement is from the hydrolysis of ATP.

Two diagrams illustrating increased contraction of a skeletal muscle are shown in Figure 21-20. Contraction begins when an electrical impulse triggers the sarcoplasmic reticulum to release calcium ions, unblocking the myosin-actin interacting sites. To obtain energy for the physical action of contraction, myosin joins with ATP from the cell. Actin has little affinity for the myosin–ATP complex. Interaction of myosin of the thick filament and actin of the thin filament is

possible because myosin has enzymatic properties. It is an *ATPase*, an enzyme that hydrolyzes ATP. This enzyme converts the myosin–ATP complex in the heads of the myosin filaments to a myosin–ADP–P_i complex. Actin has an affinity for this complex, so the thin and thick filaments join by means of cross bridges formed by the myosin heads. Energy from release of ADP and P_i from the complex causes movement of the thin filament toward the center of the sarcomere. The myosin and actin are still bound and represent a contracted state of the muscle. Since actin has little affinity for myosin joined to ATP, further contraction depends on ATP's displacing actin from the actin-myosin complex. After this displacement, the cycle repeats with reattachment of a myosin–ADP–P_i complex to another position on the thin filament. Figure 21-21 shows the various complexes formed as a muscle goes through one cycle of contraction.

At any one time there is only a small amount of ATP in a muscle. As a muscle contracts, this ATP is depleted, so that other sources of ATP must be available to the cell.

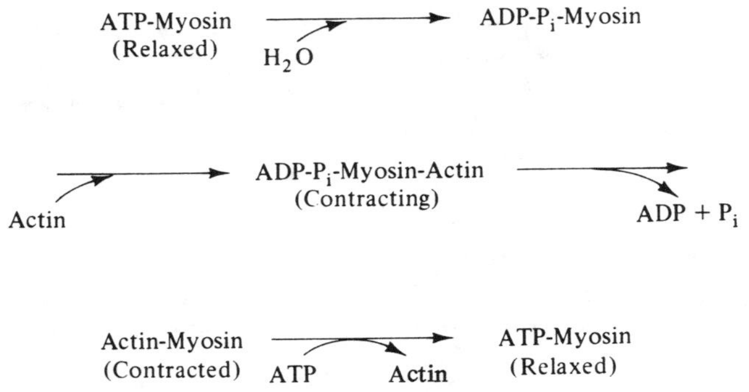

ATP-Myosin   ⟶   ADP-P_i-Myosin
(Relaxed) H_2O

⟶   ADP-P_i-Myosin-Actin   ⟶
(Contracting)
Actin   ADP + P_i

Actin-Myosin   ⟶   ATP-Myosin
(Contracted)   ATP   Actin   (Relaxed)

Figure 21-21   Complexes formed during one cycle of muscle contraction

One of these is *creatine phosphate* (see Figure 21-22), which transfers a phosphate group to ADP by the enzymatic action of creatine kinase.

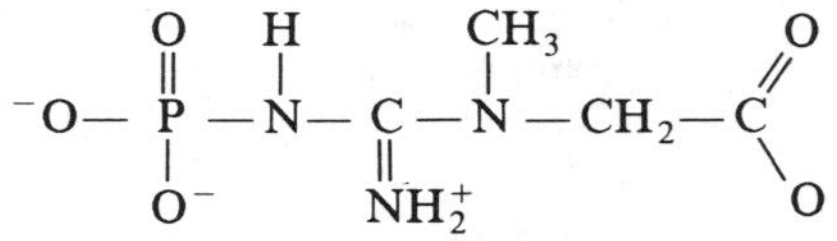

$$\text{ADP} + \text{creatine phosphate} \rightleftharpoons \text{ATP} + \text{creatine}$$

When muscles are at rest, the reverse reaction occurs, resynthesizing creatine phosphate for later use.

During moderate exercise muscle still needs more ATP. This may come from glycogen breakdown, yielding glucose for oxidation, or from oxidation of fatty acids or glucose obtained from the bloodstream. If the oxygen content of the cell decreases, anaerobic glycolysis provides the ATP with the additional production of lactic acid.

Rigor mortis

If we refer again to Figure 21-21, a muscle can complete a cycle of contraction only when the actin-myosin complex is reconverted to the ATP–myosin complex. Displacement of actin by ATP is necessary for this conversion from contracted to relaxed state. The actin–myosin complex is called a

Figure 21-22   Structure of creatine phosphate

rigor complex. The formation of rigor complexes throughout a muscle after death is responsible for the muscle stiffening known as rigor mortis.

Approximately 2 hours after death rigor mortis begins, and it continues for about 30 hours. At the time of somatic death a muscle usually has enough ATP to remain relaxed for a few hours; the ATP, however, begins to decompose, and no resynthesis is possible. Its decomposition reactions involve dephosphorylations and a deamination, which produce *inosine monophosphate* as the major decomposition product. (See Figure 21-23.)

As ATP levels decrease, muscle cells are forced into the actin–myosin complex. They remain in this state of rigor until the muscle softens and appears relaxed because of decomposition of the protein.

For many years it was believed that rigor mortis was caused by the buildup of lactic acid in muscle after death. Today, however,

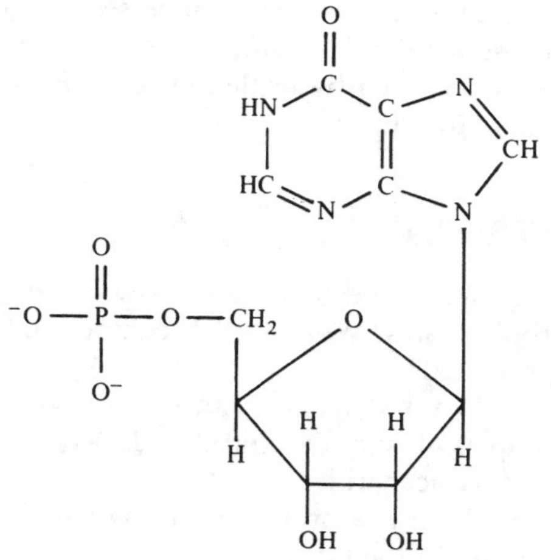

Figure 21-23 Structure of inosine monophosphate

ATP depletion is the accepted explanation. Support for this theory is found in the work of E. H. Callow.[1] It is possible to induce relaxation in a muscle in rigor by adding ATP plus an inhibitor to slow down the use of the added ATP. Muscle cells change from the contracted actin–myosin complex back to the relaxed myosin–ATP complex.

Muscles in which rigor mortis has occurred are more inflexible than muscles undergoing normal contraction. The theory of rigor mortis suggests that all, or almost all, of the fibers in a muscle are in a state of contraction during rigor mortis. During normal contraction, on the other hand, not all fibers are contracting at the same time. While some are contracting, others are relaxed. The involvement of fewer fibers in normal contraction than in rigor mortis accounts for the observed differences in muscle flexibility.

[1] Callow, E. H.: *Rigor Mortis*, in *Food Investigation*. Department of Scientific and Industrial Research, H. M. Stationery Office, London, 1956. As cited in W. E. D. Evans, M. D., B. S., *The Chemistry of Death*, Charles C Thomas, Springfield, Illinois, 1963, p. 31.

CHAPTER SUMMARY

Carbohydrates, which are composed of carbon, hydrogen, and oxygen, are structurally aldehyde and ketone derivatives of polyhydroxy alcohols. They are classified on the basis of their hydrolysis products as monosaccharides, disaccharides, and polysaccharides. Monosaccharides are further classified according to the number of carbons they contain. The most common and nutritionally important of these simple sugars are the hexoses ($C_6H_{12}O_6$): glucose, fructose, and galactose. The disaccharides ($C_{12}H_{22}O_{11}$) are sugars that can be hydrolyzed to two monosaccharide units. The three major disaccharides are lactose, maltose, and sucrose. Polysaccharides ($C_6H_{10}O_5)_X$ yield many monosaccharides when hydrolyzed. Starch with its two forms of amylose and amylopectin is a polysaccharide used by plants to store energy. Humans and higher animals use glycogen, another polysaccharide, for this purpose. Cellulose, also a polysaccharide, is the most abundant organic compound in the biosphere.

Chemical reactions of carbohydrates are as follows:

1. Some are reducing agents:

$$\text{sugar} + 2\ Cu(OH)_2 \xrightarrow{\text{heat}}$$
$$\text{carboxylic acid} + Cu_2O + 2\ H_2O$$

2. Hydrolysis:

monosaccharides $\longrightarrow$ no reaction
disaccharides $\longrightarrow$ monosaccharides
polysaccharides $\longrightarrow$ disaccharides
$\longrightarrow$ monosaccharides

3. Oxidation:

$$C_6H_{12}O_6 + 6\ O_2 \longrightarrow$$
$$6\ CO_2 + 6\ H_2O + \text{heat}$$

4. Fermentation:

$$C_6H_{12}O_6 \xrightarrow{\text{zymase}} 2\ C_2H_5OH + 2\ CO_2$$

5. Photosynthesis:

$$6\ CO_2 + 6\ H_2O \xrightarrow[\text{light}]{\text{chlorophyll}} C_6H_{12}O_6 + 6\ O_2$$

Carbohydrates function as sources of energy. The processes by which our bodies extract energy from carbohydrates and carry it in the form of adenosine triphosphate (ATP) are glycolysis, the Krebs cycle, and oxidative phosphorylation. Glycolysis is the conversion of glucose to pyruvate with a net production of two ATP's. Oxidation of pyruvate to acetyl CoA is followed by the reactions of the Krebs cycle. One turn of the cycle produces one ATP and four molecules of hydrogen carriers, three NADH's and one FADH$_2$. These compounds next undergo a series of oxidation–reduction reactions called the electron-transport chain. As electrons are passed along the chain ultimately to molecular oxygen, ATP is synthesized; hence, the name for this process is oxidative phosphorylation. The overall equation for one molecule of glucose undergoing the reactions of glycolysis, the Krebs cycle, and oxidative phosphorylation is

$$\text{glucose} + 36\ ADP + 36\ P_i + 36\ H^+ + 6\ O_2 \longrightarrow$$
$$6\ CO_2 + 36\ ATP + 42\ H_2O$$

This chapter discussed the processes by which ATP is synthesized during life, since rigor mortis is caused by depletion of ATP which occurs after death.

QUESTIONS

1. What elements are present in the carbohydrates? What organic compounds are represented?

2. List the names and sources of two examples of monosaccharides, disaccharides, and polysaccharides.

3. What is a proteoglycan? Where can it be found in the body?

4. Which carbohydrates give a positive Benedict's or Fehling's test?

5. What are the final oxidation products of carbohydrates? The final hydrolysis products?

6. What are the products of a fermentation reaction? How may this type of reaction be classified?

7. Give both the reactants and the products of a photosynthesis reaction.

8. How many ATP molecules are produced from one molecule of glucose during (a) glycolysis, (b) TCA cycle, and (c) oxidative phosphorylation?

9. Explain in simple terms what is meant by oxidative phosphorylation.

10. Compare and contrast the lactic acid and ATP depletion theories of rigor mortis.

The final class of biochemical compounds that we will discuss is lipids. The name is from the Greek *lypos*, which means "fat." Like carbohydrates, lipids are fewer in number and type in a cell than proteins; there are less than 50 different kinds of lipids in a cell. Both brain and nervous tissue are rich in lipids. Lipids function as structural components of cell membranes and as a storage form of energy.

Lipids are mainly composed of carbon, hydrogen, and oxygen; some also contain nitrogen and phosphorus. An important property of lipids is that they are usually insoluble in water; therefore, they dissolve readily in typical organic solvents such as ethers and chloroform. This insolubility in water distinguishes the lipids from carbohydrates and proteins. Monosaccharides and

SIMPLE LIPIDS

Upon hydrolysis simple lipids produce fatty acids and an alcohol. Examples of simple lipids are (1) fats and oils and (2) waxes.

Fats and oils

Hydrolysis of both of these types of lipids yields fatty acids and glycerol. Whether such a lipid is called a *fat* or an *oil* depends on its physical state. At room temperature, fats are solids or semisolids and oils are liquids.

If hydrolysis of fats and oils forms glycerol and fatty acids, then the synthesis of these lipids must involve a reaction between glycerol and fatty acids. You already know the structure of glycerol, a trihydroxy alcohol. Fatty acids were also previously iden-

Chapter 22
LIPIDS

disaccharides and many proteins are water soluble.

CLASSIFICATION OF LIPIDS

Lipids are frequently classified into three groups on the basis of their hydrolysis products. Enzymes known as *lipases* catalyze the hydrolysis reactions. The three classifications are simple lipids, compound lipids, and miscellaneous lipids.

tified as monocarboxylic organic acids. In addition they are straight chain compounds that may be saturated or unsaturated. The fatty acids that naturally occur in lipids have an even number of carbons. See Table 22-1 for a list of fatty acids and their common sources. The three fatty acids most frequently found in lipids are *palmitic, stearic, and oleic*. Palmitic and stearic acids are saturated compounds that are solids at room temperature. In contrast, oleic acid is un-

Table 22-1   Some fatty acids and their sources

Name	Formula	Source
Myristic acid	$CH_3(CH_2)_{12}COOH$	Nutmeg oil
Palmitic acid	$CH_3(CH_2)_{14}COOH$	Palm oil
Stearic acid	$CH_3(CH_2)_{16}COOH$	Beef tallow
Palmitoleic acid	$CH_3(CH_2)_5CH{=}CH(CH_2)_7COOH$	Butter
Oleic acid	$CH_3(CH_2)_7CH{=}CH(CH_2)_7COOH$	Olive oil
Linoleic acid	$CH_3(CH_2)_4CH{=}CHCH_2CH{=}CH(CH_2)_7COOH$	Soybean oil
Linolenic acid	$CH_3CH_2(CH{=}CHCH_2)_3(CH_2)_6COOH$	Linseed oil
Arachidic acid	$CH_3(CH_2)_{18}COOH$	Peanut oil
Arachidonic acid	$CH_3(CH_2)_4(CH{=}CHCH_2)_4(CH_2)_2COOH$	Lecithin

saturated and is a liquid at room temperature. It has one double bond between carbon 9 and carbon 10.

Fatty acids that our bodies need for proper functioning but cannot synthesize are called *essential fatty acids*. They must be included in our diets. The essential fatty acids are *linoleic, linolenic,* and *arachidonic* acids. Structurally they contain two, three, and four double bonds, respectively.

How do glycerol and fatty acids join to form a fat or an oil? To produce one molecule of lipid, one glycerol molecule and three fatty acid molecules react. The reaction, which is between each —OH group of glycerol and one fatty acid's —COOH group, is an esterification. (See Chapter 16.) Another way to define fats and oils is as esters of fatty acids and glycerol. If we use palmitic acid as the fatty acid, the reaction is

As in other esterifications, a molecule of water forms for each ester linkage.

A general name for a fat or oil is a *triglyceride*. The name of the fat formed by the reaction of glycerol and palmitic acid is *tripalmitin*. If three molecules of stearic acid are reacted with glycerol, the fat that is formed is *tristearin*. Likewise, oleic acid yields *triolein*. In each of these three lipids all the fatty acids are the same. They are simple glycerides. In most naturally occurring fats, different fatty acids are found within the same molecule. Then they are *mixed glycerides*.

What determines if a simple lipid formed between glycerol and three fatty acids will be a solid (fat) or a liquid (oil)? The amount of saturation controls the physical state of the lipid. Look at Table 22-2. A high content of saturated fatty acids characterizes fats and a

Table 22-2 Percentages of saturated and unsaturated fatty acids in fats and oils*

	Saturated			Unsaturated	
	Myristic	Palmitic	Stearic	Oleic	Linoleic
Fats					
Butter	8–15	25–29	9–12	18–33	2–4
Lard	1–2	25–30	12–18	48–60	6–12
Oils					
Olive	0–1	5–15	1–4	67–84	8–12
Peanut	–	7–12	2–6	30–60	20–38
Corn	1–2	7–11	3–4	25–35	50–60
Cottonseed	1–2	18–25	1–2	17–38	45–55

*Percentages may not total 100% owing to small quantities of other acids.

high content of unsaturated fatty acids is common in oils. We will see in a later section that oils are converted to fats by chemical reactions which change double bonds to single bonds.

Waxes

The other type of simple lipids are *waxes*. They are esters of fatty acids and high-molecular-weight alcohols rather than glycerol. These alcohols usually contain one hydroxy group per molecule. Some important waxes and their sources are beeswax (honeycomb), lanolin (wool), spermaceti (head of sperm whale), and carnauba (palm leaves). Carnauba wax is used as an automobile and floor wax. Lanolin forms a base for many ointments and creams. Beeswax and spermaceti are both found in candles and in cosmetics.

COMPOUND LIPIDS

The products of hydrolysis of these compounds are fatty acids, an alcohol, and other compounds. Important compound lipids are (1) phospholipids, (2) sphingolipids, and (3) glycolipids.

Phospholipids

A molecule of these compound lipids is made from one molecule of glycerol, two fatty acid molecules, one phosphoric acid molecule, and an amino alcohol. The relationship among these parts is seen in Figure 22-1. If the amino alcohol is ethanolamine, the phospholipid is a *cephalin*. When choline is the amino alcohol, the compound is a *lecithin*.

$$HO-CH_2CH_2-NH_2$$
Ethanolamine

$$HO-CH_2CH_2\overset{\overset{\displaystyle CH_3}{|}}{\underset{\underset{\displaystyle CH_3}{|}}{N^+}}-CH_3$$
Choline

Cephalins are important in the clotting of blood. They along with lecithins are also found in nerves and brain tissue. Lecithin also helps in transporting fats from one tissue to another. Egg yolk is a rich source of lecithins. They are added to many foods as emulsifying agents.

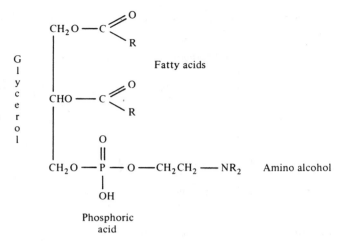

Figure 22-1   Structure of phospholipids

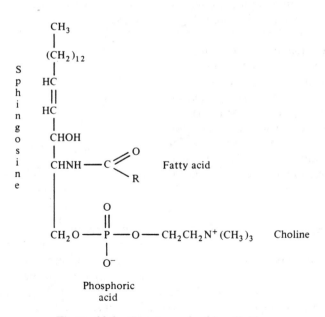

Figure 22-2   Structure of sphingolipids

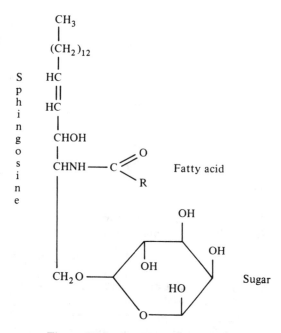

Figure 22-3 Structure of glycolipids

Sphingolipids

These compounds contain *sphingosine*, which is an unsaturated amino alcohol, a fatty acid unit, a phosphoric acid unit, and one or more cholines. The simplest sphingolipid is *sphingomyelin*. Brain tissue and the myelin sheath surrounding the axon of nerve cells are rich in sphingomyelins. Figure 22-2 diagrams the structure of a sphingomyelin, showing the component parts.

Glycolipids

A third class of compound lipids is the *glycolipids*. These contain a sugar unit, usually galactose, as well as either glycerol or sphingosine, and fatty acids. Those with glycerol are found in plants and microorganisms. The ones with sphingosine are in brain and nervous tissues of animals. A specific name for the sphingosine containing glycolipids is *cerebrosides*. Figure 22-3 shows their structure.

MISCELLANEOUS LIPIDS

The simple and compound lipids are classified according to their hydrolysis products. In contrast, *miscellaneous lipids* do not undergo hydrolysis. They are classified as lipids since they are extracted from plant and animal tissues by nonpolar solvents. Examples of miscellaneous lipids are (1) terpenes and (2) steroids.

Terpenes

These compounds contain carbon skeletons that are multiples of isoprene, a five-carbon unit.

$$CH_3$$
$$\diagdown$$
$$C-CH=CH_2$$
$$\sslash$$
$$CH_2$$

Isoprene

The simplest terpenes contain two isoprene units. One of these, *myrcene* ($C_{10}H_{16}$), is found in bay leaves. *Zingiberene* ($C_{15}H_{24}$) is a three-isoprene unit terpene found in oil of ginger. Some terpenes such as *menthol* are also alcohols. Menthol is found in peppermint oil and is used in many pharmaceuticals. These terpenes all have fragrant odors. Some others are brightly colored. The color of tomatoes and carrots is due to *carotenoids*. They have a 40-carbon skeleton which forms by the joining together of two 20-carbon units. Each is built from successive additions of four isoprene units. An extremely important terpene is natural rubber, which is a linear polymer of isoprene units.

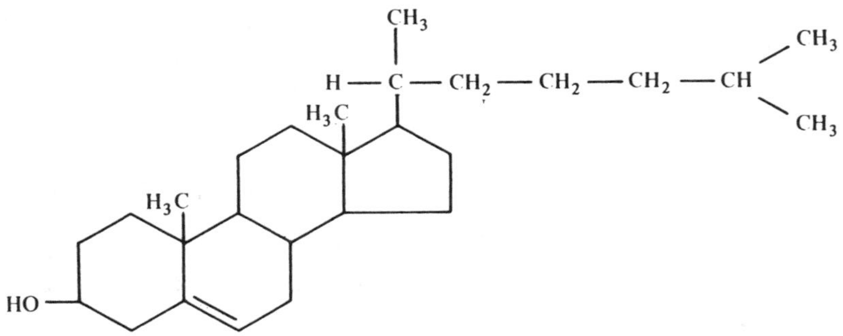

Figure 22-4 Cholesterol, a steroid

Steroids

These miscellaneous lipids all have a common parent structure called a *cyclopentanophenanthrene nucleus*. It is also called a *steroid nucleus*, which is probably easier to remember and to say! The nucleus contains three six-membered rings and one five-membered ring.

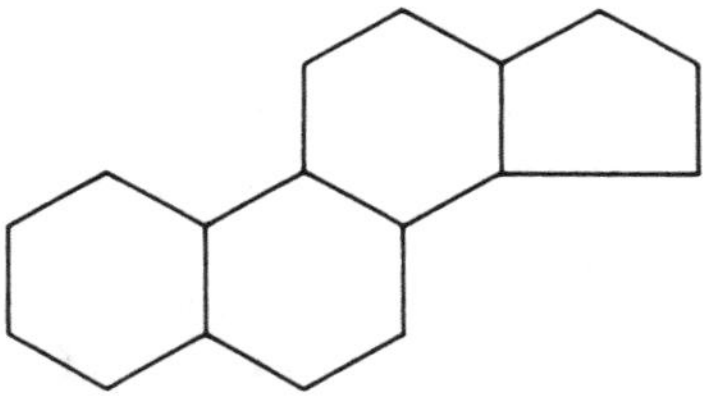

Different steroid molecules are formed by substituting functional groups and hydrocarbon chains for the hydrogens and by adding double bonds to the cyclohexane rings.

Sterols are steroids that contain an alcohol functional group. The most abundant sterol in the body is *cholesterol*. Its structure is seen in Figure 22-4. Cholesterol is found in brain and nervous tissue, in the bloodstream, and in gallstones. Since it forms deposits on the inner walls of blood vessels, cholesterol is often thought of negatively. However, it also has good effects, since it is the precursor for many beneficial compounds synthesized by our bodies. These include the bile salts, several hormones, and vitamin D.

Bile salts

Bile is a digestive fluid formed by the liver. It is stored in the gall bladder, from which it is released to help in the digestion of fats and oils. Bile contains pigments such as bilirubin, cholesterol, and bile salts. A major bile salt is *sodium glycocholate*, which has the structure diagrammed in Figure 22-5. Two important aspects of this bile salt's structure are the extensive hydrocarbon portion in the steroid nucleus and the salt portion containing positive and negative regions.

Owing to its hydrocarbon portion, a bile salt is expected to dissolve in organic compounds. Since it is a salt, it also has an affinity for polar molecules. These two qualities of a bile salt explain why bile helps in the digestion of fats and oils. Within the digestive tract, lipids do not dissolve in the essentially water-soluble contents. Other ingested food products and enzymes are water soluble. Consequently, lipids form large globules and have little contact with the water-soluble lipases. Since bile salts have a polar end and a nonpolar hydrocarbon portion, they are able to form a link between the aqueous medium containing the lipases and the lipids. By this action, the large globules

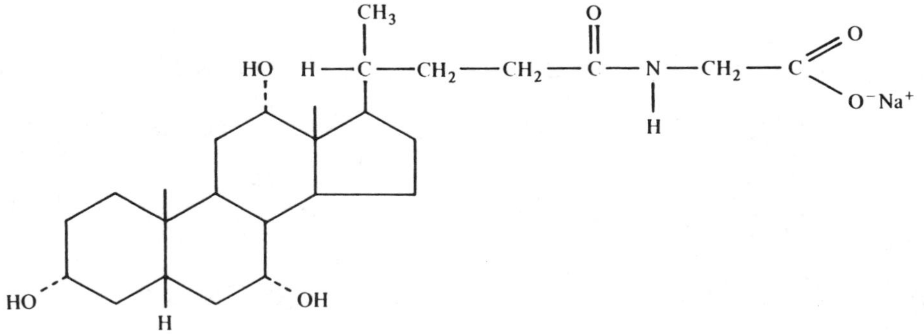

Figure 22-5   Sodium glycocholate, a bile salt

of lipids are broken down into smaller droplets, which have greater contact with hydrolytic enzymes. Since the bile salts can join together polar and nonpolar compounds and promote their solubility in one another, they are emulsifying agents. More will be said about emulsification in a later section when we discuss the cleansing action of soap.

Hormones

Some physiological functions are regulated by compounds known as *hormones*. They are best described as chemical messengers that are carried throughout the body in the bloodstream. As messengers, their levels signal the starting, the stopping, and slowing down or speeding up of chemical reactions. A few hormones are produced in the hypothalamus of the brain. Examples of these are *vasopressin* and *oxytocin*. Most, however, are produced in the endocrine glands and discharged directly into the circulatory system. Some of these are *steroids*.

The cortex of the adrenal glands produces steroid hormones. These glands are located at the top of each kidney. One group of their hormones, called *glucocorticoids*, influence carbohydrate metabolism by preventing uptake of glucose by tissues. Three of these regulators are *cortisone*, *corticosterone*, and *cortisol*. Hormones of another type produced by the adrenal glands are called *mineralocorticoids*. They influence the concentrations of electrolytes, Na^+ and K^+, and thereby regulate the body's retention of water. *Aldosterone* is a mineralocorticoid. Figure 22-6 shows the structures of some steroid hormones.

Other hormones that contain the steroid nucleus are the male and female sex hormones. In the male, they are produced by the testes and are called *androgens*. The major male sex hormone is *testosterone*. Female sex hormones are produced by the ovaries and include *progesterone* and the *estrogens*. Testosterone and the estrogens control the development of male and female secondary sex characteristics. The major role of progesterone is to prepare the uterine lining for implantation of a fertilized egg.

Structures of testosterone, estradiol (an estrogen), and progesterone are drawn in Figure 22-7. There is much similarity between the structures of the male and female hormones.

Vitamin D

Another compound for which cholesterol is a precursor is vitamin D. Actually there are two forms, vitamin D_2 and vitamin D_3.

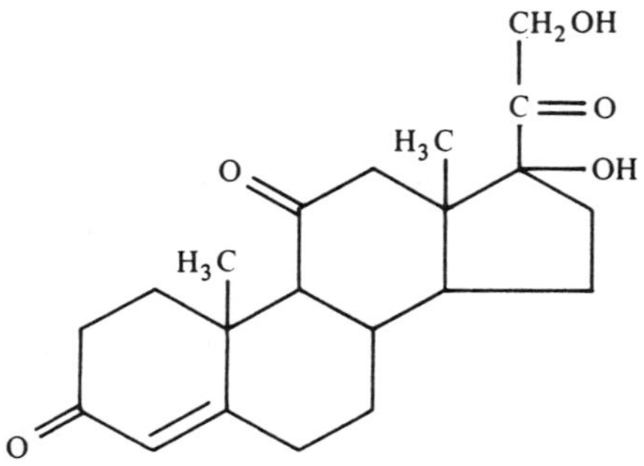

Cortisone

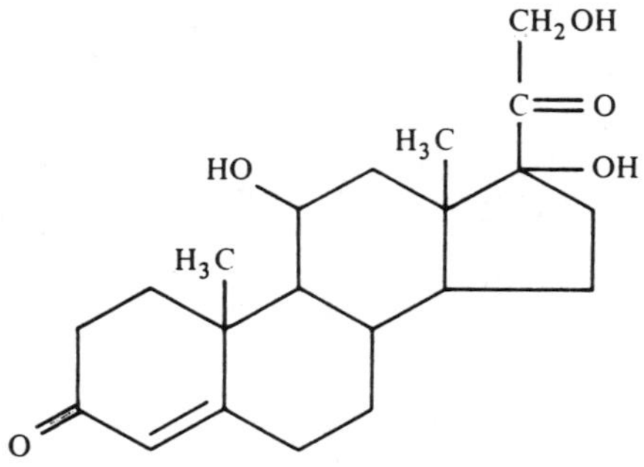

Cortisol

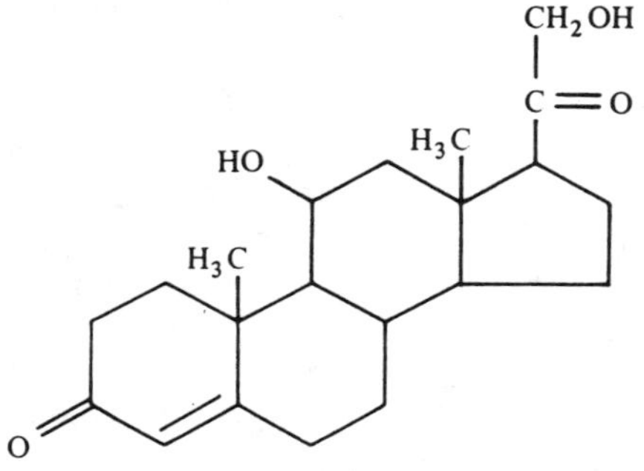

Corticosterone

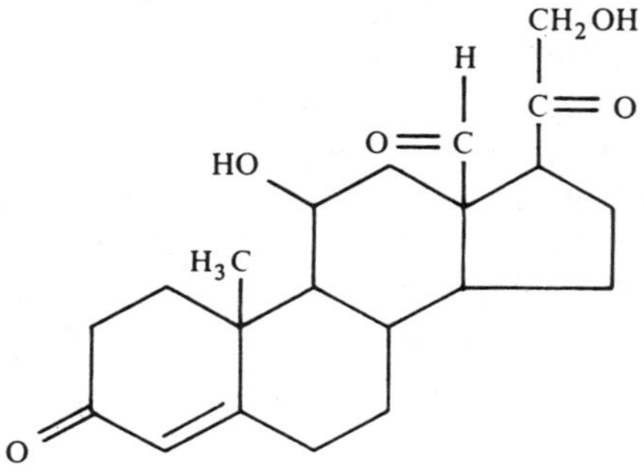

Aldosterone

Figure 22-6 Steroid hormones

Vitamin D_2 is produced by the action of sunlight on ergosterol, an ingested plant sterol, found in the skin of animals. Sunlight also converts cholesterol in the skin to vitamin D_3. Structures of the two forms of vitamin D are drawn in Figure 22-8.

Vitamin D functions in the proper formation of bones and teeth. It influences the uptake of calcium and phosphorus by these body parts. A lack of vitamin D causes the disease rickets in children.

REACTIONS OF LIPIDS

This discussion of the chemical properties of lipids will be limited to fats and oils.

Oxidation

The products of digestion of ingested fats and oils are fatty acids, glycerol, and some monoglycerides. As the name suggests, *monoglycerides* are composed of glycerol and one fatty acid. All these compounds are absorbed from the small intestine into the body's lymph system. Within the small intestine are millions of tiny fingerlike projections called *villi*. Within each villus is a lymph capillary for absorption of lipid material and a network of blood capillaries for absorption of nonlipid products of digestion. Rejoining of fatty acids and glycerol occurs in the lymph system, which empties

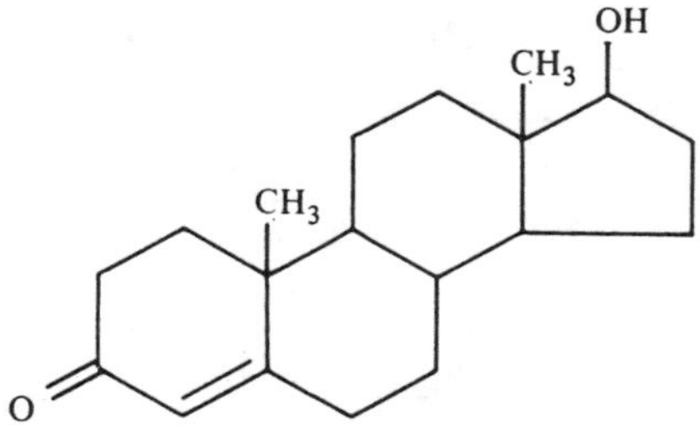

Testosterone

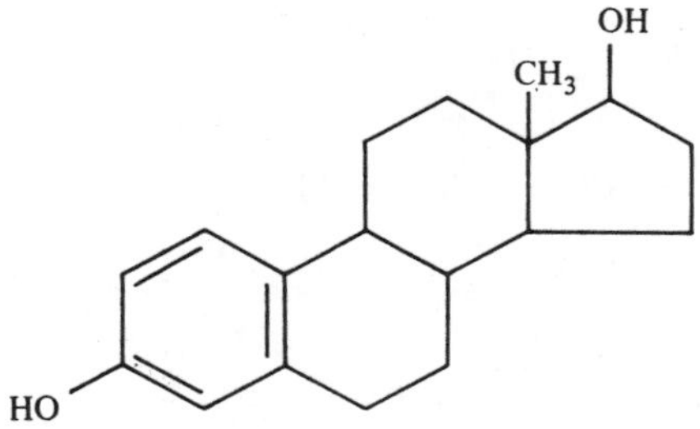

Estradiol

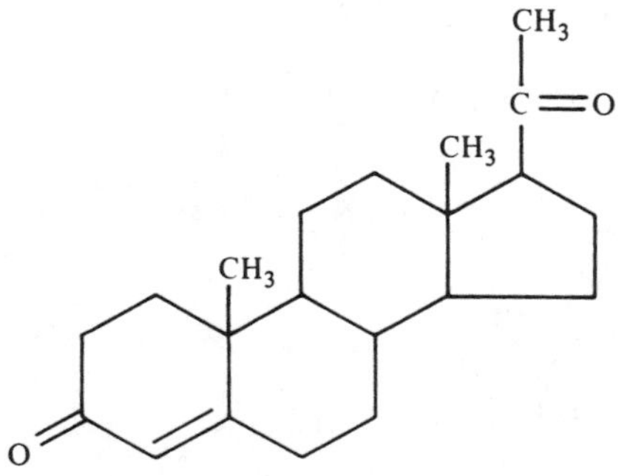

Progesterone

Figure 22-7 Sex hormones

into the bloodstream at the thoracic duct. Triglycerides travel in the blood combined with protein as lipoprotein complexes. These triglycerides maintain a relatively constant level of 150 mg/100 ml of plasma. Excess fats are removed from the blood and stored under the skin as adipose tissue and around organs such as lungs, the heart, and the spleen for protection. These stored fats may also serve as sources of energy for maintenance of bodily functions.

Complete oxidation of fats produces carbon dioxide and water and liberates nine kilocalories of energy per gram. Fats have a higher caloric value than carbohydrates or proteins. They are more efficient storage forms of energy. Nonetheless, carbohydrates provide most of the energy of the body. Generally more carbohydrate than fat is consumed as food and, in comparison to fats, little carbohydrate is stored as a reserve food supply.

A person who is fasting will initially obtain energy from carbohydrate materials. As they are depleted, the body will increase its metabolism of fats to supply energy demands. We have seen that the products of complete oxidation of fats include carbon dioxide and water. As with the carbohydrates, many intermediate steps occur as a fatty acid is broken down ultimately to these simpler molecules. One of the intermediates is *acetoacetyl coenzyme A*. Its structure may be abbreviated as

$$CH_3\overset{\overset{\displaystyle O}{\|}}{C}CH_2\overset{\overset{\displaystyle O}{\|}}{C}SCoA$$

where CoA represents a large organic molecule diagrammed in Chapter 21. In the liver it is converted to the free acid, *acetoacetic acid*, which is one of three compounds referred to as *ketone bodies*. The others are *acetone* and *β-hydroxybutyric acid*. They are both formed from acetoacetic acid with the help of certain enzymes. (See Figure 22-9.) β-hydroxybutyric acid is incorrectly called a ketone body, since the ketone functional group is not found within its structure.

Vitamin D_2

Vitamin D_3

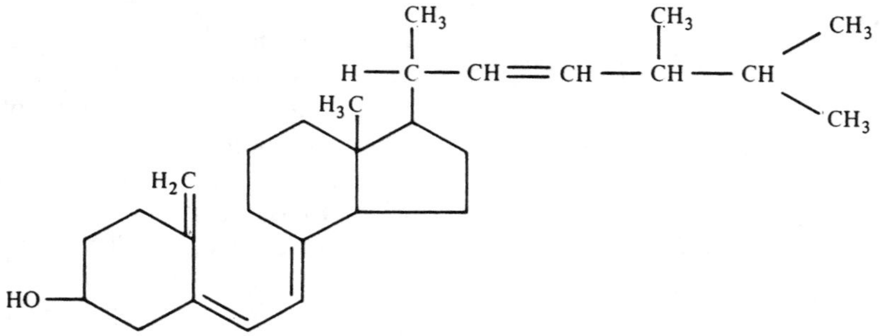

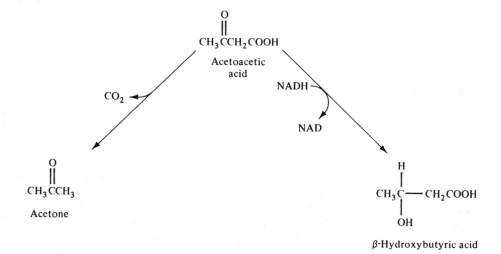

Figure 22-8 Forms of vitamin D

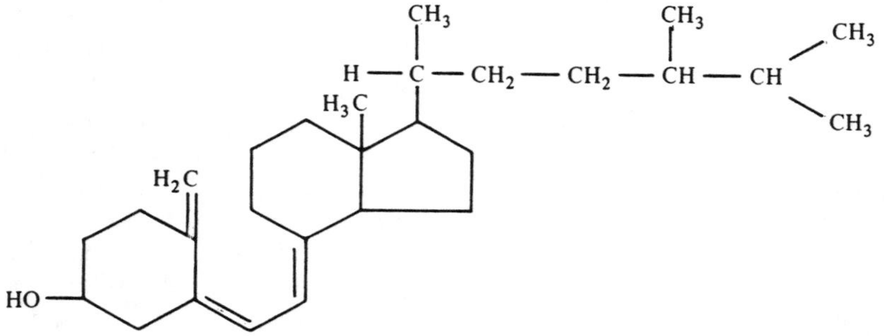

Figure 22-9 Ketone bodies

The blood and urine of a normal person contain very small quantities of the ketone bodies. An average blood level is 0.5 mg/100 ml. Approximately 100 mg are excreted daily in urine. The concentrations are low, since the normal individual mainly uses carbohydrate sources for energy and oxidizes little fat. During periods of fasting or starvation, however, the concentration of the ketone bodies increases significantly in blood and urine, as fats become the major sources of energy.

Whenever carbohydrate metabolism is restricted, an increase in the concentration of ketone bodies occurs. The sweet-smelling breath of an untreated diabetic is due to high levels of acetone. Elevated amounts of the acidic ketone bodies in a diabetic's blood can cause an acidosis, which if extreme may be fatal. As the pH of the blood is lowered, hemoglobin's ability to carry oxygen is decreased. Insufficient oxygen may lead to coma and death.

Saponification

The process of boiling fats or oils with aqueous alkali is *saponification*. The products are glycerol and metallic salts of fatty acids. These salts are commonly called *soaps*. Using the fat stearin and sodium hydroxide, we can write the following equation:

The soap that is formed is *sodium stearate*. The reaction is also an important method for the preparation of glycerin. If the alkali is potassium hydroxide, the soap is *potassium stearate*. The sodium salts are hard and are found in cake soaps. Potassium soaps are soft. They are used in shaving creams and liquid soaps.

The structure of a soap molecule contains a nonpolar part in the hydrocarbon portion and an ionic part on the other end. This structure is the basis of the cleansing ability of soaps. Dirt is essentially oils and greases, which are mainly organic nonpolar compounds. Since water is polar, water alone has very little cleansing action. Nonpolar dirt does not mix with polar water. Soaps clean by acting as emulsifying agents. An *emulsion* is a mixture of two mutually insoluble substances, such as dirt and water, with the dirt being held in suspension by a third substance known as an *emulsifying agent*. When soapy water comes in contact with dirt, the nonpolar part of the soap molecule dissolves in the dirt and the polar part is soluble in the water. In this way a link is made by the soap between the dirt and the water, enabling the dirt to be rinsed away with the water.

The action of emulsification is also explained by the concept of *micelles*. They are spherical clusters formed by soap molecules when added to water. The soap molecules orient themselves to keep their

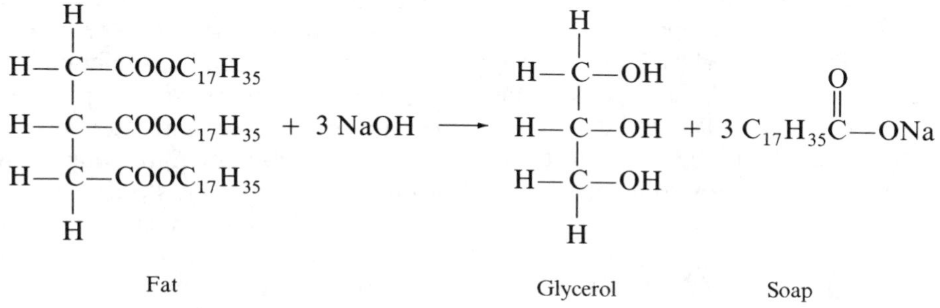

$$\begin{array}{c} H \\ | \\ H-\underset{|}{C}-COOC_{17}H_{35} \\ H-\underset{|}{C}-COOC_{17}H_{35} \quad + \quad 3\,NaOH \quad \longrightarrow \\ H-\underset{|}{C}-COOC_{17}H_{35} \\ | \\ H \end{array} \qquad \begin{array}{c} H \\ | \\ H-\underset{|}{C}-OH \\ H-\underset{|}{C}-OH \\ H-\underset{|}{C}-OH \\ | \\ H \end{array} \quad + \quad 3\,\overset{\displaystyle O}{\overset{\displaystyle \|}{C_{17}H_{35}C}}-ONa$$

Fat   Glycerol   Soap hydrophobic nonpolar portions away from the water and their ionic portions in contact with water. Individual micelles in soapy water repel one another, because each has a positively charged shell at its surface. If oil is added to the soapy water, the nonpolar portions of the micelles mix with the oil, holding it as tiny droplets at the center of each micelle. (See Figure 22-10.) The oil usually appears to have dissolved in the soapy water. Actually the solutions of soapy water, both alone and with the oil, are colloidal solutions.

We encountered the concept of emulsification earlier in this chapter in our discussion of bile salts. Both bile salts and soaps follow the same mechanism in "dissolving" substances of different polarities.

Hydrogenation

Alkenes undergo a reaction called *hydrogenation* by which they add hydrogen to the carbons of the double bond.

$$\diagdown \!\! \diagup \atop C=C \atop \diagup \!\! \diagdown + H_2 \xrightarrow{\text{catalyst}} \begin{array}{cc} | & | \\ -C-C- \\ | & | \\ H & H \end{array}$$

The reaction requires a catalyst, usually nickel or platinum, and produces an alkane. By this process an unsaturated compound becomes saturated.

The same reaction can be performed on unsaturated lipids. Margarines and shortenings for cooking are produced in this way from vegetable oils. Usually only some of the double bonds in the unsaturated compound are hydrogenated. If all become saturated, the product is too hard for commercial purposes.

$$\text{Vegetable oil} + H_2 \xrightarrow{\text{catalyst}} \text{solid fat}$$

Rancidity

Fats and oils that are exposed to warm moist air may become rancid. As a result, they have unpleasant odors and tastes. Two types of processes produce rancidity. *Hydrolytic rancidity* is caused by microorganisms hydrolyzing the lipid. If large numbers of short chain fatty acids are produced, disagreeable odors and tastes are noted. Rancidity of butter is due mainly to the characteristics of butyric acid, a four-carbon carboxylic acid.

The second form of rancidity is *oxidative*. Oxygen from the air oxidizes carbon-to-carbon double bonds in unsaturated lipids to aldehydes and carboxylic acids, many of which have disagreeable odors. Substances called *antioxidants* are added to foodstuffs to prevent this kind of rancidity. A common antioxidant is vitamin E. Oxidation of highly unsaturated lipids can also be used beneficially. When oils such as linseed oil undergo oxidation, the aldehydes and acids may polymerize to form tough films that are water resistent. Oils with this property are frequently added to oil-base house paints. They are called *drying oils*.

SIGNIFICANCE OF LIPIDS TO THE EMBALMING PROCESS

Decomposition of lipid material is not as important to the embalmer as protein breakdown. Fatty material may become rancid if microorganisms are not inhibited by the embalming process. However, lipids themselves do not produce decomposition products with the putrid odors of putrefying protein. Fat cells in the body's fat storage areas are supported by fibrous connective protein tissue. If proper embalming of these regions is not achieved, these proteins will putrefy.

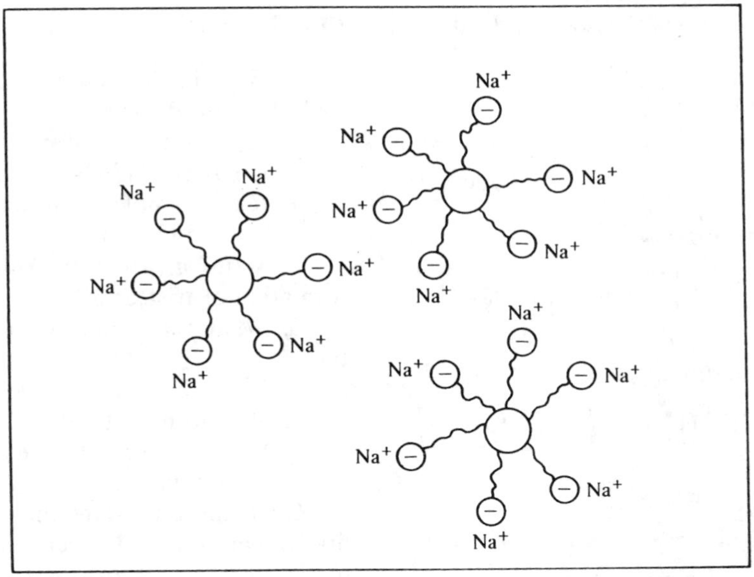

Figure 22-10 Colloidal solution of oil and soapy water

One interesting compound to the embalmer associated with lipids is *adipocere*, commonly called *gravewax*. It is a white waxy material produced by saponification of body fat. If a body is buried in alkaline soil, adipocere can be produced over a period of many years. However, the formation of adipocere is purely of academic interest. The increased use of "protective" type caskets and the cemetery requirements of outside enclosures (vaults) substantially reduce the likelihood that the body will come in contact with soil of any kind.

CHAPTER SUMMARY

Lipids function as structural components of cell membranes and as storage forms of energy. These compounds differ from other biochemical compounds owing to their general insolubility in water. Classification of lipids is based on their hydrolysis products. Three main classes are simple lipids, compound lipids, and miscellaneous lipids. Simple lipids are formed from fatty acids and an alcohol. If the alcohol is glycerol, the lipid is a fat or oil. Waxes contain alcohols other than glycerol. Examples of compound lipids are phospholipids, sphingolipids, and glycolipids. Hydrolysis of any of these compounds yields fatty acids, an alcohol, and other simpler compounds. Miscellaneous lipids do not undergo hydrolysis. Terpenes and steroids are members of this group. All steroids contain in common a nucleus which contains three six-membered rings and one five-membered ring. Steroids containing an alcohol functional group are called sterols. Cholesterol is the most abundant sterol in the body. It is the precursor to such important compounds as the bile salts, several hormones, and vitamin D.

Chemical reactions that fats and oils undergo are:

1. Oxidation:

$$\text{lipid} \longrightarrow \text{carbon dioxide} + \text{water} + \text{energy}$$

2. Saponification:

$$\text{lipid} + \text{alkali} \xrightarrow{\text{heat}} \text{soap} + \text{glycerol}$$

3. Hydrogenation:

$$\text{vegetable oil} + H_2 \xrightarrow{\text{catalyst}} \text{solid fat}$$

4. Rancidity:
   (a) Hydrolytic:

$$\text{butter} \xrightarrow{\text{microorganisms}} \text{butyric acid}$$

   (b) Oxidative:

$$\text{unsaturated lipids} \xrightarrow{O_2}$$
$$\text{aldehydes} + \text{carboxylic acids}$$

Of academic interest to the embalmer is adipocere, a white waxy substance produced by saponification of body fat when human remains are buried in alkaline soil.

QUESTIONS

1. Explain the difference between the hydrolysis products of
   (a) A fat and a wax.
   (b) A cephalin and a lecithin.
   (c) A simple lipid and a miscellaneous lipid.
2. Write a structural equation for the formation of tristearin.
3. What determines if a lipid is a fat or oil?
4. Draw the steroid nucleus. How is this modified to form a sterol?
5. What property do bile salts and soaps have in common?
6. Define and state the relationship to lipids: hormone, adipocere, micelle, ketone bodies.
7. What is the difference between oxidative and hydrolytic rancidity?
8. What physical property distinguishes lipids from the other major types of biochemical compounds?
9. What are the oxidative products of fats? Compare the energy content of fats to that of carbohydrates.
10. What effect does the embalming process have on lipids?

Section IV
APPENDICES

During chemical changes the electrons of the reacting atoms interact. The identity of the atoms remains the same before and after the reaction. Some forms of matter undergo another type of change which involves the nuclei of atoms. As a result of some nuclear processes, a reactant atom is transformed into another type of atom because of alterations in the composition of its nucleus. This chapter discusses the causes, the mechanisms, and the effects of nuclear reactions.

RADIOACTIVITY

In Chapter 4 we learned that the major parts of an atom are a nucleus and one or more electrons. Within the nucleus two types of

above 83 and some with lower numbers are naturally radioactive.

Discovery of radioactivity

In 1896, radioactivity was discovered by Henri Becquerel. While experimenting with salts of uranium (atomic number = 92), he accidentally discovered that they caused the exposure of a photographic plate in the dark. Such activity indicated that uranium was emitting some type of radiation. Two years later, Marie and Pierre Curie discovered the elements polonium (atomic number = 84) and radium (atomic number = 88). Like uranium, they were found to be radioactive.

The radiations from these elements were studied by Rutherford, who found three types

Chapter 23
RADIATION CHEMISTRY

particles found are protons and neutrons. Since the protons are positively charged, they repel each other. A function of the neutral neutrons is to stabilize nuclei by separating the protons. If the proton-proton repulsions are not counteracted by the neutrons, the nucleus decays to a more stable form. This spontaneous decay of nuclei is called *radioactivity*. All elements with atomic numbers

of radiations: he called them alpha, beta, and gamma.

Alpha radiation

This form of radiation consists of particles that each contain two protons and two neutrons. Since their atomic number is two, they are nuclei of helium. Each particle has a

Table 23-1 Characteristics of the major types of radiations

Name	Symbol	Composition	Mass (amu)	Charge	Hazard to humans
Alpha particle	α	Helium nuclei	4	+2	Internal
Beta particle	β	Electron	$\frac{1}{1837}$	± 1	External and internal
Gamma ray	γ	Energy	0	0	External and internal

double positive charge. The velocity of these particles is approximately one-tenth the speed of light.

To evaluate the effect of radiations from radioactive sources, we must consider their abilities both to penetrate matter and to ionize it. Owing to their mass and charge, alpha particles travel in air only a few centimeters. It is possible to stop them by a piece of paper. Since they can penetrate body tissue only about 0.05 millimeters, they cannot reach internal organs from outside the body. If ingested or inhaled, alpha emitters will damage cells of internal organs. This damage is caused by the high ionizing power of alpha particles. Their plus-two charge causes them to remove electrons from the outer orbits of other atoms. The properties of alpha particles are summarized in Table 23-1.

Beta radiation

The type of radiation called *beta* consists of very small particles that have a mass $\frac{1}{1837}$ that of a proton. The particles are of two types, depending on their charge. The more familiar type of beta particle has a charge of minus one and is an *electron*. Less familiar is a positively charged beta particle (charge = +1), which is called a *positron*. Electrons are formed within a nucleus by the breakdown of a neutron into a proton and an electron. The proton remains in the nucleus; the elec-

tron is emitted. If, in contrast, a proton is broken down to a neutron within a nucleus, a positive beta particle, the positron, is emitted from the nucleus. The formations of the two types of beta particles are seen in the following equations:

$$\begin{aligned} {}_{0}^{1}n &\longrightarrow {}_{1}^{1}p + {}_{-1}^{0}e \\ {}_{1}^{1}p &\longrightarrow {}_{0}^{1}n + {}_{+1}^{0}e \end{aligned}$$

In each equation the superscripts refer to mass numbers and the subscripts to charges.

Since beta particles are smaller in mass and in charge than alpha particles (see Table 23-1), they have less ionizing power but can penetrate matter farther than alpha radiation. Their range in air is several meters. They can be stopped by a piece of aluminum foil. Their penetration of a few millimeters into living tissues causes damage both external and internal. Prolonged external exposure can burn the skin.

Gamma rays

The most penetrating type of radiation from a radioactive atom is *gamma* radiation (see Table 23-1). It is a type of electromagnetic radiation. Other familiar forms of electromagnetic radiation are visible light and X-rays. (See Figure 23-1.) Similar to both of these, gamma rays travel as waves, but they are higher in energy. The exact energy of a particular gamma ray depends on its wave-

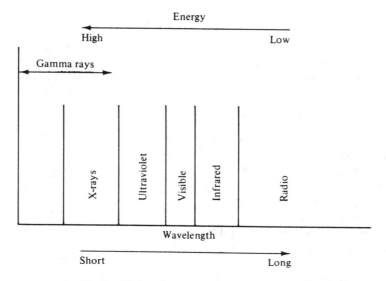

Figure 23-1 The electromagnetic spectrum

length. Frequently gamma rays are emitted from a nucleus during the process of either alpha or beta decay. In air, gamma rays can travel many meters. Dense material such as lead is necessary to stop them. Gamma rays penetrate the human body and can damage both the cells and the tissues of internal organs. The ionizing ability of this form of radiation is less than that of alpha or beta particles.

TRANSMUTATION

Both alpha decay and beta decay lead to the conversion of an atom of one element into an atom of another. This type of nuclear change is called *transmutation*. It is possible to predict the identity of the new nucleus by following the simple rules of balancing of equations. In these nuclear equations the sums of the mass numbers (superscripts) and atomic numbers (subscripts) on both sides of the arrow must be equal.

Alpha decay

As the result of alpha decay, the mass number of the reactant (decaying atom) is decreased by four and the atomic number is decreased by two. The identity of the product atom is determined by the new atomic number. An example of alpha decay is

$$^{238}_{92}\text{U} \longrightarrow {}^{234}_{90}\text{Th} + {}^{4}_{2}\text{He}$$

The radioactive atom uranium-238 has decayed to thorium-234 and an alpha particle. Another example of alpha decay is that of radium-226, which emits both an alpha particle and gamma radiation. Since gamma rays are pure energy, their atomic number and mass number are both zero. The equation for this decay process is

$$^{226}_{88}\text{Ra} \longrightarrow {}^{222}_{86}\text{Rn} + {}^{4}_{2}\text{He} + \gamma$$

Once again, notice the balance of mass numbers and atomic numbers on both sides of the arrow.

Beta decay

The thorium-234 produced by the alpha decay process previously described is also radioactive. It decays by emission of a negative beta particle and a gamma ray:

$$^{234}_{90}\text{Th} \longrightarrow \,^{234}_{91}\text{Pa} + \,^{0}_{-1}e + \gamma$$

Since the mass of an electron is so much less than that of a proton, it is given a mass number of zero. The atomic number of minus one is assigned to an electron, since the charge of an electron is equal in magnitude but opposite in sign to that of the proton. The atom of protactinium formed in this decay process is also radioactive. Actually the decay of uranium-238 begins a series of decays called a *radioactive disintegration series*. (See Figure 23-2.) The series ends with the formation of lead-206, a stable atom. Each of the decaying atoms in the series is referred to as a *radionuclide*. This is a general term used to describe any radioactive material.

An example of positron formation is the decay process of unstable carbon-9:

$$^{9}_{6}\text{C} \longrightarrow \,^{9}_{5}\text{B} + \,^{0}_{1}e$$

The boron atom that forms along with the positron continues to decay and forms stable beryllium-9:

$$^{9}_{5}\text{B} \longrightarrow \,^{9}_{4}\text{Be} + \,^{0}_{1}e$$

These last two equations can be summarized by the overall decay:

$$^{9}_{6}\text{C} \longrightarrow \,^{9}_{4}\text{Be} + 2\,^{0}_{1}e$$

HALF-LIFE

The stability of radionuclides is evaluated in terms of half-life, symbolized by $t_{\frac{1}{2}}$. The half-life of a particular radioactive atom is

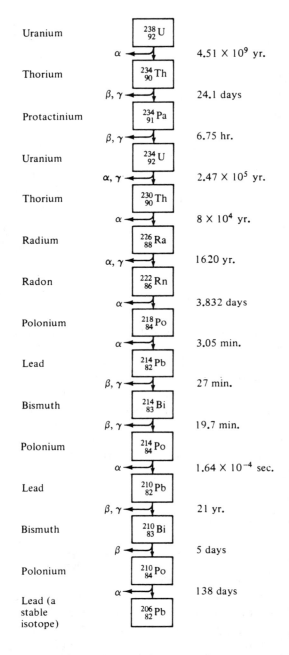

Figure 23-2   The uranium-238 disintegration series

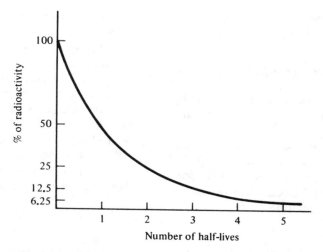

Figure 23-3 Logarithmic decay curve of a radionuclide

Table 23-2	Half-lives of radionuclides	
Element	Isotope	Half-life
NATURALLY OCCURRING RADIONUCLIDES		
Carbon	$^{14}_{6}C$	5730 yr
Radium	$^{226}_{88}Ra$	1620 yr
Radon	$^{222}_{86}Rn$	3.83 days
Thorium	$^{230}_{90}Th$	8×10^4 yr
Uranium	$^{235}_{92}U$	7.1×10^8 yr
	$^{238}_{92}U$	4.5×10^9 yr
MEDICALLY USED RADIONUCLIDES		
Cobalt	$^{60}_{27}Co$	5.3 yr*
Gallium	$^{67}_{31}Ga$	78 hr
Gold	$^{198}_{79}Au$	2.7 days
Iodine	$^{123}_{53}I$	13.3 hr
	$^{125}_{53}I$	60 days
	$^{131}_{53}I$	8.04 days
Iridium	$^{192}_{77}Ir$	74.4 days
Phosphorus	$^{32}_{15}P$	14.3 days
Radium	$^{226}_{88}Ra$	1620 yr*
Radon	$^{222}_{86}Rn$	3.83 days
Tantalum	$^{182}_{73}Ta$	115 days*
Technetium	$^{99}_{43}Tc$	6.02 hr

*Note: not all medically used radionuclides have short half-lives.

the amount of time that it takes for half of the initial amount of radioactive material to decay. Some radionuclides have very long half-lives; those of others are much shorter. The half-lives of some naturally occurring radionuclides are listed in Table 23-2. The half-life of radon-222 is 3.8 days. If initially 10.00 grams of this radionuclide are present in a sample, there will be 5.000 grams left unchanged after 3.8 days. The other 5.000 grams will have undergone the characteristic decay pattern of this isotope of radon. After another half-life passes, 2.500 grams of initial material are left. As more half-lives pass, smaller quantities (1.250 g, 0.6250 g, 0.3125 g,...) of undecayed radionuclide remain. Figure 23-3 shows the decay curve for a radionuclide. The shape of the curve is logarithmic. This means the greatest amount of change occurs in the first few half-lives.

The length of the half-life of a radionuclide is an indication of its stability. The longer the half-life, the more stable the radioactive atom. Common radionuclides used in medical procedures (see Table 23-2) have short half-lives. These materials are, therefore, not long-term radiological hazards.

ARTIFICIAL TRANSMUTATIONS

It is possible to cause a transmutation by bombarding nuclei of one element with other particles.

The first artificial nuclear transformation was performed in 1919 by Rutherford. By bombarding nitrogen gas with alpha particles having a high velocity, he formed an unstable isotope of fluorine:

$$^{14}_{7}N + ^{4}_{2}He \longrightarrow ^{18}_{9}F$$

Decay of the fluorine atom produced a stable form of oxygen and a proton:

$$^{18}_{9}F \longrightarrow ^{17}_{8}O + ^{1}_{1}H$$

The significance of this experiment was the first detection of protons. Similarly, in 1932, neutrons were discovered by Sir James Chadwick during a bombardment reaction of beryllium with alpha particles:

$$^{9}_{4}Be + ^{4}_{2}He \longrightarrow ^{12}_{6}C + ^{1}_{0}n$$

Bombardment reactions are the basis of the process of nuclear fission, splitting of a nucleus into smaller fragments. Bombardment of uranium-235 with slow neutrons breaks it apart into smaller nuclei, other neutrons, and energy.

$$^{235}_{92}U + ^{1}_{0}n \longrightarrow$$
$$^{142}_{56}Ba + ^{91}_{36}Kr + 3^{1}_{0}n + energy$$

The production of neutrons in this reaction continues the fission process in the form of a chain reaction. Large amounts of energy are released in these fission processes. Uncontrolled fission processes occur in an atomic bomb. Fission reactions may be controlled so the energy is released more slowly. Nuclear reactors in nuclear power plants operate under conditions of controlled fission. Most of the energy released is in the form of heat. Absorption of this heat by liquid coolants such as water generates steam which drives a turbine to produce electricity.

All the elements with atomic numbers greater than uranium have been artificially produced in the laboratory by bombardment reactions. The elements neptunium and plutonium were produced by bombardment of uranium-238 with neutrons.

$$^{238}_{92}U + ^{1}_{0}n \longrightarrow ^{239}_{92}U$$
$$^{239}_{92}U \longrightarrow ^{239}_{93}Np + ^{0}_{-1}e$$
$$^{239}_{93}Np \longrightarrow ^{239}_{94}Pu + ^{0}_{-1}e$$

These "transuranium" elements, as they are called, are radioactive and decay according to their characteristic half-lives. Similar equations could be written for the other known elements with higher atomic numbers.

RADIATION QUANTITIES AND UNITS

The evaluation of the effects of radiation is based on the measurement of certain quantities. Four frequently used ones are exposure, absorbed dose, dose equivalent, and activity. (See Table 23-3.)

Exposure

This quantity evaluates the ability of gamma rays to produce ions in air. It is defined as the amount of ionization produced per unit mass of air. The unit of exposure is the roentgen, abbreviated as R. In one cubic centimeter of air, one roentgen produces about two billion ion pairs. This unit is not used for either alpha or beta radiations.

Table 23-3 Summary of radiation quantities and units

Quantity	Common units	SI units
Exposure	roentgen (R)	2.58×10^{-4} coulomb/kg
Absorbed dose	rad 1 rad = 10^{-2} joule/kg	Gray (Gy) 1 Gy = 1 joule/kg
Dose equivalent	rem 1 rem = 10^{-2} joule/kg	Sievert (Sv) 1 Sv = 1 joule/kg
Activity	curie (Ci) 1 Ci = 3.7×10^{10} disintegrations/sec 1 mCi = 3.7×10^{7} disintegrations/sec 1 μCi = 3.7×10^{4} disintegrations/sec	Becquerel (Bq) 1 Bq = 1 disintegration/sec

Absorbed dose

The amount of energy absorbed by a unit mass of matter is the *absorbed dose*. Two units are used for its measurement. One, an older unit, is the rad (radiation absorbed dose), which equals 10^{-2} joules of energy absorbed per kilogram of material. The other unit is the Gray, abbreviated as Gy, which equals one joule of energy per kilogram of matter.

The amount of energy actually associated with these units may be better understood by considering the relationship between joules and calories (cal) of energy. One joule (J) = 4.184 calories (cal) of energy. This means:

1 Gy = 1 J/kg = 4.184 cal/kg

Table 23-4 shows the effects on humans of various absorbed doses of radiation.

Dose equivalent

One rad of gamma radiation does not produce the same biological effect as one rad of beta radiation. In order to compare the biological effects of the different forms of radiation, the quantity *dose equivalent* has been defined. It is equal to the product of

Table 23-4 Biological effects of acute radiation exposures

Radiation dose to whole body (rad)	Effect
0–25	No detectable clinical effects
25–100	Reduction in number of some blood cells
100–200	Nausea and fatigue. Vomiting if dose is greater than 125 rads
200–300	Nausea and vomiting first day of exposure. Within two weeks loss of appetite, fatigue, diarrhea, moderate emaciation.
300–600	Nausea, vomiting, and diarrhea in first few hours. Within one week loss of appetite and fever. Within second week fatigue, hemorrhage, diarrhea, and emaciation. If above 400 rads, death likely for 50% of untreated population.
600 or more	Nausea, vomiting, and diarrhea in first few hours. Up to 100% death within 30–60 days.

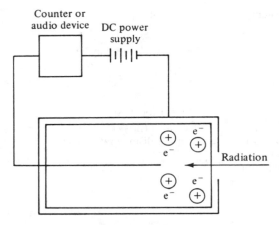

Figure 23-4 Diagram of a Geiger-Müller counter

rads of radiation and a quality factor that accounts for the biological effect of the given type of radiation:

dose equivalent = absorbed dose
× quality factor

The unit of dose equivalent is the rem (roentgen equivalent for man). It is the dose of any form of radiation that has an effect of 1 roentgen on a human.

Activity

The nuclear transformation rate of a decaying atom is given by its activity. The unit of activity is the curie, abbreviated Ci:

1 Ci = 3.7×10^{10} disintegrations/second

This very active rate is the number of radioactive disintegrations occurring per second in a 1-gram sample of radium. In practice, smaller quantities such as the millicurie and the microcurie are used.

Often the concept of *activity* is confused with *exposure*. These two terms should not be used interchangeably in describing radiations.

RADIATION DETECTORS

Detectors of radiation can be divided into two types: (1) survey meters that detect radiation and (2) dosimeters that measure individual exposures.

Survey meters

Two commonly used survey meters are the Geiger-Müller counter and the scintillation counter.

Geiger-Müller counter The parts of a *Geiger counter*, as this detector is frequently called, are seen in Figure 23-4. An ionizable gas such as argon is contained in a partially evacuated tube. Within the tube is a wire that is made positive or negative by application of a potential from a dc power supply. The sides of the tube are given the opposite charge of the wire. An audio device or counter is connected to the circuit. As radiation passes through a window into the tube, ionization of the gas produces electrons and positively charged particles. The positive and negative electrodes attract the electrons and positive ions, forming an electrical current that triggers the audio or counting device. The Geiger counter is primarily used to measure beta particles and gamma rays. See Figure 23-5 for pictures of Geiger counters.

Scintillation counter As radiations strike crystals of sodium iodide, electrons within the crystal are excited to higher energy levels. As they drop back to the ground state, light is emitted. These emissions, called *scintillations*, can be amplified and indicate the quantity of radiation. Using various scintillators, scintillation counters have been designed to detect the three types of radiation. (See Figure 23-5.)

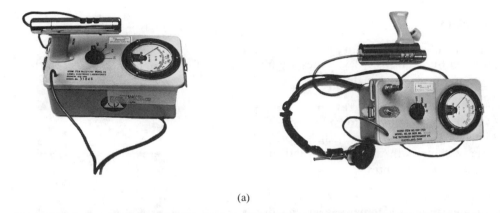

(a)

(b)

Figure 23-5 Pictures of (a) Geiger-Müller counters and (b) alpha scintillation counters (Courtesy of REAC/TS, Oak Ridge Associated Universities, Oak Ridge, Tennessee)

Dosimeters

Individual exposures to radiation are monitored by *dosimeters*. Two types are film badges and pocket dosimeters.

Film badges Photographic film is darkened upon exposure to radiations. The extent of darkening of film badges worn by people working with radionuclides indicates their radiation exposures.

Pocket dosimeters These devices are used for the detection of gamma rays which cause ionization of air within a chamber. Free electrons are attracted to a fixed metal wire and movable quartz fiber, both of which have positive charges. The instrument contains a device for reading doses of radiation. For proper reading of the dosimeter, it must be charged prior to use. (See Figure 23-6.)

PROTECTION FROM RADIATION

Anyone who lives in today's world knows that exposure to radiation is harmful to man. What is the source of this danger? As radiations travel through living tissue, the interaction may form highly reactive particles called *free radicals*. A free radical has an unpaired electron which causes it to continue to react after its formation. If these reactions occur in the nucleus of a cell, the molecules of the genes may be altered. Some of the effects could be death of the cell, formation of a malignant carcinoma, or transmission of a genetic mutation.

An example of a free radical is the hydroxyl radical. It can form by a reaction between a high-energy alpha particle and water.

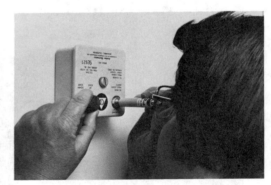

Figure 23-6 Devices for dosimetry (Courtesy of REAC/TS, Oak Ridge Associated Universities, Oak Ridge, Tennessee)

$$\ce{^4_2He} \quad + \quad \overset{\cdot\,\cdot}{\underset{H\quad H}{O}} \quad \longrightarrow \quad \ce{^4_2He} \quad + \quad \left[\overset{\cdot\,\cdot}{\underset{H\quad H}{O}}\right]^{+} \quad + \quad \ce{^0_{-1}e}$$

The products are an alpha particle that has lower energy than the reactant alpha particle and an ion of water in which the oxygen has lost an electron. This compound dissociates into a proton and a hydroxyl radical, which is very reactive.

$$\left[\begin{array}{c} \ddot{O} \\ / \quad \backslash \\ H \qquad H \end{array} \right]^{+} \longrightarrow \quad H^{+} \quad + \quad : \ddot{O}\text{-}H$$

How do people protect themselves against exposure to radiations? Three factors can be considered: time, distance, and shielding.

Time

Minimizing the amount of time one is in contact with a radioactive material is a protective measure against radiation. If at a certain location a person received 5 mrems of radiation per hour, he would receive a dose of 2.5 mrems if he stayed there only half an hour.

The expression used in this example of mrems/hr is called an *exposure rate*. The National Council on Radiation Protection and Measurement (NCRP) has set certain limits on exposure rates. For a person working in the nuclear industry, 5 rems/yr of on-the-job exposure is allowed. Nonnuclear industry workers should only receive 0.5 rems/yr beyond exposures due to background radiation and medical procedures. Natural background radiations are cosmic radiations, which are high-energy gamma rays coming from outer space, and gamma rays emitted from naturally occurring radionuclides. Radiations from atomic-weapons fallout and from some consumer products such as luminous watch dials, television tubes, and smoke detectors are sources of man-made background radiations.

Distance

Radiation intensities follow an inverse-square law. Measurement of the intensities of radiations at various distances from a source shows that the intensity (I) decreases with the square of the distance (d) from the source. In the form of an equation, this relationship is expressed as

$$I \propto \frac{1}{d^2}$$

where $\propto$ means "is proportional to." According to this equation, at a distance 3 meters from a source the intensity is one-ninth of what it is at the source itself. Similarly, a reduction in radiation intensity of $\frac{1}{100}$ is found 10 meters from a source.

Shielding

In discussing alpha, beta, and gamma radiations, we saw that a piece of paper can stop alpha particles, a thin piece of aluminum foil stops beta particles, and gamma rays are stopped only by dense materials such as lead. These materials all act as shields of each of the indicated type of radiation for a person exposed to them. Shielding is a very effective protection against radiations. Radionuclides are usually stored in lead containers for this purpose. However, although it can be effective, complete shielding from high-energy gamma radiation may be impractical in a given situation dealing with radionuclides.

SOURCES OF RADIATION ENCOUNTERED BY EMBALMERS

The two most common examples of radiation that are found in human remains are due to

1. Occupational exposure
2. Radionuclide therapy

Occupational exposure

The first source is the less likely to pose a problem to the embalmer for two reasons. First, there have been only 22 fatal radiation accidents in the world (7 in the U.S.) over a period of 39 years. The likelihood, therefore, of the average embalmer encountering one of these cases is very low. Second, a body that has been contaminated with dangerously high levels of radiation will not be released to the embalmer until radiation levels have been reduced to an acceptable level by standard decontamination procedures. These procedures are carried out under the supervision of the health physics officer of the associated industry. These personnel have undergone rigorous training, as the nuclear industry is the most highly regulated one in the world. By the time the embalmer receives one of these remains, the only problems he should encounter will be those associated with delayed embalming and refrigerated or frozen bodies.

Radionuclide therapy

The second source, radionuclide therapy, presents a different problem. High levels of radiation can occur during treatment of malignant diseases. Patients receiving large doses of radionuclides are usually required to remain hospitalized until their content of radioactivity is less than 30 mCi. This requirement, which is called the *30 mCi rule*, may not be the best criterion for release of a patient from the hospital. NCRP No. 37[1] recommends that exposure rate rather than activity be used. The basis for using this factor is that radionuclides differ in their exposure rates and half-lives. Patients who receive gamma-emitting nuclides with half-lives greater than 125 days are hospitalized for the duration of their treatment. Examples of nuclides in this category are radium-226, cobalt-60, and cesium-137. These sealed sources are removed from the patient before discharge from the hospital. Such a patient is no longer radioactive as soon as the source is removed. Those receiving nuclides with half-lives of less than 125 days are governed by a series of restrictions determined by their various degrees of radioactivity. There is one overlying principle of radionuclide therapy that is of paramount significance to the embalmer. Radionuclides are not given to moribund patients. Consequently, deceased patients with large amounts of radionuclides will be encountered only rarely in most hospitals. In the event that this does occur, hospital personnel (radiation safety or radiation protection personnel) are required by the conditions of the license for the use of these substances to monitor and certify to the embalmer the radioactive condition of the patient. Their duties include providing knowledgeable personnel to the funeral home to monitor the embalming procedure and to certify that no one is overexposed and nothing is contaminated. The physician or the hospital would be liable to lose their license if such should occur.

VEHICLES OF RADIONUCLIDE THERAPY

Common methods by which radionuclides are introduced into a body are by ingestion, injection, and implantation. Radioactive colloids may be injected directly into localized

---

[1] Guidelines given on the handling, embalming, and cremation of radioactively contaminated remains are adopted from NCRP Report No. 37, *Precautions in the Management of Patients Who Have Received Therapeutic Amounts of Radionuclides*, © National Council on Radiation Protection and Measurements, 1970.

malignant growths. Implants are usually in the form of radioactive needles, seeds, wires, and pellets. These types of therapy cause different patterns of dispersal of the radionuclide in the body. Ingested and injected radionuclides are generally disseminated throughout body fluids, organs, and their protective serous membranes. Implanted materials usually remain in one place, unless the accidental rupture of seeds, pellets, or needles causes generalized dissemination. The danger to the embalmer from any of these antemortem treatments is influenced by whether or not an autopsy has been performed.

PREPARATION OF THE BODY WITHOUT AUTOPSY

Embalmers rarely will be exposed to high levels of radiation from patients treated with radionuclides who die outside the hospital. Provided these bodies are embalmed without opening the cavities, the exposure to the embalmer will most likely be minimal—the maximum exposure that an embalmer may receive in a year is 0.5 R. Assuming that the average embalmer will only encounter, at the maximum, a few such cases each year, his exposure is not expected to exceed this level. The major protective measure that should be taken during such an embalming is the wearing of rubber gloves. They prevent possible contamination by radioactive body fluids. In addition, a waterproof apron should be worn over the standard protective clothing. Heavy fluoroscopic lead-rubber aprons were once thought to provide considerable protection, but gamma rays are much more penetrating than the diagnostic X-rays for which these aprons were designed. Aprons of this type reduce the gamma-ray exposure rate by only

10% and therefore serve no useful purpose. Effective protection against gamma radiation requires an apron with a minimum of 4 inches of solid lead! Time, distance, and shielding are the keys to the control of exposure to radiation. Of the three, shielding has the least significance to the embalmer.

More elaborate procedures may need to be taken in an unautopsied case if a patient dies within a few hours of being treated with gold-198 or phosphorus-32. These radionuclides are injected as colloidal suspensions. When introduced into the abdomen, they contaminate serous fluids by settling out on the surface of serous membranes. Embalmings of these cases should be performed in the hospital autopsy room under the direction of a radiation protection supervisor. Special precautions include removal of the serous fluid from the body by a trocar which is fixed so that no person must hold it or the tubing while the fluid is being withdrawn. Such fluid should be aspirated into a closed system followed by flushing into the sewer system with large amounts of water. The blood and urine may be disposed of normally, since they contain no appreciable radioactive material.

In contrast, the blood and urine of a patient who dies during the first 24 hours after administration (orally or intravenously) of iodine-131 may contain considerable amounts of radioactivity. These fluids should be aspirated and disposed of like the serous fluid contaminated with the colloidal suspensions.

Iodine-131 is used in the treatment of thyroid disease. One day after administration, if 50 mCi (an amount more than expected even from large initial doses) were concentrated in the thyroid, an exposure rate of approximately 1R/hr at a distance of 10 cm could be produced. If an embalmer spends 20 to 30 minutes doing cosmetic restoration of the face, the dose of radiation received by his fingers is within acceptable limits.

PREPARATION OF THE AUTOPSIED BODY

Radiation encountered from nonautopsied bodies is in the form of gamma rays, which have the highest penetrating power of the three types previously described. Radiation exposure from autopsied remains involves beta particles in addition to gamma rays. These beta particles, normally blocked by the intact remains, now have no barrier to keep them confined to the interior of the body. However, exposure to these radiations present much more of a hazard to the pathologist than to the embalmer. Autopsies of this nature are performed under the direction of the radiation protection supervisor. Removal of implants, and decontamination of body fluids, viscera, and cavities are carried out at this time. Provided that all these procedures are strictly adhered to, the embalmer is actually presented with less of a radiation hazard by the autopsied case than by the nonautopsied remains. Once the source of radiation is removed from the body, it no longer contains radioactivity. In the event that an implant has not been removed, it is important to realize that it should never be touched directly with the hands. The implant should be removed with long forceps (8 inches) and placed in appropriately shielded containers for storage or transportation.

CREMATION

If a body is to be cremated without embalming, there will be no radiation hazard from external handling. Persons who may be endangered by the cremation process are those living in the vicinity of a crematory who could be exposed to radioactive material emitted with the stack gases, and crematory employees who may inhale dust while handling radioactive remains.

NCRP No. 37 estimates that radiation exposures to the general public and to crematory workers would be within acceptable limits if each crematory were to handle in a year an overall amount of no more than 200 mCi of iodine-131 and 2000 mCi of all other commonly used therapeutic radionuclides, excluding implants. It is required that implants of any type be removed prior to cremation under the direction of a radiation protection supervisor.

SUMMARY OF PRECAUTIONARY PROCEDURES

1. Rubber gloves, preferably two pairs, should be worn throughout the entire embalming operation. Double surgical gloves should be sufficient because the use of heavy gloves could reduce dexterity and thus increase contact time. Plastic aprons should be worn to help prevent contamination of the clothing or skin with radioactive fluids.

2. Large quantities of running water should be used at all times during the embalming to dilute and flush away the drainage material.

3. The time of close contact with the body should be kept to a minimum. Remember time, distance, and shielding.

4. Special care should be taken to prevent the floor from being contaminated. It is recommended to tape a large sheet of absorbent material, underlaid with plastic, to the floor. Protective shoe covers should be worn by everyone working in this region, and removed when it is left.

5. Great care should be taken that all body fluids are properly discharged down the drain. In case of overflow this fluid should immediately be taken up with dry disposable waste held in forceps, and put into a suitable container.

6. Instruments should be soaked in soap or detergent, then rinsed well with running water.

7. Clothing, towels, etc., should be surveyed and stored for appropriate radioactive decay before being sent to the laundry.

8. Disposable wastes should be collected in a waterproof garbage bag and disposed of by incineration in consultation with the State Radiological Health Department.

9. Gloves should be thoroughly flushed with water before being removed from the hands, then placed in a container of soap and water and allowed to soak. The container should then be stored in a suitable place until the radioactivity has decayed to a safe level.

10. If the embalmer suffers any introduction of material from the remains into lesions on his hands, he should wash the affected area with copious amounts of running water and thereafter consult with his personal physician or a radiation safety officer.

It is important for funeral service practitioners to be aware of the scope of the problem of radioactivity, and how to deal with it. It is equally important not to exaggerate the danger and not to be unreasonably fearful when the hazard is minimal or nonexistent.

CHAPTER SUMMARY

Certain atomic nuclei are unstable, owing to the ratio between their protons and neutrons. The spontaneous decay of these nuclei is called radioactivity. All elements with atomic numbers above 83 and some with lower atomic numbers (carbon-14 and potassium-40) are naturally radioactive. Three types of radiations are emitted from radioactive nuclei: alpha particles ($^4_2$He), beta particles ($\pm e$), and gamma radiation (a form of electromagnetic radiation). Of the three, alpha particles have the highest ionizing ability and gamma rays are the most penetrating to matter. Emission of both alpha particles and beta particles results in changes, called transmutations, in the identity of nuclei. Transmutations may be artificially caused by bombarding nuclei with particles. Nuclear fission (breaking apart of nuclei) and formation of the transuranium elements occur by bombardment.

A general term for any radioactive material is *radionuclide*. The stability of radionuclides is evaluated in terms of half-life, $t_{\frac{1}{2}}$, which is the amount of time for half of a sample of radioactive material to decay. Radionuclides with long half-lives are more stable than ones with short half-lives.

Four quantities and their units that measure radiations or their effects are exposure (roentgen), absorbed dose (rad, Gray), dose equivalent (rem), and activity (curie). Radiation is detected by Geiger-Müller counters and scintillation counters. Individual exposures to radiations are measured by dosimeters, such as film badges or pocket dosimeters.

To be protected from radiation, three factors—time, distance, and shielding—should be considered. Personal exposure time to radionuclides should be minimized. Since radiation intensity decreases with the square of the distance from a radioactive source, moving away from a source is also a protective measure. Materials such as paper (alpha particles), thin metal foils (beta particles), and lead (gamma radiation) are shields against the corresponding radiations.

The most likely sources of radioactive bodies to the embalmer are patients receiving radionuclides. The chance of embalmers encountering high levels of radiation in these remains is low because radionuclides are not given to moribund patients. If an embalming is performed on a remains with radioactivity, different procedures are used for nonautopsied and autopsied cases. In nonautopsied cases, the danger to the embalmer is due to gamma rays. Radiation exposure from autopsied cases involves both gamma rays and beta particles. The latter cases, however, will probably have been decontaminated by the pathologist before the body is released to the embalmer. Direct disposal of a radionuclide-treated remains by cremation may present a hazard to the community at large and crematory employees, but little or no danger to external handling. A summary of precautionary procedures for embalming radioactive cases is listed at the end of the chapter.

QUESTIONS

1. Define: radioactivity, radionuclide, fission, free radical, transmutation.

2. Characterize by charge, by mass, and by symbol the three types of radiations that nuclei emit.

3. When alpha particles are emitted from a nucleus, they often have higher energies than beta particles or gamma rays. Why, then, are they the least penetrating of the three forms of radiation?

4. Write a balanced nuclear equation for each of the following decays:
    (a) Beta decay of $^{14}_{6}$C.
    (b) Positron decay of $^{122}_{53}$I.
    (c) Alpha decay of $^{212}_{84}$Po.

5. Give the names and abbreviations of the quantities that are used for radiations.

6. A radionuclide has an activity of 15 mCi. What does this mean?

7. $^{24}_{11}$Na is a synthetically produced radionuclide with a half-life of 15 hours. If 1.0 gram of $^{24}_{11}$Na is produced, what amount will have decayed in 45 hours?

8. The activity of a radionuclide is measured at 8 A.M. and again at 8 P.M. on the same day. The activity at 8 P.M. is one-eighth of the original value (8 A.M.). What is the half-life of the radionuclide?

9. Compare the intensity of radiation from a radionuclide at the source with the intensity 4 feet away from the source.

10. Rank in order of importance to the embalmer the three protection measures against radiation. Explain.

11. What is the difference in procedure in embalming a body treated with Au-198 and one with I-131?

12. What is the most important consideration in preventing contamination of the embalmer by radioactive fluids?

The three divisions of this text have illustrated the many and diverse applications of chemistry to both decomposition and its temporary arrester, the embalming operation. Embalming chemistry is a synthesis of applications of many facets of inorganic, organic, and biochemistry. This chapter will both summarize and review the major topics involving the chemistry of disinfection, preservation, and decomposition, including the major components of embalming fluids.

ACTIONS OF PRESERVATIVE CHEMICALS

Four major types of preservatives are used in embalming fluids: aldehydes, alcohols, phenols, and formaldehyde "donor" com-

and quaternary structure manifested in the characteristic structure and appearance of human tissue. Hydrolysis initiates the denaturation of protein and changes the alignment of the "active" chemical groups with respect to each other. This results in their subsequent reactions with substances that they are normally not in contact with, further contributing to the process of decomposition. When tissue fixation with preservative chemicals occurs, the "active" chemical groups are rendered inactive by being maintained in a similar alignment to that which they possess during life.

Inhibiting further decomposition

Preservative chemicals inhibit or arrest decomposition. They do not reverse decom-

Chapter 24
SUMMARY OF THE ACTION AND COMPOSITION OF EMBALMING FLUIDS

pounds. Their individual modes of action vary, but they all share five common actions.

Inactivating the active chemical groups of proteins or amino acids

Since proteins are polymers of amino acids, they share the same active terminal carboxyl and amino groups. In addition, proteins possess various active side-chain groups. The interactions among all the active chemical groups in proteins produce the tertiary

position, they simply retard it. For this reason, it is important that embalming is done as close to death as is reasonably possible. The further away from death, the more decomposition has occurred, thus the less tissue available for preservation.

Inactivating enzymes

Two types of proteolytic enzymes are significant in the process of decomposition. The proteolytic enzymes are singled out because of the important structural role of protein in the human body. One type comes from putrefactive bacteria and the other type from the digestive organelles of the cells themselves (autolytic enzymes). Since enzymes are important catalysts of hydrolysis, it is important that they are rendered inactive. One of the significant properties of enzymes is that they are a type of protein. Preservative chemicals, then, will have an effect on these dynamic proteins similar to their effect on structural proteins.

Killing microorganisms

In addition to being one of the sources of proteolytic enzymes, putrefactive bacteria employ other chemical secretions in order to utilize dead human tissue as a source of nutrition. The killing of these microorganisms by preservative chemicals (disinfection) is accomplished by two different means. First, denaturation of the structural protein of the human remains deprives these bacteria of their primary source of nutrition. Second, the preservative chemicals denature the structural proteins of the bacteria themselves. The physiological chemistry of bacteria has many things in common with that of human cells. Therefore the same chemical actions which cause fixation of the tissues of the remains will also produce fixation of the bacterial invaders. In this manner the action of preservative chemicals aids in the control of a major source of decomposition.

Destroying odors and eliminating their further production

Decomposition odors are principally due to the formation of various amines (putrescine, cadaverine, indole, skatole) resulting from the hydrolysis, deamination, and de-carboxylation of structural proteins. The decomposition of sulfur-containing proteins also contributes to these obnoxious odors. The true destruction of these odors is accomplished by the use of a chemical agent called a *deodorant*. Preservative chemicals counteract the odors of decomposition in two ways. First, they react with the nitrogen in these compounds to effectively neutralize the odor. Second, they react with the sources of decomposition (i.e., putrefactive microorganisms and their enzyme products) to eliminate the further production of these odors.

PRESERVATION BY FORMALDEHYDE

Formaldehyde is the most widely used of preservative chemicals found in embalming fluids. Fluids must contain a minimum of 5% formaldehyde in order to comply with state regulations regarding the transportation or treatment of victims of so-called "acute contagious diseases."

Reactions of formaldehyde

This preservative reacts with a variety of substances.

Reaction with water The major source of formaldehyde in embalming fluids is an aqueous solution containing 37% HCHO gas by weight (40% by volume) called *formalin*. Although this has been traditionally described as a mixture, more than just a physical change takes place. When formaldehyde gas is "mixed" with water, most of it is converted into methylene glycol. Very little "free" formaldehyde is present in these aqueous solutions. However, this apparently has no effect on the preserving and disinfecting action of the fluids. Both these processes are accomplished by fixing the proteins due to the donation of a methylene (CH_2) group. It does not matter what the source of the methylene group is; in fact, the Japanese have experienced a good deal of success using methyl alcohol as the methylene donor.

Reaction with methanol   Formaldehyde has a strong tendency to polymerize. This is an undesirable condition for liquid solutions. Methanol acts as an antipolymerizing agent in embalming fluids. Even the commercial grade of formalin contains approximately 7% methanol for this specific purpose.

Reaction with amino acids   Since amino acids are the depolymerized units of proteins, formaldehyde will react with them in a similar manner. However, since they are much smaller units than proteins, the gross appearance of "coagulated" amino acid is substantially different from that of "coagulated" protein. Thus the term *noncoagulability* of amino acids found its way into the literature of embalming.

Reaction with proteins   The main chemical action of HCHO in embalming is the coagulation of protein.[1] This is brought about through denaturation of the protein by cross-linking the peptide bonds of adjacent polypeptide chains. Unembalmed tissue is pliable and flexible. Embalmed tissue is rigid as a result of the cross-linking of protein. The methylene bridges that bond the adjacent polypeptide chains together eliminate the movement that is characteristically present in non-cross-linked protein. The gross changes in proteins brought about by for-

[1]Sleichter G. M., "A Study of the Combining Activity of Formaldehyde with Tissues"; thesis submitted in partial fulfillment of the requirements for Master's degree, University of Cincinnati (1939).

maldehyde and other coagulating agents are:

○ The viscosity is increased.

○ The resistance to deformation by external forces is increased; i.e., the material becomes harder.

○ The resistance to digestion by enzymes is increased.

○ The water sensitivity (hydrolysis) and water solubility are decreased.

The last point merits special attention. The changes in protein with respect to water brought about by formaldehyde apply to normal amounts of water. Cross-linking of protein removes a molecule of water for every cross-link that is formed. The presence of an abundance of water may reverse this process by hydrolyzing the cross-linkages. Therefore, the embalming results may also be reversed by the presence of an excess amount of water.

Formaldehyde demand

The total amount of formaldehyde with which protein will combine to be completely preserved is termed *formaldehyde demand*. As decomposition progresses, hydrolysis of proteins exposes more and more amino groups. In undecomposed tissue one molecule of formaldehyde bonds two peptide links. After hydrolysis breaks the individual peptide bonds, each amino group will react with a formaldehyde molecule. This effectively doubles the formaldehyde demand. Thus, embalming recommendations for cases of advanced or advancing decomposition include a large volume of a high-index arterial fluid. Two factors, then, become essential in the reaction of formaldehyde with protein. First, embalming should be done as close to the time of death as is reasonably possible in order to circumvent the problems generated by hydrolysis. Second, the tissues of the body should be supplied with an excess of formaldehyde above that which is actually needed to enter into chemical union with the proteins and their decomposition products.

The walling-off action of formaldehyde

The key to the preservation of tissue by formaldehyde is the distribution and diffusion of the fluid. *Distribution* refers to the movement of fluid from the point of injection to the tissues. *Diffusion* describes the movement of fluid into the tissues. This latter movement is often hindered by what is called the *walling-off action* of formaldehyde. This action is best described as follows: A piece of biopsied tissue is immersed in a solution of formaldehyde for a certain period of time. When removed from the solution, the tissue exhibits a hard, leathery appearance. It seems to be "preserved." If a section is made with a scalpel, the interior appears pink, moist, and virtually untouched by the formaldehyde. Walling off of tissue does not exclusively occur with immersion. If the embalming solution is too concentrated, the capillaries in the tissues will be seared and sealed by the formaldehyde, thus effectively inhibiting diffusion of the fluid into the tissues by walling off the unexposed areas.

Indirect action on fats

Adipose tissue contains very little nitrogen. Since the preservative action of formaldehyde works by cross-linking nitrogen atoms, it would seem that there would be no effect at all upon fatty tissue. However, the fat deposits of the body are not isolated islands of tissue. Instead, they are found embedded in a supporting, protein-rich connective-tissue network. The indirect action of formaldehyde on fats, then, actually involves the preservation of the matrix in which the fat is embedded rather than the preservation of the fat itself.

EMBALMING FLUIDS—BASIC TYPES

Arterial fluid: components and functions

Embalming fluid is an aqueous solution of gases, liquids, and solids. The components of this mixture are preservatives, supplementary germicides, modifying agents, anticoagulants, surfactants, dyes, reodorants, and vehicles.

Preservatives Chemical preservatives denature the protein of the body in such a manner that the enzymes of decomposition cannot work. There are two reasons for this action. First, the substrate is changed by the process and the enzyme cannot "fit" into the structure. Second, the enzymes, being protein themselves, are also denatured and therefore lose their function. The following substances are most commonly found as the preservative components of arterial embalming fluid.

Aldehydes All aldehydes function by cross-linking protein. The manner in which the cross-linking occurs is reflected in the tissue firmness and fixation. Lower monoaldehydes such as formaldehyde produce more firmness than dialdehydes like glutaraldehyde or adipaldehyde. The reason is that the smaller aldehydes produce many more cross-links than the larger aldehydes, in which steric inhibition limits the number of linkages formed. The more links, the less flexibility of the protein, and therefore the greater the firmness or hardness of the tissue. Hardness, however, is not a proper criterion for preservation; lack of decomposition is the only true indicator. Formaldehyde and glutaraldehyde are the most commonly used mono- and dialdehydes in embalming-fluid compilations. In addition to possessing excellent fixative properties, glutaraldehyde has such outstanding disinfectant qualities that it has been labeled a "cold chemical sterilant."

Alcohols Lower alcohols such as methanol, ethanol, and isopropyl alcohol are often used in combination with aldehydes as preservatives. Alcohols also have the ability to cross-link proteins, but to a lesser extent than aldehydes. Methanol is used more often than ethanol because of its dual ability to (1) act as a methylene group donor for the cross-link and (2) function as an antipolymerizing agent for the aldehydes. Isopropyl alcohol has the best germicidal qualities of the three.

Phenolic compounds Phenols and phenolic compounds function as both preservatives and disinfectants, owing to their ability to precipitate protein. Phenols, when used by themselves, serve as bleaching agents for discolorations on skin surfaces. When used in combination with aldehydes, however, these compounds tend to produce a putty-gray effect on tissues. Therefore, high-phenol-content arterial embalming fluids are confined more to the preservation of anatomical specimens.

Formaldehyde "donor" compounds These substances are condensation products of formaldehyde. The formaldehyde is held in chemical combination with another compound but may be released by an activating substance such as potassium carbonate. The advantage of formaldehyde donor compounds is the ability to produce a "fumeless" arterial chemical which will not be irritating to the operator. Their disadvantage is that they have a slow reaction rate with the tissues, since the release of formaldehyde is slow.

Supplementary germicides Quaternary ammonium compounds are excellent surface active agents and are widely used for the disinfection of skin, oral, and nasal cavities and of instruments. However, since they are cationic detergents, they are effectively neutralized by anionic substances. Embalming fluids contain a number of anionic substances. Therefore, these substances are not compatible with arterial fluids, and their use should be restricted to surface disinfection and specialty fluids.

Modifying agents The standard preservatives and disinfectants found in embalming fluids are, by themselves, extremely caustic and astringent. The same chemical action which brings about preservation and disinfection also interferes with distribution and diffusion by searing capillary walls and causing a "short circuit" of embalming circulation. Various chemicals are incorporated into embalming fluids for the purpose of "modifying" the action of these harsh substances by delaying their activity until the tissues have received a sufficient supply of arterial fluid. The following classes of substances control the rate of reaction of the preservatives and disinfectants.

Humectants Dehydration is a byproduct of the reaction of aldehydes, alcohols, and phenols with body tissue. A *humectant* is a moisture-retaining agent. These substances help to offset dehydration by imparting a pliable and flexible effect to the tissues. Examples are glycols (dihydroxy alcohols), glycerol (a trihydroxy alcohol), sorbitol and other polyhydroxy alcohols, and lanolin (an oil).

Buffers Substances which resist changes in pH when an acid or a base is added to a solution are called *buffers*. Somatic death is followed by a pH shift to acidic. Decomposition swings the pH to the alkaline side, owing to the hydrolysis of protein into alkaline products. Highly acidic conditions accelerate the polymerization of formaldehyde. Strongly basic solutions cause the decomposition of formaldehyde (Cannizzaro reaction). Therefore, it is extremely important that formaldehyde solutions contain buffers. Slightly acidic formaldehyde produces better tissue fixation than alkaline solutions, but also causes putty-gray discolorations. Slightly alkaline solutions improve the tissue coloration and enhance the action of dyes. As a result, most arterial fluids are buffered to pH's of 7.2–7.4. Some examples of embalming-fluid buffers are borax, sodium phosphate, citrates, and EDTA.

Anticoagulants Ionized calcium is one of the key factors in blood coagulation. All tap water contains some dissolved calcium. The amount found in water is expressed as the degree of "hardness" of that water. Since, in the embalming operation, water is the principal diluent (or "vehicle," as discussed later), the amount of calcium must be regulated. Very hard water contributes to blood clotting and interferes with its removal from the circulatory system. Anticoagulants are substances that react with the ionized calcium, thus keeping the blood in the liquid state and facilitating its removal. Anticoagulants are sometimes termed *water-conditioning agents* because of the contribution of hard water to the increase of calcium-ion concentration. Historically, oxalates and citrates were the most commonly used anticoagulants. Contemporary formulations have largely abandoned these two classes of compounds. Oxalates are no longer used because of their toxicity to the operator. Citrates will actually contribute to blood clotting in the presence of certain bacterial enzyme systems associated with septicemia. Chelating agents such as EDTA have largely replaced oxalates and citrates as anticoagulants. In addition to its action against calcium ions, EDTA serves double duty in arterial fluids as a buffer. (See the previous paragraph on buffers.)

Surfactants At the surface of a liquid, water molecules are pulled inward. This draws the surface molecules more tightly together, forming a kind of "skin" called *surface tension*. A similar interfacial tension occurs between liquids and the surface of cell membranes, interfering with the penetration of the liquid into the cell. *Surfactants* (surface-active agents, wetting agents, surface-tension-reducing agents) facilitate the flow of embalming chemicals through the capillary walls and into the tissues to ensure complete distribution and saturation of the tissue cells by the preservatives. Sulfonates and sodium lauryl sulfate are two examples of surfactants used in arterial fluids.

Dyes In addition to disinfection and sterilization, the definition of embalming has a third component: restoration. Tissue color as well as texture must be taken into account for restorative purposes. Dyes are incorporated into arterial fluids for this reason. Synthetic dyes, derived from hydrocarbons, are most commonly used because of their small molecular size which allows them to diffuse easily into the tissues, thus producing a uniformly distributed color. These colors range from pale yellow to bright red. Some examples of dyes used in embalming fluids are *eosin* ($C_{20}H_8Br_4O_5$), a yellowish-orange colored tetrabromo derivative of fluorescein; *erythrosin*, a red substance formed by the oxidation of the amino acid tyrosine; and *ponceau red* ($C_{19}H_{16}N_2Na_2O_7S_2$), a non-staining dye used primarily to color the fluid rather than stain the tissues, which produces a cherry-red color.

Reodorants Also called *perfuming* or *masking agents*, these substances cover up the harsh odors of the preservatives and disinfectants found in arterial fluids. Reodorants are distinguished from deodorants, which actually destroy the odor by chemically reacting with its source. True deodorants would destroy not only the odor of the preservative-disinfectant agents but their primary actions as well. Reodorants have their source in a wide range of organic compounds. Some examples are *benzaldehyde* (C_6H_5CHO) and other aromatic aldehydes; *oil of cloves*, which is a derivative of eugenol ($C_{10}H_{12}O_2$),

Eugenol

a hybrid of a phenol and an ether; *oil of sassafras*, a derivative of safrole, the constituent of several essential oils;

Safrole

and *methyl salicylate* (oil of wintergreen), an ester of methyl alcohol and salicylic acid.

Vehicles   Since embalming is accomplished by injection of the blood vascular system, the chemical components must be suspended in a liquid medium. This solvent is known in embalming terminology as a *vehicle*. Water, methanol, and glycerin are the most commonly used vehicles. The choice of a vehicle is limited by two major considerations. First, the vehicle should not react with the active components of the embalm-

ing fluid, thereby rendering them useless. Second, the vehicle should not react with the tissues of the circulatory system, since this would interfere with the distribution and diffusion of the preservatives and disinfectants.

Cavity-fluid: components and functions

Arterial embalming alone will not thoroughly disinfect and preserve a human remains. The thoracic and abdominal cavities and the organs they contain must receive supplementary embalming treatment. Fluids formulated for this purpose are designated *cavity fluids* and have a different composition than arterial fluids. This difference in composition is twofold. First, cavity fluids contain a much higher concentration of disinfectants and preservatives than arterial fluids. (See Table 14-1.) Second, cavity fluids generally do not contain dyes, reodorants, or modifying agents. Since cavity treatment involves direct, thorough saturation of tissues, there is no need either to delay the action of the primary chemicals or to provide a restorative effect to the treated areas. Aside from these two differences, the types of preservatives, supplementary germicides, surfactants, and vehicles used in cavity fluids are exactly the same as those found in arterial fluids.

Accessory fluids (supplemental or additive)

Pre-injection   The purpose of a *pre-injection fluid* is to prepare the blood vascular system for the injection of preservatives and disinfectants. As a result, pre-injection fluids are formulated exactly the opposite of cavity fluids. They contain water-conditioning agents, anticoagulants, surfactants, and humectants together with very low concentrations of preservatives. Some pre-injec-

Table 24-1 General types of embalming preparations

Ingredient	Composition
Type I (nonformaldehyde)	
ethylenediaminetetraacetate	3.0%
monosodium phosphate	1.0%
sodium citrate	1.0%
sorbitol	10.0%
methanol	10.0%
water	74.0%
nonionic surfactant	1.0%
Type II (primary fluid)	
borax	4.2%
boric acid	2.5%
glycerin	16.8%
water	47.0%
methanol	17.5%
formalin	11.0%
anionic or nonionic surfactant	0.6%
reodorant and coloring agents, as desired	0.4%
Type III (arterial fluid)	
glutaraldehyde	8%–12%
formalin	8%–25%
water	27%–42%
glycerin	6%–12%
borax	2%–6%
methanol	15%–26%
tetrahydrofurfuryl alcohol	5%–10%
alkyl aryl sodium sulfonate	0.5%–1.0%
reodorant and coloring agents, as desired	
Type IV (arterial fluid)	
glycerin	20 lb
polyacrylic acid (Carbopol 934)	4 lb
sulfonated naphthenic mineral oil (Atlantic Soluble Oil No. 1)	25 lb
formaldehyde (46% solution in methanol)	516 lb
p-dichlorobenzene	20 lb
o-dichlorobenzene	42 lb
pine oil	20 lb
Rhodamine B (2% aqueous solution)	2000 ml
Bismarck Brown (3% aqueous solution)	2500 ml
sodium hydroxide (crystals)	38 oz
water	528 lb
methanol	53 lb
Type V (arterial fluid) [a]	
trimethylolnitromethane	200 g
potassium carbonate	5 g
anionic surfactant (wetting agent) [b]	5 g
sulfanilimide	1 g
eosine dye and perfume, as desired	

Table 24-1 (*Continued*)

Ingredient	Composition
Type VI (cavity fluid)	
formalin	70.0%
alcohol[c]	29.5%
wetting agent[d]	0.5%

SOURCE: Reprinted with permission, "Embalming Chemicals" by Leandro Rendon, p. 163, *Encyclopedia of Industrial Chemical Analysis*, ed. Snell, Volume 12, © 1971 by John Wiley & Sons, Inc.
[a] The powdered mixture is added to a sufficient quantity of water to make 1 pint of full-strength embalming fluid.
[b] A phosphated higher (e.g., capryl) alcohol.
[c] Methanol, ethanol, or isopropyl alcohol.
[d] Triton X-100 or equivalent.

tion fluids contain no formaldehyde at all. (See Type I, Table 24-1.)

Co-injection A co-injection fluid is very similar in composition to a pre-injection fluid. Although the formulations of a co-injection will vary depending upon requirements, the main difference is the time of injection. Pre-injections are introduced into the blood vascular system against closed drainage before the actual arterial embalming begins. Co-injections are mixed with the arterial fluids and are therefore introduced concurrently with arterial embalming.

Humectant or restorative fluids Although both moisture-retaining agents and cosmetic dyes are routinely incorporated into arterial embalming fluids, it is sometimes necessary to use additive fluids that are specially formulated to contain unusually large amounts of those substances. Lanolin-based fluids are most frequently used for this purpose.

Fluids for special conditions

Jaundice fluids Jaundice is a pathological condition which results in a yellow discoloration of the skin due to excessive amounts of the bile pigment bilirubin. High concentrations of formaldehyde convert bilirubin into biliverdin which produces a greenish discoloration. Since neither one of these discolorations is acceptable for funeral viewing purposes, several different types of jaundice fluids have been developed.

○ *Low-index arterial fluids* These fluids contain a concentration of formaldehyde low enough to prevent the conversion of bilirubin to biliverdin.

○ *Masking fluids* These fluids contain both a medium concentration of formaldehyde and cosmetic dyes in order to mask the yellow discoloration of bilirubin.

○ *Bleaching fluids* These formulations contain chemicals that will have a lightening or bleaching effect on the bilirubin. They also have a medium formaldehyde content.

○ *Nonformaldehyde fluids* Since, by definition, these fluids contain no preservative, they are designed to remove the discolorations by flushing them from the tissues and the blood vascular system.

Special preservative fluids The maximum concentration of formaldehyde in embalming fluid is limited by its solubility in water. When higher concentrations are desired, it is necessary to employ an additional solvent such as ethyl alcohol. These special preservative fluids are used to treat cases with advanced decomposition and unusual pathological conditions.

Autopsy chemicals   In post-mortem examinations the thoracic and abdominal organs are removed from their respective cavities, sectioned, and replaced. Since this interrupts the vascular supply to both the viscera and the cavities, special supplemental embalming treatment is required. The substances used to treat the viscera are direct-contact solid chemicals, which are referred to as *hardening compounds*. The specific purposes of hardening compounds are dehydration, preservation, and disinfection. Some common components of solid autopsy chemicals are:

○ Paraformaldehyde, $(CH_2O)_x$: preservative, disinfectant

○ Aluminum chloride, $AlCl_3$: dehydrating agent, disinfectant

○ Alum, $KAl(SO_4)_2 \cdot 12\,H_2O$: dehydrating agent, disinfectant

○ Wood flour (finely powdered sawdust): dehydrating agent, preservative

○ Plaster of Paris, $(CaSO_4)_2 \cdot H_2O$: dehydrating agent

Chemical substances used to treat the cavity walls of autopsied remains are prepared as gels. These gels have basically the same composition as cavity fluids, except that they are suspended in a gelatinous matrix to ensure ease of application to the cavity walls.

FACTORS INFLUENCING STABILITY OF FLUIDS (SHELF LIFE)

Temperature

Extremes in temperature have a detrimental effect on the shelf life of embalming fluids. Elevated temperatures accelerate polymerization of formaldehyde and cause decomposition of the other disinfectant and preservative components. Depressed temperatures cause precipitation of the endothermic solutes.

Time

All organic compounds exhibit a tendency to form polymers. Methanol is incorporated into embalming fluids as an antipolymerization agent for formaldehyde. Nonetheless, the average shelf life of fluids is between two and five years.

pH

One of the purposes of adding buffers to embalming fluids is to prolong their shelf life. Strongly alkaline solutions cause decomposition of formaldehyde (Cannizzaro reaction). Highly acidic solutions promote polymerization.

Light

In Chapter 6 light was cited as one of the factors influencing the speed of chemical reactions. Light has two effects on embalming fluids: (1) it causes a color change, thus interfering with the eventual reaction of the cosmetic dyes; (2) it increases polymerization of the formaldehyde. As a result, some manufacturers have adopted tinted containers to prolong the shelf life of their products.

CHAPTER SUMMARY

The three essential components of the definition of embalming are disinfection, preservation, and restoration. Chemical means are employed to achieve these goals, since existing physical methods are too uneven in their effects. For example, steam-pressure sterilization could achieve excellent disinfection and preservation but would be counterrestorative.

Preservative chemicals will generally double as disinfectants. However, supplementary germicides are included in embalming-fluid formulations, and modifying agents are added in order to augment restoration.

This chapter dealt first with the general effects of preservative-disinfectant chemicals on the human remains. Since formaldehyde is the most widely used of these chemicals, the specific chemical reactions of this substance are thoroughly discussed. The components and functions of arterial fluids, cavity fluids, and accessory fluids all are outlined and illustrated in detail. The chapter concluded with a discussion of the factors which influence the shelf life of embalming chemicals.

QUESTIONS

1. Explain how the action of preservative chemicals also produces disinfection.

2. What is meant by the "noncoagulability of amino acids"?

3. How does advancing decomposition increase formaldehyde demand?

4. Define: formaldehyde donor compound, humectant, surfactant, sequesterant, reodorant, vehicle.

5. Describe two differences between arterial embalming fluid and cavity fluid.

6. List and describe four types of jaundice fluid.

7. What is the functional difference between a pre-injection fluid and a co-injection fluid?

8. What single chemical change shortens the shelf life of embalming fluid more than anything else?

9. List and give the function of four different components of hardening compound.

10. If the function of embalming is to coagulate protein, why doesn't the blood, which also has a high protein content, coagulate as a result?

INDEX